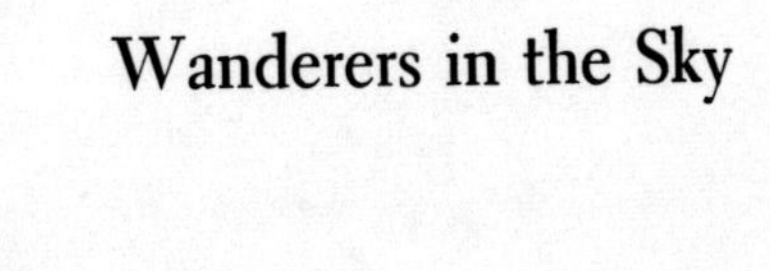

# Wanderers in the Sky

# Wanderers in the Sky

## THE MOTIONS OF PLANETS AND SPACE PROBES

EDITED BY THORNTON PAGE & LOU WILLIAMS PAGE

VOLUME I *Sky and Telescope* Library of Astronomy

Illustrated with over 100 photographs, drawings, and diagrams

The Macmillan Company
Collier-Macmillan Limited, London

The articles in this book were originally published in slightly different form in *The Sky*, copyright American Museum of Natural History 1936; 1938; 1939; copyright Sky Publishing Corporation 1940; 1941; in *Sky and Telescope*, copyright © Sky Publishing Corporation 1942; 1943; 1944; 1946; 1947; 1948; 1949; 1950; 1951; 1952; 1953; 1954; 1955; 1956; 1957; 1958; 1959; 1960; 1961; 1962; 1963; and in *The Telescope*.



*Third Printing 1970*

The Macmillan Company
866 Third Avenue, New York, N.Y. 10022
Collier-Macmillan Canada Ltd., Toronto, Ontario

Printed in the United States of America

Library of Congress catalog card number: 65-12722

# Contents

## 3. Recent Probing of Space

## 4. The Hazards of Interplanetary Space



## 5. Our Moon, a Big Satellite

# Illustrations

*Figure*

*Figure*

## Tables

# Preface

Wanderers are always on the move. In the sky, planets have long been identified simply by their motion among the apparently immobile stars. The word planet means wanderer, but this kind of wandering is no haphazard meandering. In fact, the precision of celestial motion has now spread to terrestrial artifacts—the space probes launched by men to circle the earth, visit the moon, or journey even farther into interplanetary space. In less than a decade, this probing has provided a great deal of new information about the universe, and it promises to provide much more. As new facts are obtained, and as old facts are reinterpreted in the light of new ideas, man's understanding of the celestial wanderers is growing.

These changing concepts are themselves interesting, and show how science progresses. This book (like the others in this series) has been compiled from articles published during the last thirty years in The Telescope, The Sky, and the periodical which they merged to form, Sky and Telescope, a magazine read by amateur astronomers as well as professionals, by students of astronomy, and by their professors. The series is designed to show, among other things, how astronomical ideas develop, which ideas have held firm since Telescope (parent magazine of the present periodical) was first issued in 1931, which ideas have changed, and—by extension—how much of what astronomers now think about the universe is likely to be modified in the future.

For instance, the age of the earth is now thought to be almost four billion years; in 1931 it was thought to be two billion. In 1931 Pluto had just been discovered, and the nine planets going around our sun were thought to be unusual; now we have reason to think that many other stars have similar families. Entirely new methods of observing planets, stars, interstellar material, and galaxies have come into being since 1931, including space probes, radar, and radio-telescopes.

The history of Sky and Telescope is recounted in Appendix I. The magazine is available at most libraries in bound volumes. After reviewing its many articles, the editors decided to present in Macmillan's Sky and Telescope Library of Astronomy several individual trends, each with some degree of unity. Historical development is the general motif, but it is not followed slavishly. Dates of original publication are given with each selection, and each topic is carried through the most recent published research, often in intentional contrast with earlier views.

All the articles in this volume deal with the exploration of the solar system: how man can get to the moon or to another planet, and what to expect on the way. No attempt is made, however, to cover all of the engineering aspects of launching space probes. Rather, in Chapters 1 and 2 it has seemed wise to show the foundations of celestial mechanics, fundamental to space exploration. This leads naturally to the early ideas of interplanetary travel—part of science fiction in 1931 and now a practical possibility. Vertical rocket firings, Sputniks, manned satellites, lunar probes, and shots at Mars and Venus are all described in articles written at the time they occurred.

Later sections tell about interplanetary space and the moon, primarily in terms of ground-based observation and with emphasis on what still remains uncertain. Is the lunar surface covered with dust or with a frothy fiberglass? Why is Venus so hot? What causes the change in the dark areas on Mars? Man-made wanderers will undoubtedly settle many of these questions in the next decade—and raise a new crop for astronomers to puzzle over. Several problems of current astronomical interest will be treated in other volumes: What is the atmosphere like on Venus? Is there life on Mars? What keeps the sun hot? How is it aging? What was the origin of the solar system—and many questions concerning the more distant stars, nebulae, and galaxies.

Each of the articles in this volume is reproduced essentially as it originally appeared in Telescope, The Sky, or Sky and Telescope with minor modifications for consistency of style. In order to maintain continuity, some tangential material has been cut. When short in length, these deletions have not been indicated, but omissions of one or more paragraphs have been designated by ellipsis. Occasional minor changes have been made in the wording to improve clarity or to eliminate repetition. A few explanatory additions have been introduced, usually designated by brackets.

Selections for which there is no author credit were prepared by the

*the staff of the applicable magazine. Footnotes supplied by the editors bear the intials* TLP, *as do the passages of interspersed editors' comments throughout the volume.*

*Editors' comments are intended to help today's reader; they are certainly not intended to criticize views of authors who wrote ten to twenty years ago; in fact, just as they were sometimes "wrong," so may our interpretations be "wrong" today.*

THORNTON PAGE
LOU WILLIAMS PAGE

*January, 1964*

## About the Editors

Dr. Thornton Page is now Fisk Professor of Astronomy at Wesleyan University, Middletown, Connecticut, and Director of the Van Vleck Observatory. After studying at Yale University, he went to England as a Rhodes Scholar, where he received a Ph.D. from Oxford University in 1938. Dr. Page then spent twelve years on the faculty of the University of Chicago and at the Yerkes Observatory, interrupted by five years' military service with the Navy. Dr. Page has written articles in scientific journals and has been the editor of two books: *Introduction to Physical Science* (3 vols.), and *Stars and Galaxies.*

Mrs. Page, a geologist, also taught in the College of the University of Chicago and is the author of two science books for young readers, *A Dipper Full of Stars* and *The Earth and Its Story*. The Pages have made use of their experience in several scientific disciplines in the preparation of *Wanderers in the Sky.*

# 1

# The Dawn of Understanding

*Man is a curious animal and has demonstrated his curiosity in many targets of exploration—the New World, Mount Everest, the Arctic, and the Antarctic. There is wide interest today in space exploration—manned space flight and expeditions to the moon, Mars, and more distant points. In a way, these goals reflect a widespread understanding of astronomical concepts that did not exist a few centuries ago.*

*Sensible exploration implies some such understanding; one has to know that there is a North Pole of the earth before one can set out to get there. In space exploration, moreover, the method of travel requires a good deal of technical understanding. The articles in Chapter 1 show how man's concepts of the planets and their motions have developed.*

TLP

## Old and New Ideas of the Solar System

ERNEST CHERRINGTON, JR.

(*The Sky*, June 1938)

Man cannot touch any of the great heavenly bodies except that small one upon which he finds himself at home. He perceives their existence only through the sense of sight. To him their reality is no more definitely established than that of the light waves which they send earthward. To him the nature of the universe depends upon the interpretation of his observations.

For thousands of years man has gathered observations on the universe. His imagination has raced ahead of his eye, piecing the fragmentary data into a cosmic picture. As observational technique was improved and as the data grew more abundant the picture changed radically from time to time. So, while the universe remains the same through countless ages, our ideas regarding its nature are continually modified and broadened. . . .

The cosmic picture of today differs greatly from the universe as described by the writers of yesterday. Our current picture is not only of greater breadth and depth, but many of its details stand forth more clearly. Yet a great deal of the canvas is still untouched, and in many portions we find only the vague lines of a preliminary sketch. Man's horizon has broadened with the development of his mind. It has left the earth and receded into the depths of space. How far it will continue to advance depends not so much upon how large the universe actually is but more upon the degree of refinement of which the human brain is capable.

History has left no entries upon the pages of time a million years ago, but on them modern science has scribbled a few notes. We see primitive man struggling against the great odds that nature seems to have set against him. His world is a very small one. It extends over a few square miles surrounding the hut to which he retires at sunset.

Man becomes conscious of the sun as it rises in the morning and sets in the evening. He perceives his shadow. It is long at sunrise and sunset but short at midday. At length he attributes daylight to the presence of the sun in the sky and darkness to the absence of the sun. Each evening the sun sets behind the hills to the west. Curious man journeys westward across those hills, but when evening overtakes him the setting sun appears no nearer. The earth must be very large and the realm of the sun must be great also. The universe is steadily growing.

Night comes and man watches the moon. It must be akin to the sun since it rises in the east, moves across the sky above, and sets in the west. Night after night he watches it grow from a slender crescent to a full, bright disk. Its changing form puzzles him. He begins to wonder about the sun and the moon. Here we see the first astronomer. The motive that incited him to gaze upon the heavenly bodies and later fabricate explanations for their apparent motions was simple curiosity, a human characteristic that began to develop early in the evolution of man's mind. Out of curiosity came science.

One of the earliest civilizations of which we have more than a few scattered records grew up in the valley of the Nile. The country of Egypt comprised the world of that period. For generations the forefathers of the Egyptians wandered up and down the Nile. Their world was much larger than that of primitive man. Nevertheless they felt that the earth must have a definite boundary. This idea was substantiated by reports from those who wandered farthest. At the mouth of the Nile the Egyptians encountered the Mediterranean, which stretched northward apparently without limit. To the east lay the Red Sea. Evidently the earth was a flat slab of dirt and rock surrounded by and floating upon a great body of water.

So the traditional picture of the universe inherited by civilized Egypt was a flat disk of earth as large, perhaps, as the state of Texas floating upon a vast ocean. Surmounting the earth was a hemispherical dome upon which were fastened the stars and under which glided the sun and moon in their daily journeys from east to west. Later it occurred to some thoughtful person that something must hold back the water upon which the earth floated, and so a rather indefinite ocean basin was postulated.

The religious history of the Egyptians is similar to that of other races.

*Fig. 1.* To the Chaldeans the earth was a mountain rising from the eternal waters in the enclosed chamber of the universe. (From Gaston C. C. Maspero, *The Dawn of Civilization*; Yerkes Observatory photograph)

They worshiped the sun as the chief source of light and heat. They worshiped the moon, whose gentle light dispelled the blackness of many nights. Since fire was the only source of light known to ancient peoples, the sun was pictured as a bowl of celestial fire. Every morning the fire was kindled on the eastern horizon, where it began to glow with a dull, red light. As the bowl rose into the sky its contents blazed brighter. As evening drew near the combustible material in the great bowl was nearly consumed, and the fire began to die down. Only the glowing embers were left to shed the feeble red light of sunset.

Once in a great while the deities who attended to the refueling of the sun made a mistake. They failed to pile enough combustibles into the bowl at dawn, and consequently the fire burned out before sunset. Thus eclipses of the sun were explained. Although the gods always came to the rescue and quickly righted their mistake, it must have given weak, mortal man much satisfaction to feel that even the gods could err.

The moon was regarded as a dish of fire much weaker in luminosity than the sun. Out of this naïve concept developed an explanation for the phases of the moon that probably brought wide acclaim to its originator. The bowl containing the lunar fire turned around and around in the sky within a period of twenty-eight days. When a very tiny portion of the fiery contents was turned toward the earth, new moon was observed. First-quarter moon occurred when half the burning bowl was visible, and so on.

At first glance the explanation sounds rather good, but ask yourself the question: "What shape would a bowl of fire have to have in order to reproduce the phases of the moon by rotation?" An ordinary circular bowl would be needed for full moon, but what about the other phases? With such an arrangement new moon would appear not as a crescent but cigar-shaped, and first-quarter moon would be elliptical rather than semicircular. But the early philosophers did not bother to go into details. This idea of the nature of the moon and its phases must have been expounded for many hundreds of years, for we find it taught as late as the year 500 B.C. by Heraclitus the Greek philosopher. . . .

We do not know just when astronomical ideas developed sufficiently to give the sun a permanent identity in the mind of man. The Greeks of the fifth century B.C. believed that a new sun graced each day. Yet we find evidence that their predecessors the Egyptians finally came to regard the sun of each day as identical with the sun of the day before. What gave rise to such an important change in belief? Possibly the occurrence of a sunspot of unusually large dimensions. Spots big enough to be observable with the naked eye appear once in a while upon the surface of the sun. They may be observed through thin clouds or at sunset or sunrise. Indeed we find records of a few scattered sunspot observations made in China thousands of years before the invention of the telescope.

The question that then arose was: "If the same sun is to set in the west each evening and rise in the east the following morning, how does it manage to pass under the earth at night?" That was a real nut for the philosophers to crack, but they finally worked out a solution to their own satisfaction. There must be a tunnel, they reasoned, running under the earth from east to west. A canal passes through this tunnel and forms a part of the great ocean surrounding the earth. In the evening a boat waits to pick up the sun at the western horizon. During the night the gods row the boat through the canal and arrive at the eastern horizon just in time for sunrise. This idea is described pictorially upon some of the records of ancient Egypt. The sun was still regarded as a relatively small body.

For thousands of years astronomers (if early philosophers may be called astronomers) paid little attention to the stars. The 5000 stars visible to the naked eye altogether send us less than one-tenth of 1 per cent as much light as does the full moon. Hence the ancients looked upon the stars as minor bodies—mere points of light, as they seem to be. How the old philosophers would have scoffed at the assertion that one of those very faint little stars actually gives off 500,000 times as much light and heat as does the sun! They left the unimportant stars to the simple shepherds and other common people who spent the long nights out-of-doors and whiled away the lonely hours of darkness by watching the stars.

As the nocturnal pastime of pointing out and watching the constellations came into vogue certain startling discoveries followed. Let us suppose, for instance, that a group of star-gazers had agreed to call a certain group of stars the Bull. The Bull consisted of a very bright yellow star, a bright red star, and several fainter stars including the Pleiades. After a number of nights had passed someone noticed that the brightest star in the Bull—the yellow one—no longer occupied the same position in relation to the others that it had on the occasion of first observation. His friends agreed that the constellation did look changed. They noticed that none of the stars except the bright yellow one had moved with reference to each other. Further investigation showed that the brightest star in the Bull was actually moving eastward among the other stars. In the course of time five bright stars were found which continually changed their positions in the sky. They were called planets or wanderers, while all the others were designated fixed stars since they apparently occupied the same positions in relation to each other night after night, year after year.

In the second century of the Christian Era, Ptolemy, the famous Egyptian mathematician, wrote a text of astronomy called the *Almagest*. This historic work is a complete treatment of the ancient universe in which the heavens revolved about a motionless earth. Surrounding the earth, wrote Ptolemy, is a hollow sphere on which all the fixed stars are fastened. This sphere revolves on an axis, passing through the earth, once in twenty-four hours. The sun and moon are each attached to smaller transparent, hollow spheres. These spheres also have the earth at their center, and each revolves at a different speed.

*Ptolemy's* Almagest *(Universe) merits an extended comment. A summary of practically all astronomical knowledge at the time it was written, it developed a model of the universe dating back to the Greek philosopher Plato in the fifth century* B.C. *In this carefully worked-out theory, all celestial motion was interpreted as the rotation of spheres, or the combination of rotating spheres, an idea that held sway for more than 1400 years.*

*In his preface, Ptolemy gives interesting reasons for studying astronomy, a subject "suitably located between the extremes of theology and physics." The former is limited by the incomprehensibility of the divine and the latter by the instability of the natural, neither being susceptible of agreement among philosophers. Mathematics applied to astronomy, on the other hand, is based on observation and is certain. Moreover, the law and order uncovered in such study will improve the moral character of man by "augmenting his taste for the eternal truth."*

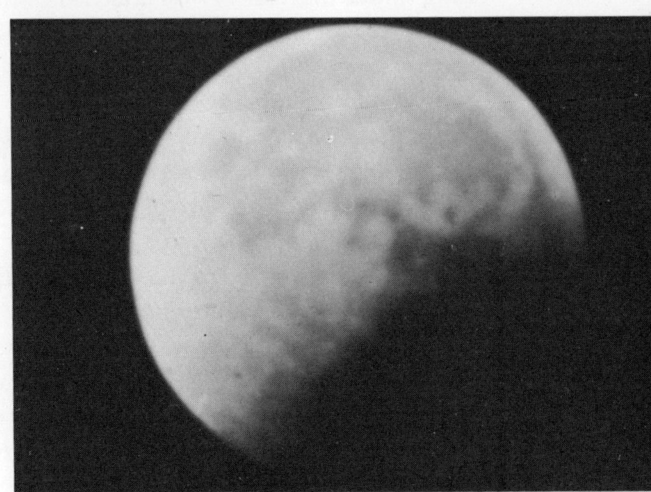

*Fig.* 2. The earth's shadow on the moon. (Yerkes Observatory photograph)

The Almagest proceeds to "assemble all former thoughts on the subject, to present them clearly, concisely, and in proper order, to develop a celestial theory, and to demonstrate all the concepts mathematically." The celestial theory was built on five basic truths, in Ptolemy's words: "(1) The sky is spherical in form, and moves in the manner of a sphere. (2) The earth, considered as a whole, is also sensibly a sphere. (3) The position of the earth is in the middle of the universe, very near the center. (4) The size of the earth and its distance from the center is negligible relative to the sphere of the fixed stars. (5) The earth undergoes no movement or displacement."

The sky is a sphere, Ptolemy reasoned, because the stars attached to it move in circles from east to west during the night, all these circles having the same center (at the pole of what astronomers today call the celestial sphere, used to measure directions in space). His arguments for the spherical earth are the same we learn in school today, and his reasons for the earth being at the center were sound. "If we were off center we would not see the stars move uniformily around us during the night." He goes on to explain how the seven wanderers—sun, moon, Jupiter, Saturn, Venus, Mars, and Mercury—could move irregularly among the stars. This explanation was accomplished by accepting the assumption that the planets move in epicycles—circles—that themselves move in circles around the earth. Ptolemy pictured each planet attached to a rotating sphere that was in turn attached to the rotating sky (or to another sphere so attached), and all these spheres were connected or geared together in a complicated way in order to explain the observed motions of the wanderers in the sky.

The Ptolemaic principle that all celestial motions are produced by rotating spheres was based essentially on our view of the night sky shown in Figure 3, a time-exposure photograph showing nearly two hours' motion of stars around the north pole of the sky. Today we say that this apparent motion is due to the earth's rotation, carrying us with it—but the sky does seem to "turn like a sphere."

The diagram in Figure 4 shows clearly the motions of one of the "wanderers" that the ancient astronomers were trying to explain. Considering that they had no telescopes, it is remarkable that they understood so much. Their ideas were used as late as 1492.

TLP

# The Pardonable Errors of Christopher Columbus

E. RUSSELL PATERSON

(*Sky and Telescope*, October 1952)

It is not to the discredit of Christopher Columbus to state that his discovery of the New World was the lucky outcome of miscalculations founded on scientific errors. The greatness of Columbus rests on his dogged acting on his convictions, his courage, and his powers of leadership. The basis of his convictions was the faulty science of the fifteenth century, for which he was in no way responsible, and which was the cause of his miscalculations.

The theory of the spherical shape of the earth appears very early in the story of science. . . . Columbus inherited it, but the theory was not generally accepted until explorers had succeeded in circumnavigating the earth in the following century.

The size of the spherical earth was the next factor in Columbus' calculations. The best modern measurement gives a circumference of

*Fig.* 3. Star trails. *a.* Near the pole of the sky. *b.* Near the equator. (Yerkes Observatory photograph)

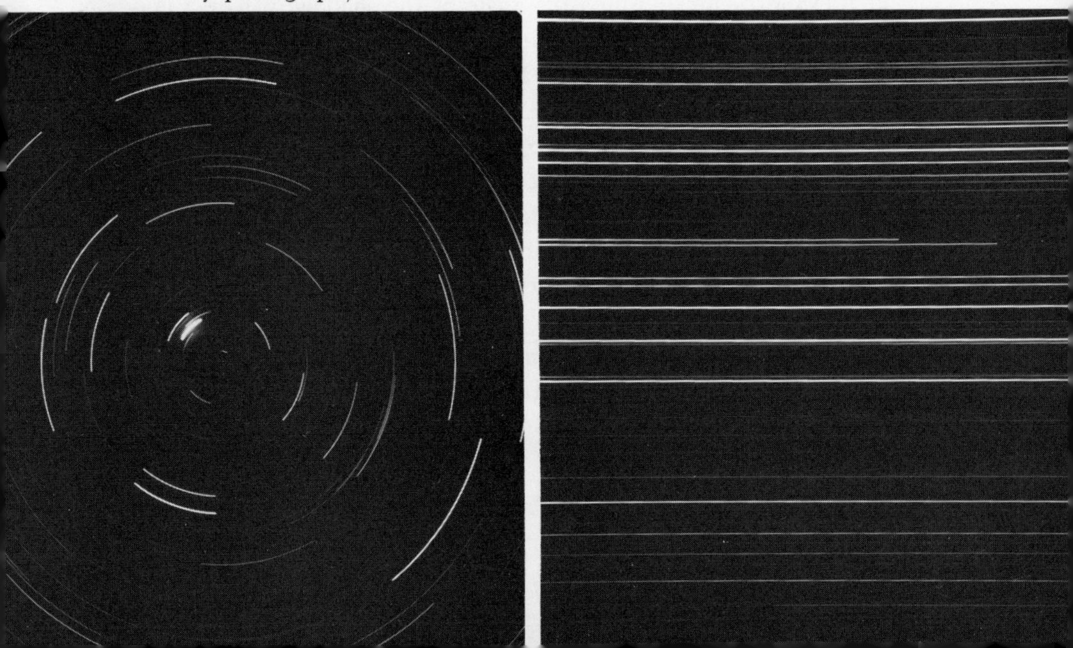

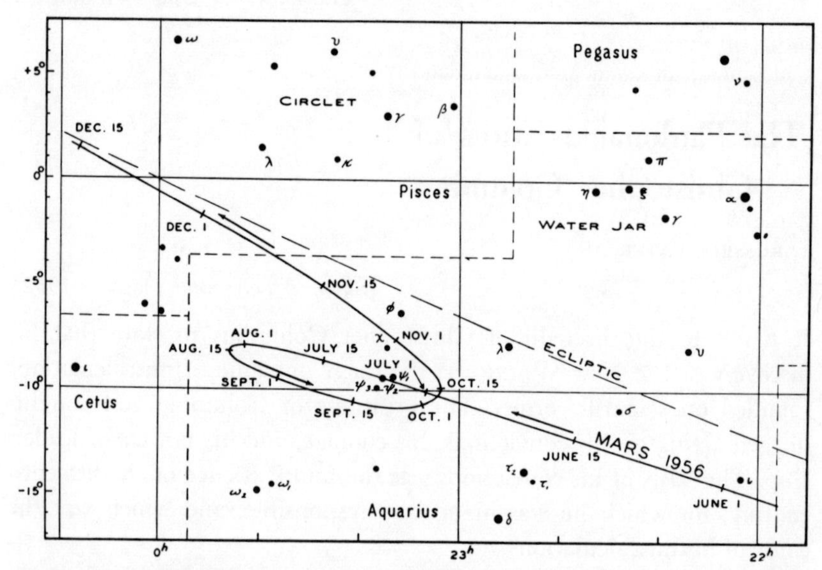


*Fig. 4.* The path of Mars in 1956. Until August the planet moved eastward among the stars and then began its westward (retrograded) travel, resuming direct motion in October.

24,900 miles. The earliest truly scientific attack on the problem of which we have a record was the work of Eratosthenes of Alexandria in the third century B.C. He noted (or heard the report) that at noon at the summer solstice the sun shone directly down deep wells at Syene (modern Aswan), in Egypt, 500 miles south of Alexandria. Working at Alexandria, he measured the angle of the shadow cast by a gnomon (a post) at noon on Midsummer's Day. Simple geometry (as illustrated in Fig. 5A) showed that this was also the angle at the center of the earth subtended by the line between Syene and Alexandria. As he read it as 1/50 of a circle, he concluded that the circumference of the earth must be 50 × 500 miles, or 25,000 miles. While his method is perfectly correct in principle, the details of his calculations were erroneous (Syene is not exactly south of Alexandria), and the amazingly accurate result is due to Eratosthenes' good fortune in that his errors pretty well canceled out.

The estimates of circumference of the earth made by Eratosthenes and later Greeks were expressed in *stadia.* The *stadion* was the standard length of the athletic field in Greek games. Unfortunately, the standard varied in different parts of the Greek world, and it is never clear what stadion was referred to by an author. The variation was between 172 yards and 202 yards. For the sake of clarity, this article translates the stadion as 1/10 mile.

Eratosthenes' estimate of the earth's circumference was 250,000 stadia. The Greek mind always liked to keep things tidy, so he cheerfully added 2000 stadia so that his total (252,000) would be simply divisible by 360 degrees.

About 100 B.C., Posidonius of Rhodes attacked the problem using the maximum altitudes of the star Canopus as seen from Rhodes, where it appears just over the horizon, and from Alexandria (see Fig. 5). From this he deduced that the angle at the center of the earth formed by radii to these two places was 1/48 of a circle. The distance between them he accepted as 375 miles, using the rough guesses of mariners sailing from one port to the other. This gave a circumference of only 18,000 miles—a much smaller earth than that calculated by Eratosthenes.

The third factor in Columbus' calculations concerned the extent of the land mass. To the Greeks (and this belief persisted through the Middle Ages) there was only one land mass—an irregular but rather narrow strip running east and west from Spain to the Orient, bounded by the all-surrounding ocean. . . .

The length of the land mass, and the size of the earth around which it was wrapped, determined all estimates of the extent of the gap between Spain and the Orient. Columbus was not the first by any means to consider sailing westward to the Orient; the possibility of doing so was discussed by Strabo, the famous Greek geographer of the first century B.C., but he believed it could not be done. The problem was that of supplies, for if an unbroken ocean stretched between the two ends of the land mass, ships would have to carry sufficient food and water for the whole trip.

At the time of Eratosthenes, India was known through the conquests of Alexander the Great, and the scientist estimated that the land mass stretched around 130° of his larger earth, leaving an unbroken ocean of 230° width.

It is known that Columbus' principal source of geographical ideas was a book entitled *Imago Mundi*, written about 1400 by the French Cardi-

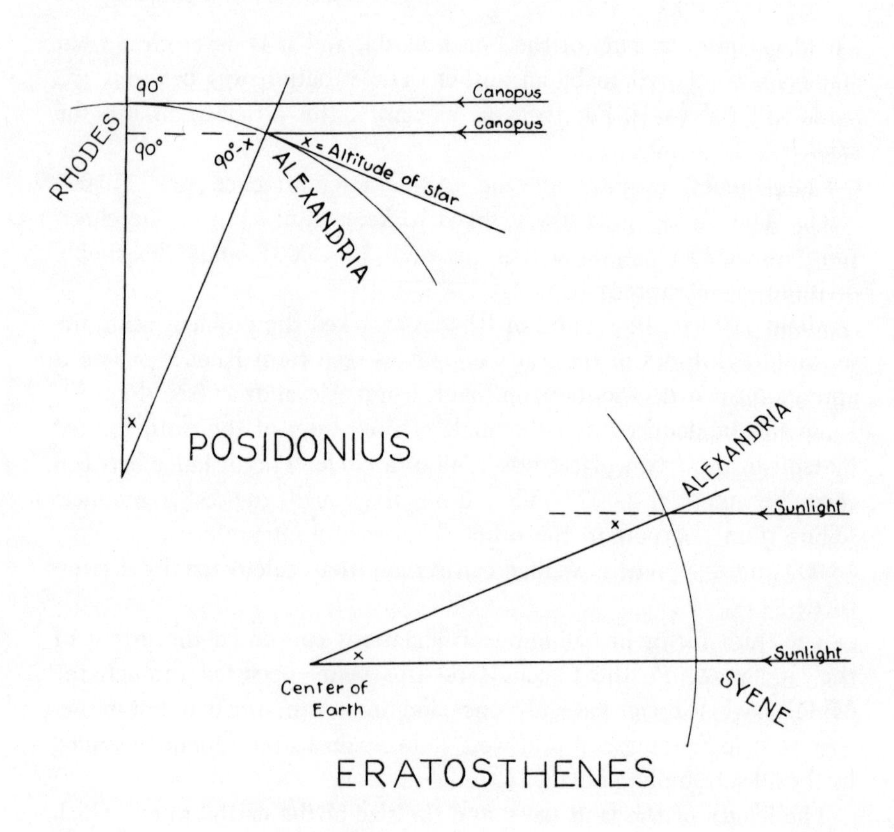


*Fig.* 5A. (*above*) The principles of two methods of measuring the size of the earth in ancient times, one by the altitude of the star Canopus above the southern horizon, the other by the noontime altitude of the sun at the summer solstice. *Fig.* 5B. (*below*) The "land mass" at Lat. 36° N.

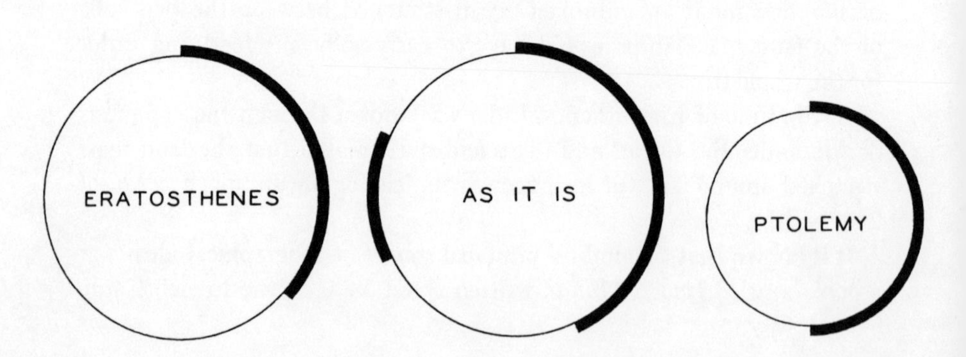

nal Pierre D'Ailly; Columbus carried a copy with him on his voyage and made marginal notes as he proceeded. This book incorporated an ocean of 135°. By this time, however, lands still farther east had been visited by explorers, including Marco Polo, and Columbus revised the figures to a land mass of 240° and an ocean of only 120°.

The final problem was the translation of measurement in degrees to actual mileage. Columbus seemingly misinterpreted the Arabian mile as the Italian nautical mile, which he was accustomed to use. The consequence was that he greatly underestimated the actual mileage across his assumed 120° ocean. It was this miscalculation which gave him confidence that a flotilla of ships could carry sufficient supplies to make the passage. . . .

When Columbus received the authorization he sought, he set sail and after two months reached "San Salvador," usually identified as Watling Island in the Bahamas. Methods available at that time of keeping track of distances sailed east and west were very crude, as there was no scientific method of calculating longitude, and Columbus reported that he had sailed not merely 120° (his own forecast), but 135° west from Spain. The truth was that he had proceeded 65°. Undoubtedly, the expedition would have been disastrous if his theories had been correct. His good luck was that he encountered the New World en route.[1]

*With this historical account of Columbus' good fortune in geographic miscalculation, we conclude the discussion of early ideas about the earth, and turn to motions in the sky. Today every schoolchild is taught that the earth rotates on its axis and moves around the sun in an ellipse, along with eight other planets. But such an orderly solar system is not at all obvious from what can be seen in the sky. In fact, Ptolemy's geocentric model seems to fit the apparent motions of celestial objects far more readily. These seeming motions are briefly summarized as follows:*

*1. The sky turns westward every twenty-four hours (one full day), carrying all celestial objects with it, the stars in their fixed relative positions.*

*2. The moon moves eastward among the stars (not exactly opposite to the daily westward motion), taking 27½ days to go once around the*

[1] Fuller details concerning the theories of Columbus can be found in *The Story of Human Error*, edited by Joseph Jastrow (Appleton-Century, 1936). The geographical section of the book, on which this article is mainly based, was written by Prof. John Barger Leighly, of the University of California.

*sky and back to the stars where it started. This was explained by Ptolemy as a separate circular motion on a circle carried around by the first (1).*

3. *The sun also moves eastward among the stars, taking 365¼ days (one year) to go once around. Its path, the* ecliptic, *takes it first somewhat north, then somewhat south, thus accounting for the seasons.*

4. *The other wanderers (planets) move eastward among the stars most of the time, but execute loops toward the west at regular intervals, different for each. Ptolemy explained the looping by his assumed epicycles. The moon and planets are always fairly near the sun's track, and the band centered on the ecliptic is named the* zodiac. *The groups of bright stars along the way are called the constellations of the zodiac.*

*Motions (1) and (2) are apparent to anyone who looks at the clear night sky for a few weeks, but since the stars cannot easily be seen by day, motion (3) must be inferred from the first stars seen in the western sky just after sunset (or the last seen in the eastern sky just before sunrise). These are found to be the signs of the zodiac in sequence from west to east. Of course, it is assumed that if the stars could be seen by day the sun would be located just west of the constellation on the western horizon immediately after sunset.*

*It was quite reasonable to consider the earth fixed in this system, just as we do today when we describe an airplane in flight or a space probe after launch moving at a speed of several hundreds or thousands of miles per hour. The earth certainly* feels solid and fixed; *what is wrong with the idea that it is at rest?*

TLP

## Direct and Retrograde Motions

J. HUGH PRUETT

(*Sky and Telescope*, October 1950)

All the planets—even the thousands of tiny asteroids—revolve around the sun in the direction known as eastward, or counterclockwise as viewed from the north pole of the sky. But when we watch their apparent motions among the stars from night to night, we frequently get an entirely different impression. For a time they move as we believe they should; but then they apparently reverse and travel westward. For example, Jupiter at the beginning of 1950 was gaining about a minute in right ascension each day, in eastward motion. This daily motion continued for several months, but by May 13 had slowed to ½ minute daily. On June 28, Jupiter stopped its previous motion and apparently began to move westward among the stars.

Such contrary motion confused the ancients who held to the geocentric (earth-centered) theory of the solar system. But the accompanying diagram (Fig. 6) shows the simple solution possible with the heliocentric (sun-centered) system. When the planet appears to move eastward with an increase in right ascension, its motion is said to be *direct*; when westward, *retrograde*. As it ceases its apparent motion in right ascension just before reversing, it is said to be *stationary*. This term in some almanac or astrological literature recently caused a correspondent to ask me, "Does the statement that Mars was stationary February twentieth mean it actually stopped its motion in its orbit?" The planet, of course, always continues its orbital motion, but the apparent motion projected onto the background of fixed stars appears to stop. An examination of the diagram shows that opposition occurs at the middle of the retrograde motion. . . .

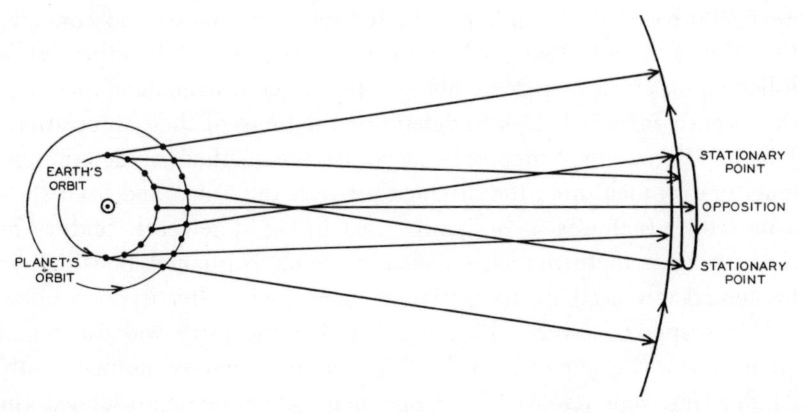


*Fig. 6.* As the faster-moving earth passes a superior planet, our line of sight to that planet swings backward for a time to produce the apparent retrograde motion.

# Astronomy in the Dark Ages

PERCY W. WITHERELL

(*Sky and Telescope,* May 1944)

In the "dark" period between Ptolemy and Copernicus there were a few bright spots. In the ninth century, al-Battani, also known as Albategni, a prince of Syria, made many observations and prepared astronomical tables that were more accurate than those of Ptolemy. He also determined the eccentricity of the solar orbit and the rate of the precession of the equinoxes more precisely, and he stated that the place of the sun's "apogee" was not fixed.

In the fifteenth century Ulugh Bey, a prince of Tartary, founded an astronomical academy and made many personal observations. Among the instruments he had constructed was a gnomon 180 feet high. The results obtained compare favorably with those made later by Tycho Brahe. A catalogue of fixed stars prepared under the patronage of Ulugh Bey ended the gap of sixteen centuries that had elapsed since Hipparchus produced the first list.

In the fifteenth century, the Austrian mathematician and astronomer Georg Purbach and his pupil, Johann Müller, translated and corrected the *Almagest* and other ancient treatises. Müller and Walther established an observatory in Nuremberg with unique instruments; they used the recently invented clock to determine the times of their observations. Johann Werner of Nuremberg suggested the method of determining longitude by measuring the distance between the moon and fixed stars, a procedure that was so brilliantly used in the nineteenth century by the American mathematician and astronomer Nathaniel Bowditch in his remarkably accurate navigation so many years after its innovation.

Handicapped, however, by the belief that the earth was the center about which the universe revolved, astronomy remained dormant until its shackles were removed by Copernicus when he reproclaimed the theory of Aristarchus (the Greek astronomer of the third century B.C.) that the earth and the other planets revolved about the sun.

Copernicus showed that a daily revolution of the earth on an axis inclined to the ecliptic explained the apparent motion of the stars. He still clung to belief in the uniform circular movements of the planets, and in order to explain their observed motions was forced to the hypothesis that the center of each orbit was different and did not coincide with the position of the sun. Nevertheless, the simplicity of his universe helped to establish its probability in the minds of men. . . .

## The Copernican Theory

**EDWARD ROSEN**

(*The Sky*, September 1940)

The present year marks the four-hundredth anniversary of a momentous event in the development of modern astronomy. For in 1540 there appeared the first printed exposition of Copernicus' heliocentric system. The book was written by an enthusiastic young man, George Joachim Rheticus, who gave up a teaching job in a German university

*Fig.* 7. Nicholas Copernicus (1473–1543). (American Museum of Natural History)

in order to visit the celebrated astronomer and master the new system at its source.

Why was a personal visit necessary? The answer is that there was no other way to become acquainted with the new doctrine. For Copernicus was unwilling to release his book for publication. He had thought the whole thing through; he had worked out the proofs and the calculations; he had consummated his life's work. But he clung tenaciously to his manuscript and would not turn it over to a printer.

What is the proper explanation of this conduct? Perhaps Copernicus was antisocial, unwilling to share his discovery with others? No; he communicated his ideas to his personal friends without hesitation, and through this channel they spread. The truth is that he was obsessed by a fear. For over a thousand years men had been taught to believe that the earth was motionless and that it was the center of the universe. Only a few weak voices had been raised in dissent. What reception would be given to a book that subverted concepts established since remote antiquity? In an age torn by religious controversy, what would happen to the author of a treatise that seemed to many persons to contradict the Bible? It was prudent to keep one's peace.

Then in 1539 the eager young professor arrived on the scene. Rheticus was at once enormously impressed by the genius of his host, and realized that failure to publish, or even delay in doing so, meant a serious loss to science. He therefore took upon himself the responsibility of announcing the new system. After all, he had just given up a university job; but he was not anxious about his future because he knew that he was widely regarded as a very promising young man.

Rheticus set himself the task of composing a palatable presentation of his master's system. But he employed an entirely different style of writing. Copernicus' treatise *On the Revolutions of the Celestial Spheres* was cast in a forbidding mold. From start to finish, it was a continuous mass of closely reasoned arguments, careful geometrical demonstrations, and precise arithmetical computations. For Copernicus believed that "mathematics is written for mathematicians," and upon the title page he placed the old Greek warning, "Let no one enter here who is not trained in geometry."

Rheticus adopted a less severe tone. He made plentiful use of the attractive artifices of rhetoric, and embellished his book with astrological flourishes. The scientific material was presented, but it was not packed quite so hard. Even the diagrams, of which there were a great many in Copernicus' *Revolutions* and which made the argument easier to understand, were omitted by Rheticus, so that his tract did not look like an astronomical treatise.

His book, entitled *Narratio prima* or *First Account of the Revolutions of Nicholas Copernicus,* was so favorably received that a second edition was run off in the following year, 1541. Its popularity was enduring, for within the next eighty years it was reprinted three more times. In all probability its success, more than any other single factor, removed Copernicus' fear of adverse criticism and controversy, so that he finally agreed to put his own manuscript into the hands of a printer.

Rheticus arranged to have the printing done at Nuremberg, many hundreds of miles from Copernicus' home. The great astronomer was almost seventy years old, seriously ill, and in no condition to supervise the work. This task therefore fell to Rheticus, who was, however, unable to see it through because he had accepted a teaching post elsewhere. To carry on the supervision of the printing, he selected a prominent clergyman, Andreas Osiander, who had shown a lively interest in the mathematical sciences.

When the great treatise came off the press, its very first section was a brief Address to the Reader. This declared that no doubt some learned men had been offended by the assertion of the earth's motion; but, after all, astronomical hypotheses need not be true, or even probable.

The result was that readers did not know how to interpret the author's position. The body of the work flatly affirmed the motion of the earth as a physical fact; yet the introductory Address to the Reader said that hypotheses need not be true or even probable. What did the author intend to say? What was the reader to believe?

More than sixty years passed before the confusion was cleared up by another great astronomer—Kepler. He declared that the author of the Address to the Reader was not Copernicus at all, but the German theologian, Andreas Osiander. Even Kepler's great prestige did not suffice to clinch the matter, for many eminent authorities continued to believe that Copernicus wrote the Address. The final piece of evidence that established Osiander's authorship was provided by the edition of Kepler's complete works, the first volume of which appeared in 1858.

*Fig. 8.* The Copernican system as depicted in an early eighteenth-century atlas. (American Museum of Natural History)

This contained an essay which had never been printed before, because it was left unfinished by Kepler. It quoted correspondence that passed between Copernicus and Osiander, which made it absolutely certain that Osiander wrote the Address and that Copernicus disagreed basically with Osiander.

Shortly before the publication of this correspondence, the original manuscript of the *Revolutions* in Copernicus' own handwriting came to light. It now became clear for the first time that Osiander had suppressed Copernicus' dignified Introduction to Book I on the value of studying astronomy, and had replaced it by the Address to the Reader, which he himself wrote but from which he withheld his signature.

In his *Watchers of the Sky*, the British poet Alfred Noyes has drawn an imaginative picture of Copernicus' last days:

The neighbors gossiped idly at the door.
Copernicus lay dying overhead.
His little throng of friends, with startled eyes,
Whispered together, in that dark house of dreams,
From which by one dim crevice in the wall
He used to watch the stars.
"His book has come
From Nuremberg at last; but who would dare
To let him see it now?"—
"They have altered it!
Though Rome approved in full, this preface, look,
Declares that his discoveries are a dream!"
"He has asked a thousand times if it has come;
Could we tear out those pages?"—
"He'd suspect."—
"What shall be done, then?"—
"Hold it back awhile."
That was the priest's voice in the room above.
"He may forget it."

## A Tribute to Copernicus (I)

**MAUD W. MAKEMSON**

(*Sky and Telescope*, May 1943)

The revolutionary hypothesis of a heliocentric universe gave an impulse to scientific thought that has gathered momentum with the centuries.

Looking backward over four centuries, some may wonder at the length of time required for the new system to become firmly rooted in the minds of men. Probably no scientific theory was ever so widely discussed or so passionately and bitterly contested by its opponents and defenders over so long a period. More than a century after the publication of *De Revolutionibus*, the Italian Jesuit Father Giovanni Battista Riccioli wrote a book in which he produced forty *new* arguments in behalf of the heliocentric theory and seventy-seven against it.

The objections to the theory were tangibly associated with everyday experience; the arguments in its favor were abstract, nebulous, and unsatisfactory. The concept of a moving earth conflicted with common sense. Even today, when the earth's rotation has become commonplace, a considerable effort of the imagination is required to visualize the vast and stable earth whirling like a top as it rushes through space with the speed of a cannon ball without destroying all life on its surface. Copernicus pictured a kind of "natural" motion which left the exterior of the sphere undisturbed, and his opponents unconvinced. He also pointed out that the far vaster crystal sphere of the fixed stars would be in much graver danger of flying to pieces if it revolved, as they insisted, around the earth.

In the second place, the hypothesis of a stationary sun was at variance with the Bible. What better proof could be found that the sun was habitually in motion than the statement that Joshua commanded the sun to stand still? Thus, Catholic and Protestant alike were necessarily aligned against the new teaching.

The scientists were disturbed by the undoubted fact that no annual oscillation of the stars was observed. Although the Italian philosopher Giordano Bruno had rashly argued for an infinite universe as early as 1585, even Tycho Brahe and Kepler firmly believed that the stars were attached to the surface of a crystalline sphere which marked the boundary of space. If, therefore, the earth describes an orbit about the sun, the stars in a given region of the sky should appear brighter and farther apart when the earth is closest to them, and fainter and more compact six months later when the earth approaches the opposite point of its path. Since no such parallactic motion was observed, Copernicus was compelled to expand the radius of the celestial sphere to such a vast extent that the earth's orbit became immeasurably small in comparison. The vacuous immensity thus interposed between the solar system and the starry heavens was considered extremely wasteful by Tycho Brahe, who remained an opponent of the heliocentric system to the end.

The hypotheses of a rotating and revolving earth are susceptible of exact observational proofs, but such proofs were forced to await the slow development of precise methods of measuring small angles on the celestial sphere and the evolution of a new science of mechanics. The minute effect of stellar parallax was eventually detected by Prussian astronomer Friedrich Wilhelm Bessel in 1838 by a method proposed by Galileo; but in the persistent search for this proof through the centuries, astronomy was enriched by a succession of remarkable discoveries which the world assimilated reluctantly. The rotation of the earth on its axis was first demonstrated by the Foucault pendulum experiment in 1851.

Let it not be thought that a theory of the cosmos springs fully perfected from a single mind. The strength and beauty of the Copernican system lay in the fact that it contained the elements of growth and development which will not have reached completion until the origin of solar systems and galaxies and other controversial problems of the present day have been satisfactorily explained in the far-distant future. During the first half-century after its inception, the theory was generally accepted as a simplified method of calculating the positions of sun, moon, and planets for the annual almanacs which were in demand as the basis for astrological predictions. In 1551, Erasmus Reinhold published his "Prussian Tables," derived by the new system, and they immediately superseded the less accurate Alphonsine Tables based on the Ptolemaic theory. Before the close of the sixteenth century, however, four men were born who were destined to carry on the work of Copernicus in a manner which would stir men's minds and souls to their depths, and revolutionize their concepts of the universe, although only two of them were ardent defenders of the system. They were Tycho Brahe, born in 1546; Galileo, in 1564; Kepler, 1571; and Descartes, 1596.

Tycho Brahe became the most assiduous observer of the heavens that the world had yet produced. His thoughts were first turned to astronomy by the solar eclipse of 1560. In 1563 he observed a close conjunction of Jupiter and Saturn, and noted that neither the Alphonsine Tables nor those of Reinhold had predicted it exactly, the former being wrong by an entire month, the latter by several days. Although impressed by the necessity for continuous and systematic observations, he was not ready to begin his own great program until 1576.

A brilliant new star appeared in Cassiopeia in 1572, which shook Tycho's faith in Aristotle, who had pronounced the heavens unchangeable and incorruptible; for the nova had no measurable parallax and obviously belonged among the fixed stars. Yet the classical teaching held so firm a grasp on the times that Tycho immediately wrote a treatise in which he argued that planets were carried around the earth by revolving crystalline spheres, and comets were generated in the earth's atmosphere.

As if in answer to this challenge, the comet of 1577 trailed brilliantly across the orbits of the inner planets. Tycho measured the parallax, a difficult feat on account of the motion, and concluded that the object was at least three times as far away as the moon and probably beyond the distance of Venus. As the years passed and he followed the bright comets of 1580, 1582, and 1585, his convictions gradually gave way before the evidence of his observations, and he was moved to write a book about these strange visitors from transplanetary space in which he reasoned that they revolved in orbits about the sun and were not part of the earth's atmosphere. Although he thus abandoned the crystal planetary spheres, Tycho could not reconcile himself to a moving earth. He devised a compromise between Aristotle and Copernicus, in which the planets revolved around the sun, which carried them in an annual orbit about the centrally located earth. Any motion of the inert and heavy earth he dismissed summarily as "contrary to physical principles."

Tycho's observations continued until his death in 1601, seven years before the invention of the telescope. Johannes Kepler, whose almanac for 1595 had gained him an unwarranted reputation as an astrologer and prophet, joined the Danish astronomer at Prague a few months before his death. Kepler has been derided as a mystic, three-fourths of whose work was valueless; but his insistent conviction of the divine harmony of the universe, combined with a boundless imagination and a scientific integrity not contented with half-measures, enabled him, after years of failure and discouragement, to discover the true laws of planetary motion. Perhaps the dying plea of Tycho Brahe, that his life's work might not have been in vain, gave strength in the darkest hours of Kepler's arduous search.

When Kepler assumed his heritage, he found that Mars stood 4 or 5 degrees from the place predicted by the tables of Reinhold. Copernicus once remarked that he would be more than satisfied with his theory if it represented the positions of the planets with an accuracy of ten minutes of arc, about one-third the diameter of the moon. Tycho

Brahe's observations with the great mural quadrant attained the surprising accuracy of one or two minutes of arc. So Kepler set out to improve the Copernican system for Mars, until the large discrepancy between observations and prediction was removed. For years he juggled epicycles, equants, and eccentrics of various sizes to attain the desired end. At one point he succeeded in building a structure which reduced the discrepancy to only eight minutes; but steadfastly refusing to accept a result which he considered unworthy of the foundation laid by Tycho, he discarded this system and began once again from the beginning.

At last his perseverance was crowned with success. He saw that the vagaries of Mars could be completely explained within the accuracy of the observations on the assumption that the planet moved in an ellipse with the sun at one focus. Aristotle's declaration that only the circle was sufficiently perfect to become the path of a celestial body now followed the crystalline planetary spheres into the rubbish heap. Kepler was also able to show mathematically why there are fewer days in the period of the year from autumnal to vernal equinox[1] than there are between the vernal and autumnal equinoxes, that is, why the earth moves fastest in its orbit in midwinter when nearest the sun. This reason was stated in his second law: Every planet moves in such a way that its radius vector (the line joining it to the sun) sweeps over equal areas in equal intervals of time. The third or harmonic law, relating the squares of the periods of revolution of the planets with the cubes of their mean distances from the sun, led directly to the inverse square law of universal gravitation, formulated by Newton nearly a century later. The *Epitome of Copernican Astronomy*, published by Kepler in 1618, applied his new laws to all the planets and the moon, as well as to the satellites of Jupiter.

In 1609, Galileo turned his rude telescope skyward and discovered an entirely undreamed-of aspect of the universe. To those who were willing to see, the perfection of the cosmos on which Aristotelians had insisted for 2000 years became no longer tenable. The moon's smooth spherical surface was found to be marred by mountains and pitted by innumerable craters. In the Milky Way countless stars were visible

[1] The vernal equinox in late March, and the autumnal equinox in late September, are the two days of the year when the sun rises due east and sets due west. They mark two opposite points on the earth's orbit around the sun, and would bisect the orbit exactly if it were a circle.—TLP

where there should have been empty space. The glowing Venus revealed waxing and waning phases exactly like those of the moon, proving that it shone only by reflected sunlight and was indeed a satellite of the sun.

Four tiny spheres were seen to perform endless revolutions about Jupiter like children playing around their parent; and the planet continued to pursue its way through the heavens without losing one of them, in spite of the fact that Galileo's opponents pronounced such behavior as "unscriptural." Finally, the sun, in which if anywhere immutability was to be expected, was scarred by dark spots and rotated about an axis!

Even in the face of such overwhelming evidence that the universe was not in conformity with the teachings of Aristotle, the vast majority of scholars still refused to accept the implications. In 1622 the English philosopher Francis Bacon wrote: "Copernicus' scheme is inconvenient; it overloads the earth with a triple motion; it creates a difficulty by separating the sun from the number of the planets with which it has much in common; and the introduction of so much immobility into Nature . . . and making the moon revolve around the earth in an epicycle and some other assumptions of his are the speculations of one who cares not what fictions he introduces into Nature, provided his calculations answer."[2]

## The Astronomy of Tycho Brahe

C. M. HUFFER

(*Sky and Telescope*, December 1946 and January 1947)

Tycho Brahe—the four-hundredth anniversary of whose birth we celebrated in 1946—was the last of the great astronomers who lived and worked before the invention of the telescope. His birth on December 14, 1546, followed by only three years the death of Copernicus, and his

[2] The remainder of this article appears at the end of this Chapter (p. 42), so that the ideas of Tycho Brahe, Kepler, and Galileo can first be described in more detail.—TLP

*Fig. 9.* Tycho Brahe (1546–1601). (American Museum of Natural History)

death in 1601 preceded by eight years the astronomical use of the telescope by Galileo.

Tycho was only twelve years old when he was sent to the university at Copenhagen to study to be a statesman. This career was chosen by his uncle, who had raised Tycho from early childhood, probably with the consent of his father. Such a choice was to be expected for a boy who belonged to the nobility of the Denmark of that time. . . .

The first observations made by Tycho were of a conjunction of Jupiter and Saturn in 1563, when he was sixteen years old. His first instrument was a pair of compasses. He sighted along the two legs of the compasses at a planet and at a nearby star or, as in this first observation, at the two planets, and later measured the angle on a divided circle. Thus he found the time at which the two planets were nearest together—a date which was in disagreement with the two popular tables in use at that time. This error in the tables helped the young astronomer to decide that accurate observations were very desirable, a decision which he spent the rest of his life in carrying out. . . .

Tycho began serious work in astronomy in 1569 and 1570 while living in Augsburg, Germany. The intervening years had been spent in study and travel in various parts of Europe, and he had apparently built several small instruments in his attempts to make accurate observations. In Augsburg he was associated with two brothers, one of whom, Paul Hainzel, agreed to pay the cost of construction of a large quadrant, since Tycho thought a large instrument would give more accurate

*Fig. 10.* Tycho's mural quadrant at Uraniborg. By sighting on a star or planet through the window, Tycho could determine the star's angle above the horizon with an accuracy of 1/1000 of a degree. (Bettmann Archive)

angles. So with the help of skilled workers, the quadrant, with a radius of about nineteen feet, was built and erected in Hainzel's garden.

Since the quadrant and the sextant were the principal instruments used during the lifetime of Tycho, a short description of each should be in order.

One of the two forms of the sextant as used by Tycho had a fixed horizontal arm to which was attached a circular arc, as shown in the Eichner model (Fig. 11). This arm was oriented by means of a plumb line attached to its center. One end was the center of the graduated arc. Another arm was movable about the center and its position was read off a graduated scale with diagonals as in the mural quadrant. The observer sighted along the movable arm and the reading indicated the angle between the line of sight and the horizontal. This instrument was mounted on a stand which could be turned in any direction.

By the middle of 1601 Tycho was in such bad health that although he was only fifty-four Kepler remarked, "the feebleness of old age was upon him." He died on October 24, 1601.

*Fig. 11.* Model of Tycho's astronomical sextant made by L. C. Eichner. Sightings on two stars are made from the tabs on the arc at the left across the pin at the upper right, and the angle between them is read from markings on the arc. (American Museum of Natural History, an L. C. Eichner instrument)

Tycho is almost certainly best known for his planetary observations, used after his death for the theories of planetary motion worked out by Kepler. But his observations of the sun and moon, continued over a lifetime of observing, gave more accurate data regarding the sun's motion than had been known before, and led to the discovery of new inequalities in the motion of the moon. He corrected the tables of refraction and correctly interpreted refraction as being caused by the earth's atmosphere. He cataloged the positions of 1000 stars and found no parallactic or other changes in their relative positions. He made his own instruments with accuracy unsurpassed before the invention of the telescope. His observations of comets proved that they are more distant than the moon, and settled forever the arguments that comets are part of the earth's atmosphere. He had observed the aurorae and thought them to be "sulphurous exhalations ignited in the air, and not clouds illuminated by the sun, as the latter was too far below the horizon in winter."

Tycho's observations stand ahead of those of Hipparchus for accuracy. His theory of the structure of the universe ranks with that of Ptolemy, but was inferior to the Copernican system. It is unfortunate that he did not live another ten years to share Galileo's knowledge of astronomy as improved by telescopic observations. But the brilliance of Tycho's methods of observing without optical assistance places him equal to the most famous astronomers of all time.

## Tycho Brahe's Theory of the Solar System

(*Sky and Telescope,* March 1960)

Many textbooks contain reproductions of the diagram Tycho Brahe published in 1588 to illustrate his plan of the arrangement of the solar system. He proposed that only the moon and sun revolved about the stationary earth, while the other planets and comets had orbits around the sun. Thus Tycho's theory was a compromise between the ancient idea of an immovable earth and the sun-centered arrangement proposed by Copernicus.

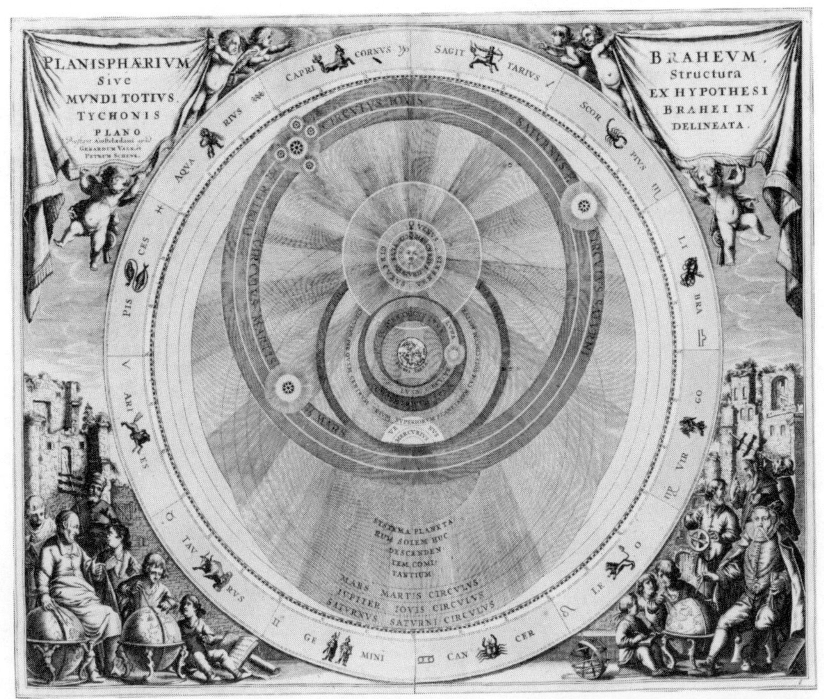


*Fig. 12.* Tycho's system as depicted in an eighteenth-century atlas. The planets are shown revolving around the sun, which in turn revolved around the earth. (American Museum of Natural History)

Until recently, the original Latin text of Tycho's description of his theory had not been published in an English version. This has now been done at the University of California by Marie Boas and A. Rupert Hall, whose translation appears in *Occasional Notes* of the Royal Astronomical Society (Vol. 3, No. 21, November 1959). They present the pertinent portion of his long treatise on the comet of 1577.

Tycho's model eased the way for the gradual acceptance of Copernicanism. The Danish astronomer demolished the traditional belief that the planets were carried along by actual spheres of hard and impervious material. Comet motions indicated to him that the solar system bodies were moving freely through space, in obedience to natural law, and he even suggested that the path of the comet of 1577 might not be "at all points exquisitely circular, but somewhat oblong, in the manner of the figure commonly called ovoid." Tycho's assistant, Johann Kepler, later applied the idea of elliptical orbits to the entire family of planets.

*Tycho Brahe's life was interesting in itself (see Alfred Noyes,* Watchers of the Sky*), and his influence on Kepler (as well as his data on planetary motions used by Kepler) undoubtedly changed the history of science.*

*Kepler's life is well portrayed in Arthur Koestler's* The Sleepwalkers. *Here we are concerned primarily with his contribution to a better understanding of how planets move. Kepler is often cited as a man who made a great scientific discovery by accident—a "sleepwalker." He earned his living as an astrologer, and his* Epitomy *contains a good deal of fruitless numerological nonsense. Nevertheless, his faith in numerical order may have been the basis for his remarkable persistence.*

TLP

## Johann Kepler and the Laws of Planetary Motion

**RUFUS SUTER**

(*Sky and Telescope*, July 1961)

If you stick two tacks through a sheet of paper, tie a thread loosely around them, and, with a pencil holding the thread loop taut, trace the resulting curve, you will draw an ellipse with the tacks as its foci.

Kepler's first law of planetary motion states that a planet travels in

*Fig. 13.* Johann Kepler (1571–1630). (American Museum of Natural History)

an ellipse with the sun at one of the foci. The publication of this law in 1609 marked a very important advance in astronomy. All of Kepler's predecessors—whether like Ptolemy they believed the heavenly bodies to move around the earth, or like Copernicus to move around the sun—held that celestial bodies swung in perfect circles. Even Galileo seems to have regarded Kepler's ellipses as visionary nonsense. But Kepler found from Tycho Brahe's observed positions of Mars that its orbit was in fact an ellipse, and this led him to state his first law.

Another ancient prejudice, that each planet moves at an unvarying speed in its orbit, was refuted by Kepler's second law, also announced in 1609. According to this principle, the radius vector of a planet sweeps over equal areas in equal intervals of time. In the diagram, the shaded areas are all equal; hence the planet requires the same length of time to move from A to *B* in its orbit as it does from C to *D*, or from *E* to *F*. Thus it travels fastest when nearest the sun (at perihelion), and slowest when farthest from the sun (aphelion). (See Fig. 14.)

In this second law, Kepler made a major innovation. Previous astronomers had treated the apparent motions of the heavenly bodies as a problem of geometric perspective. Kepler's approach was in a sense that of an engineer rather than a geometer. While he was interested in the purely geometric aspects of planetary motions, he also pondered the mechanical causes of these motions. Consideration of how the planets should move if there were a center of power in the sun gave him his first inkling that each planet travels faster when nearer the

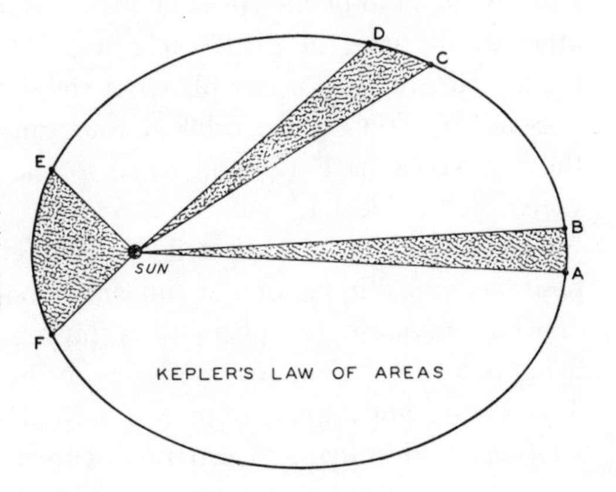


*Fig. 14.* The equal, shaded areas indicate that a planet would move from A to *B* in the same amount of time as from C to *D* or *E to F*.

cause of its motion. In the older approach, it was possible for an astronomer to deny that he asserted anything about the *real* movements of the heavenly bodies when he adopted the Copernican or heliocentric hypothesis. He was merely choosing one of several sets of geometric patterns for simplicity in calculation or for subjective esthetic reasons. This expedient became quite popular among scientists when the issue of the heliocentric theory versus theological authority arose. Kepler, with his dynamical point of view, could no more use it than could an engineer in a later age believe that a wheel connected to a steam engine by a belt made the engine run, rather than vice versa.

TABLE 1. KEPLER'S HARMONIC LAW

| *Planet* | *Distance A. U.* | *Period Years* | *Distance Cubed* | *Period Squared* |
|---|---|---|---|---|
| Mercury | 0.387 | 0.241 | 0.058 | 0.058 |
| Venus | 0.723 | 0.615 | 0.378 | 0.378 |
| Earth | 1.000 | 1.000 | 1.000 | 1.000 |
| Mars | 1.524 | 1.881 | 3.54 | 3.54 |
| Jupiter | 5.20 | 11.86 | 141 | 141 |
| Saturn | 9.54 | 29.46 | 868 | 868 |
| Uranus | 19.18 | 84.01 | 7,060 | 7,060 |
| Neptune | 30.06 | 164.79 | 27,160 | 27,160 |
| Pluto | 39.52 | 248.43 | 61,720 | 61,720 |

Kepler's third law, announced in 1619, is a relation between the revolution times of the planets and the sizes of their orbits. It states that the ratio of the squares of the periods of any two planets is the same as the ratio of the cubes of their mean distances from the sun. In other words, with the earth's year and distance from the sun as units, the period squared for any planet is equal to its distance cubed. Thus, one moving in a circular orbit at four times the earth's distance from the sun would have a period equal to the square root of $4^3$, or eight years. (See Table 1.)

These three laws made possible much better predictions of planetary positions and eclipses of the sun and moon. They could be used for drawing up accurate ephemerides [astronomical almanacs], and for fixing dates in ancient history. Later in the seventeenth century, Newton's law of gravitation, from which Kepler's laws are deducible, gave a rational and unifying explanation of them. It could then be seen that

Kepler's laws are actually close approximations, which would be exact if the masses of the planets were negligible compared to the sun's.

Some of Kepler's contemporaries, among them Galileo, were seeking a physical proof for the theories of the earth's motion and the central position of the sun. Few at that time recognized it in the Keplerian laws. Nevertheless, from our hindsight we can see today that the proof was there.

There is no need to detail here how meticulously Kepler checked his rules against the observations of Tycho Brahe, whom he had served as an assistant before succeeding him as imperial mathematician at Prague. He was fully aware of the importance of empirical or observational proof in astronomy. But there was another side to Kepler, more difficult for us in the twentieth century to understand.

He was a metaphysician and mystic, whose mind was filled with the lore of Plato, Pythagoras, and Plotinus [a Roman neoplatonic philosopher of the third century A.D.]. Thus, while he laid the foundations of celestial mechanics, all his life he was entranced by the hope of finding a relationship between distances of the planets from each other and the ancient doctrine of the five regular solids. He tried to establish a connection between planetary orbits and the rules of musical harmony. Indeed, his passion for the harmony of the spheres probably first attracted him to astronomy and kept him there despite the practical difficulties of living in the midst of tremendous political and religious chaos.

A further aspect of Kepler's complex personality deserves mention. He was not eaten up by a passion to be the first to make a scientific discovery, and did not have the secretiveness characteristic of some brother astronomers. Instead, he sought cooperation among astronomers, for example in observing the total solar eclipse of October 12, 1605. In an age of religious controversy, he was without bigotry. Although a Lutheran, he sided with the Calvinists on some theological points, and at the same time remained on good terms with the Roman Catholics. When Jesuit missionaries at the court of the Son of Heaven in Peking failed to persuade Galileo to send them eclipse calculations, Kepler immediately supplied a part of the Rudolphine Tables which he was compiling. The fact was that Kepler's vision of the harmony of the universe raised him above the strife of his time.

# The Astronomical Work of Galileo Galilei (1564–1642)

I. BERNARD COHEN

(*Sky and Telescope*, January 1942)

January 8, 1942, marked the three-hundredth anniversary of the death of one of the greatest astronomers who ever lived, Galileo Galilei. Galileo's career and Newton's are similar in many ways—both made important contributions to mathematics, physics, theoretical astronomy, the use of scientific instruments—of the telescope in particular. And both made vital contributions to the understanding of what science is, what its methodology is, and what it can do.

Galileo's discoveries in mechanics alone (described by him chiefly in *Discorsi e dimonstrazioni matematiche intorno à due nuove scienze* . . . [Leyden, 1638]) entitle him to an important place in the history of science. His interest in astronomical matters was aroused by a "new star" which was seen in the sky on October 10, 1604. This nova was the most brilliant object in the heavens with the possible exception of Venus, and it aroused a great deal of attention, just as an earlier one had done in 1572, when Tycho Brahe was attracted to astronomy. Aristotle had taught that the heavens were immutable and could not change, that stars could neither be created nor destroyed. The strict followers of Aristotle and Ptolemy were concerned, therefore, to "demonstrate" that the "new star" was no star at all but an illusion—a "collection of vapors" in the sky, or something like an aurora. Galileo, glad to find an opportunity to attack older astronomical thought, gave three public lectures in which he showed that this new star was like all other stars except insofar as it was "new," a nova. . . .

But the most impotrant event in Galileo's career as astronomer occurred in 1609. He wrote:

Ten months ago, nearly, a rumor came to our ears that an optical instrument had been elaborated by a Dutchman, by the aid of which visible

*Fig. 15.* Galileo Galilei (1564–1642). (American Museum of Natural History)

objects, even though far distant from the eye of the observer, were distinctly seen as if near at hand; and some stories of this marvelous effect were bandied about, to which some gave credence and which others denied. The same was confirmed to me a few days after by a letter sent from Paris by the noble Frenchman Jacob Bavodere, which at length was the reason that I applied myself entirely to seeking out the theory and discovering the means by which I might arrive at the invention of a similar instrument, an end which I attained a little later, from considerations of the theory of refraction; and I first prepared a tube of lead, in the ends of which I fitted two glass lenses, both plane on one side, one being spherically convex, the other concave, on the other side.

With these words did Galileo begin his book entitled *The Starry [Sidereal] Messenger* in which he described what he had accomplished by means of the new instrument.[1] The Preface to this book is dated March 4, 1610, and Galileo's invention, or reinvention, of the telescope was apparently made in June or July 1609. The early form of Galileo's telescope appears to have been trumpet-shaped, but later he made use of a straight leaden tube.

*The Starry Messenger* begins with a description of the moon, the first object of Galileo's telescopic attention. His instrument was not sufficiently powerful to show much detail; it was hardly as effective

[1] *Sidereus nuncius* . . . (Venice, 1610); *The Sidereal Messenger of Galileo Galilei* . . . translated with introduction and notes by Edward Stafford Carlos (London, 1880).

as a better grade modern field glass. Yet, until this time, no one had seen the moon magnified at all, and most astronomers believed it to be a smooth globe—clear and perfect as befitted a celestial object. Many explanations of the "apparent" dark spots had been invented—a typical example is in Dante's *Paradiso*, Canto II.

Galileo noticed many smaller markings on the moon's surface, and correctly identified the bright spots seen near the terminator as mountaintops shining in the sunlight, while the surrounding lunar area is still in darkness. With precision and ingenuity characteristic of his research, he calculated the height of the more conspicuous mountains on the moon, estimating that the largest must be in the neighborhood of 4 miles high, a figure closely agreeing with modern observation and calculation. But the most important part of his observation was the fact that the moon greatly resembles the earth, having mountains and rough spots, and large dark spots which he thought (erroneously) were due to the presence of water, and thus named "seas." He doubted the existence of lunar *seas,* however, in a later book.[2]

He next turned his telescope to the fixed stars, and found that the glass did not appreciably magnify the size of the stars, but that it appeared to increase their number vastly. . . .

On January 7, 1610, Galileo turned his telescope toward Jupiter. He noticed that it presented a round appearance much like the sun and the moon; its disk was of greater magnitude than the inferior planets, but, save for the matter of size, there was no apparent difference between the inferior planets and the superior planets.

On close examination, he noticed three very small but bright "stars" in the vicinity of Jupiter, two to the east of the planet, and one to the west. He imagined them to be fixed stars, but he could not help but be struck with the unusual fact that they were disposed with Jupiter in a straight line which was parallel to the ecliptic. Chancing, by merest accident, to look again at Jupiter the following night, he was surprised to find that these three "stars," still arrayed in a straight line, were all to the west of the planet and nearer to each other than the preceding night. Then on January 10, he observed only two "stars," now to the east of Jupiter, and he supposed that the third was concealed by the

[2] *Dialogo di Galileo Galilei . . . sopre i due massimi sistemi del mondo, Tolemaico, e Copernicano . . .* (Florence, 1632).

planet itself. At this point he was unable to account for the phenomenon by means of the motion of Jupiter, and he wondered whether the apparent motions should be referred to the "stars" themselves, rather than to the planet. Here was a matter of great importance and he decided to give it his closest attention.

On the eleventh, he again saw two "stars" to the east of the planet, but one now appeared twice as large as the other. This fact, together with the constant change of the position of these "stars" relative to Jupiter, and the complete disappearance of one of them, gave him the key to their real character: There are three "stars" revolving around Jupiter just as the planets revolve around the sun in the Copernican system. On the twelfth, Galileo saw three "stars," again, but on January 13 he finally saw four of them. On the fourteenth he again saw four. His future observations left no doubt that these were satellites of Jupiter.

Soon after the publication of his book, Galileo discovered the existence of sunspots. . . .

Another discovery made in the year 1610 was the phases of Venus. He announced this on December 11, 1610, in the form of an anagram as follows:

*Haec immatura a me jam frustra legentur*
*o·y*

which can be translated as: "These immature things are read by me now in vain." It really meant: *Cynthiae Figuras aemulatur mater*

*Fig. 16A.* (*left*) The surface of the moon as seen and drawn by Galileo. (Yerkes Observatory) *Fig. 16B.* (*right*) The satellites of Jupiter as observed on successive nights by Galileo. (Yerkes Observatory)

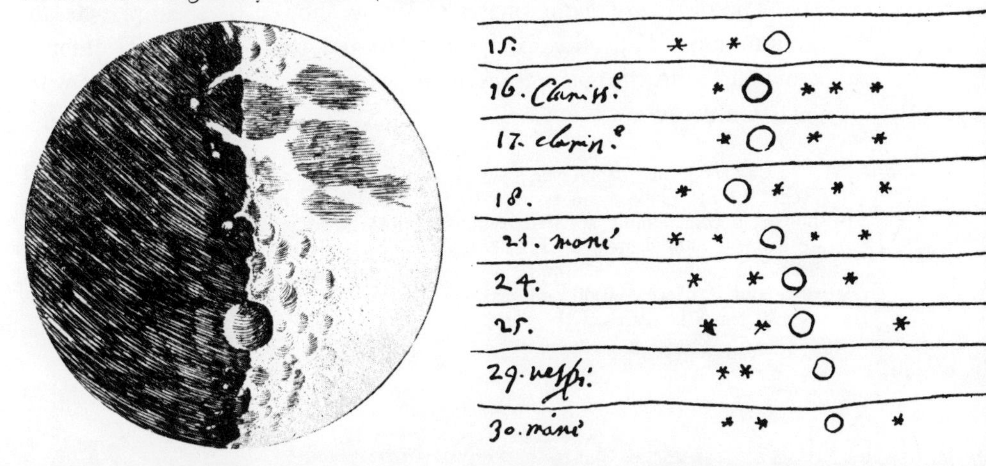

*arorum*—"The mother of loves [Venus] emulates the figures of Cynthia [the moon]." In other words, Venus has phases just like the moon. The moon, the earth, and the other planets all shine by reflecting the light of the sun.

This chain of discoveries in descriptive astronomy had strong theoretical consequences in Galileo's mind. They all were grist for the Copernican mill and each of them was a blow struck at the Ptolemaic system. Let us consider them in the order in which they were made and in which they have been described.

1. The nova of 1604 showed that the ancients were wrong in declaring that there could be no "new stars."
2. The observations of the moon showed it to be like the earth in appearance.
3. The existence of the myriads of stars shown by the telescope proved the unreliability of ancient writers who had never seen these telescopic stars.
4. In the telescope the fixed stars appeared as mere luminous points, so that the apparent diameters of several minutes of arc, attributed to them by previous observers, were proved to be nonexistent.[3]
5. The discovery of the satellites of Jupiter presented nature's model of the Copernican system in operation, and put an end to the difficulty raised by those who asked why the moon alone formed an exception to the general rule by moving around a planet instead of around the sun.
6. The discovery of sunspots supplied a striking refutation of the Aristotelian doctrine of the perfection of celestial objects, and indicated that the sun, like the earth and moon, rotated about its axis.
7. The discovery of the phases of Venus showed that the planets are nonluminous. Thus the fixed stars, "to use the words of [Giordano] Bruno, are suns, the planets are moons or earths," as Kepler wrote with joy to Galileo.

[3] This, according to Dreyer, "swept away the very serious objections raised by Tycho [to the Copernican system] that a star having no annual parallax and yet showing a considerable apparent diameter must be incredibly large." [A minute of arc is 1/60 of a degree, or 1/21,600 of a full circle, about as large as a 50-cent piece 100 yards away. A bright star may look this large to the naked eye, but if it were, and if it were 1000 times as far from us as the sun is, the star would be over 30 times larger than the sun.]

Firmer than ever in his conviction that the Copernican system represented the only true picture of the solar system, Galileo spent the years from 1625 to 1629 writing a treatise that he intended to be "the sum and culmination" of his life's work. This was the famous *Dialogues concerning the Two Principal Systems of the World, the Ptolemaic and the Copernican* [*Dialogo di Galileo Galilei* . . .]. Despite the avowal of impartiality and even of favor to the Ptolemaic system, this book was an effective and crushing attack on Ptolemaic astronomy and a convincing proof of the Copernican system.

The result, as everybody knows, is that Galileo was brought before the Inquisition, and there did he "abjure, curse, and detest" his "errors and heresies," while his book was placed on the Index. The Inquisitors were relatively lenient; they allowed him to teach and to continue with his work, and he not only wrote his *Dialogues on Two New Sciences*,[4] but he was able to make another astronomical discovery, namely, the libration of the moon [wobble of the hemisphere facing the earth]. Galileo was the final victor. His works were eventually removed from the Index and a Vatican Observatory was founded.

Whether or not Galileo actually invented the telescope, or whether, as he says himself, he reinvented it, makes little difference. The important thing is that he was the first person to use a telescope to view the heavens. With the insight which is the characteristic of genius, he grasped at once what purposes the new instrument might serve. In every direction in which he looked with the telescope he saw something new—the moon, the Milky Way, Jupiter, the sun, Venus. He had an experience which was unique in the history of mankind; he was the first person to view a hitherto undiscovered universe, the very nature of which had been unknown to all members of the human race before him. And his genius made the most of his opportunity.

*Man's understanding of celestial bodies—what they are and how they move—took a gigantic leap in the century of Copernicus, Tycho, Kepler, and Galileo. But even further progress was to come through working out the Copernican system.*

TLP

[4] *Discorsi e dimostrazioni matematiche intorno à due nuove scienze* . . . (Leyden, 1638); *Dialogues concerning Two New Sciences by Galileo Galilei*. Translated by Henry Crew and Alfonso de Salvio (New York, 1914; New York, 1933; Evanston, Ill., 1940).

# A Tribute to Copernicus (II)

MAUD W. MAKEMSON

(*Sky and Telescope*, May 1943)

Galileo's experiments in mechanics opened a new field for exploration as far-reaching in its potentialities as the sidereal world he had discovered. He established the principle of inertia, later to be restated by Descartes in his laws of nature and embodied by Newton in the first law of motion. Galileo applied it to the moving earth to explain why birds flying through the air, and the atmosphere itself, are not left behind by the planet's motion. Yet, inconsistent as it may now appear, he explained tides as the effect of the earth's rotation, scornfully rejecting Kepler's [correct] suggestion that the ocean responded to an influence emanating from the moon.

Descartes taught men to reason and to doubt. Voltaire said of him that he was "born to discover the errors of antiquity and at the same time substitute his own." Apart from his invaluable contributions to mathematics, he advanced indirectly the evolution of the Copernican theory by pointing out that it was possible for the earth to describe an orbit about the sun without actually stirring, if it were swept along by a great current as a motionless ship is borne upon the tide. Thus he reconciled the concept of a moving earth with the Scriptures and by his "vortices" prepared men's minds to accept the law of gravitation. He treated his own system, as he did those of Copernicus and Tycho Brahe, merely as a working hypothesis which "saved the phenomena." His theory was not stated with such exactitude that it could be subjected to experimental tests, yet it was held by many scholars on the Continent until the early part of the eighteenth century.

Descartes attributed "conductivity" to interplanetary space, which he regarded as filled with a "subtle matter," suggestive of the more modern "ether." His proposition that "God . . . always preserves an equal amount of movement in the universe," sounds very much like the modern principle of the conservation of momentum. Other propositions which indicate the extent of his thinking along purely astronomical lines are: that the earth viewed from the heavens would not appear otherwise than as a planet smaller than Jupiter or Saturn; that the sun and fixed stars shine by their own light; that the moon and the planets derive light from the sun; that the moon when it is new is illuminated by the earth; and many others.

During the seventeenth century astronomy progressed along a variety of lines. In 1655, the Dutch physicist and astronomer Christian Huygens discovered the first satellite of Saturn and announced that, since the quantity of planets and satellites in the solar system had attained the perfect number *twelve,* no others remained to be discovered. Later he established the nature of Saturn's rings and must have seen other satellites without recognizing their character. He invented the pendulum clock in 1656, thus making possible more accurate measures of time, so essential a part of astronomical observations. The micrometer for precise estimates of very small angles in the sky was developed by several observers. French scientists focused attention on the determination of the length of a degree of the earth's meridian in various latitudes and discovered the flattening of the earth at the poles. Polish astronomer Johannes Hevelius charted the features of the moon.

In the Observatory of Paris, the anti-Copernican Jean Dominique Cassini measured the rotations of Jupiter and Mars and discovered new satellites of Saturn; and Danish astronomer Olaus Roemer established the finite velocity of light from a study of the times of eclipses of Jupiter's moons. These same "Galilean planets" led the Italian physicist and astronomer Giovanni Borelli to announce in 1666 that the heavenly bodies moved as if acted upon by a central force at right angles to the direction of motion, which prevented them from flying off along the tangent.

In 1677, Edmund Halley observed a transit of Mercury across the disk of the sun and suggested how it could be utilized to determine the distance of the sun from the earth—a proposal which was carried out the following century during a transit of Venus. From a comparison of ancient and modern observations, Halley identified returns of the comet which bears his name. From the behavior of Jupiter and Saturn, he suspected the existence of a trans-Saturnian planet, which was verified by the discovery of Uranus 100 years later by William Herschel.

These and many other important discoveries marked the passage of the years. The greatest individual contribution to theory, however, was the work of Isaac Newton. His law of universal gravitation and three laws of motion became the foundation for the celestial mechanics of the eighteenth and nineteenth centuries. He introduced the entirely new concept of *mass* as the "quantity of matter," and derived the masses of the sun and of those planets which possess satellites by comparing their gravitational attractions. . . .

It has been said of Newton that he explained the "why" of things; but even he regarded the mutual attraction of two bodies, distant from each other in space, as merely a convenient hypothesis for describing an inexplicable phenomenon.

The history of the evolution of the Copernican theory does not end with the triumphs of the eighteenth century; nor can an adequate account of its far-reaching consequences be presented without sketching the entire history of astronomy to the present day. With each new proof of the validity of the theory, new and grander fields for exploration have been revealed. In each of the four centuries since the birth of the Copernican system, there have been pioneers who caught the gleam of something beyond the ever-widening horizon, waiting to be discovered and explained. And so the situation still remains in the twentieth century.

# 2

# Newton's Mechanical System

*The advance in man's understanding of celestial motions described in Chapter 1 was truly remarkable. Flying in the face of established authority and contradicting traditional views that had been accepted for more than fourteen centuries, a few men literally had revolutionized thought about the earth, the planets, and their place in the universe. The idea that the earth revolves about the sun, laughable in 1550 and heretical in 1630, was not yet "proved" in the narrow-minded sense of that word. Strict proof was not in fact possible until two centuries later.*

*However, the early concepts of a fixed earth, rotating sky, and planets moving in epicycles—the Ptolemaic system that was finally considered "wrong"—served an important purpose in establishing a kind of order. Without it and its defects, Copernicus' idea might not have gained men's interest; Tycho Brahe's measurements might not have been made.*

*Many other factors undoubtedly played a part—the Renaissance and the consequent broadening of intellectual viewpoints influenced much of European life—but it was the idea of Copernicus, the accurate measurements of Tycho, the persistence of Kepler in his calculations, and the rigorous thinking of Galileo that made possible the great advance.*

*When Newton was born, in 1643, it was at least plausible that the earth and planets moved in ellipses about the sun in the manner described by Kepler's laws. What is more, it was known that the moon moved in a similar way around the earth, and other moons moved around Jupiter. Galileo had shown that falling weights were accelerated toward the center of the earth, the acceleration (increase in speed) being the same for both light and heavy weights if the effects of the air are accounted for. These findings were what Newton referred to when he later said that if he had seen somewhat farther than others it was because he stood on the shoulders of giants. Still, conflicting ideas were popular, and it required exceptional vision to pick the right giants.*

TLP

## Isaac Newton (1643–1727)

**I. BERNARD COHEN**

(*Sky and Telescope*, January 1943)

If someone were to ask which two successive years were the greatest—from the point of view of anniversaries—in the history of science, he would be hard put to find a more significant pair than '42 and '43. They commemorate the death of Galileo, the birth of Newton, the death of Copernicus and the publication of his *De Revolutionibus*, and the publication of Vesalius' *Anatomy*. These last two books were both published in the same year, 1643, and they mark, in an exact sense, the beginning of the modern scientific era. One dates the beginning of modern astronomy and cosmology, the other, of anatomy and physiology. . . .

*Fig. 17.* Sir Isaac Newton (1643–1727). (American Museum of Natural History)

On January 4, 1643, Newton was born in the little hamlet of Woolsthorpe, some seven miles south of Grantham, in Lincolnshire. We may mark the time in our minds by recalling that Harvard College had been founded some six years earlier; that Louis XIV, the "grand monarch," was then but five years old; and that Shakespeare had been dead for twenty-two years.

For the purposes of discussion, we may divide Newton's life conveniently into three periods. The first of these ends with his appointment, at the age of twenty-seven, to the Lucasian Professorship of Mathematics at the University of Cambridge in 1669. For the history of science, the most interesting—as well as the most significant—part of this period is the two years which Newton, after graduation from Cambridge, spent in seclusion at his birthplace in Woolsthorpe. Newton's most recent biographer, Dean More,[1] remarks: "There are no other examples of achievement in the history of science to compare with that of Newton during these two golden years." From August 1665 to March 1667, young Newton made three great discoveries, each of which alone would have entitled him to a most distinguished position in the history of science.

The first of these was purely mathematical. The second was the law of dispersion and composition of white light.

Newton had been experimenting with the well-known effects of passing white light through a prism. He discovered that white light is broken up by the prism into light of different colors, and, in addition, that if he separated light of one color from the dispersed light and passed it through a second prism, there was no further decomposition.

[1] Louis Trenchard More, *Isaac Newton, a Biography* (New York, Charles Scribner's Sons, 1934).

He also found that a second prism placed in a diametrically opposite position to the first would recombine the many colors into white light once again.

Newton was quick to realize that herein lay the key to the nature of color and the explanation of the rainbow. He also saw that the disturbing colors in lens telescopes were a result of this, and he therefore designed the reflecting telescope.

The third discovery made by Newton during this two-year period was the law of universal gravitation. The best statement of its importance is that of Pierre Simon de Laplace, the great French astronomer, who was notorious for his refusal to praise the work of others, whether contemporaries or predecessors. Laplace wrote, "It was reserved for Newton to make known to us the general principle of celestial motions."

One of the anecdotes which everyone knows is that Newton arrived at the law of universal gravitation by observing the fall of an apple. However absurd it may be, it is nevertheless true. Recently an unpublished life of Newton came to light. It was written by the Rev. William Stukeley, physician and divine, and one of the best-known antiquaries of the eighteenth century.[2]

Stukeley was a friend of Newton's, a Fellow of the Royal Society, and, in his own phrase, "a countryman of Sir Isaac Newton's"; he lived a number of years in Grantham. His account, which follows verbatim, corroborates the story told by Voltaire (who had got it from Newton's niece) in every detail. Here it is:

> After dinner, the weather being warm we went into the garden and drank thea [!], under the shade of some apple-trees, only he and myself. Amidst other discourse, he told me, he was just in the same situation, as when formerly, the notion of gravitation came into his mind. It was occasion'd by the fall of an apple, as he sat in a contemplative mood. Why should that apple always descend perpendicularly to the ground, thought he to himself. Why should it not go sideways or upwards, but constantly to the earth's centre? Assuredly, the reason is, that the earth draws it. There must be a drawing power in matter: and the sum of the drawing power in the matter of the earth must be in the earth's centre, not in any side of the earth. Therefore does this apple fall perpendicularly,

[2] William Stukeley, M.D., F.R.S., *Memoirs of Sir Isaac Newton's Life—1752—Being some account of his family and chiefly of the junior part of his life* (A. Hastings White, editor; London, Taylor and Francis, 1936).

or towards the centre. If matter thus draws matter, it must be in proportion of its quantity. Therefore the apple draws the earth, as well as the earth draws the apple. That there is a power, like that we here call gravity, which extends itself thro' the universe.

And thus by degrees he began to apply this property of gravitation to the motion of the earth and of the heavenly bodys, to consider their distances; their magnitudes and their periodical revolutions; to find out, that this property conjointly with a progressive motion impressed on them at the beginning, perfectly solv'd their circular courses; kept the planets from falling upon one another, or dropping all together into one centre; and thus he unfolded the Universe. This was the birth of those amazing discoverys, whereby he built philosophy on a solid foundation, to the astonishment of all Europe.

. . . The second period of Newton's life ends with his appointment as Warden of the Mint some twenty-five years after the Lucasian Professorship appointment, in 1669, had opened his public career. In this interval, he produced the great works which brought him scientific fame, and which consummated the three chief discoveries of the first period.

Newton's first published paper was devoted to an account of his investigation of the prismatic spectrum. Several writers, chief among them the English mathematician Robert Hooke, objected to Newton's advocacy of the corpuscular theory of light.[3] Newton replied to the objections and a long controversy ensued. He found this controversy so disagreeable that he declared: "I intend to be no more further solicitous about matters of philosophy [science]." And he blamed "my own imprudence with parting for so substantial a blessing as my quiet to run after a shadow."

So repugnant to him was this consequence of fame—the possibility of criticism—that he protested he would not allow his works to be published until after his death. "It may be said, without great exaggeration," writes Dean More, "that it was as difficult to force his mind to divulge his ideas as it had been for him to create them." The nineteenth-century

[3] Newton developed an ingenious explanation of the refrangibility of light—different bending of the different colors by a prism. He assumed that light was a stream of small particles, red-light particles differing from blue-light particles. An alternative theory, explaining colors as waves of different sizes, was favored over Newton's "corpuscular theory" until about 1900, when the quantum theory combined aspects of both.—TLP

English mathematician, Augustus Morgan, tells us that a discovery of Newton's was "of a twofold character—he made it, and then others had to find out that he had made it."[4] . . .

Newton's *magnum opus,* insofar as the world is concerned, is his *Principia Mathematica.*[5] This book elaborates the law of universal gravitation, according to which bodies attract each other in direct proportion to their masses and in inverse proportion to the square of the distance between them. It is the first complete treatise on celestial mechanics in which the major known facts were accounted for.

With one broad stroke of genius, a new era was ushered in; man no longer had to invent special hypotheses to explain planetary motion, nor need he endow the planets with "special intelligences" to direct them in their paths. Small wonder that the succeeding century had such great veneration for Isaac Newton, that Alexander Pope was able to write:

*Nature and Nature's law lay hid in night,*
*God said, Let Newton be, and all was light.*

Newton's achievement was based on the work of predecessors. The immediate past had produced the analytical geometry of Descartes and his contemporary, the French mathematician, Pierre de Fermat, the algebra of the English mathematicians William Oughtred, Thomas Harriot, and John Wallis, Huygens' discovery of centrifugal forces, Kepler's laws of planetary motion, Galileo's law of falling bodies, and the law of the composition of velocities—to mention but a few of the ingredients present and waiting for the grand Newtonian synthesis.

One of the greatest debts of Newton to his predecessors was that which he owed to Galileo. Prior to the time of Galileo, it had been generally agreed that there was a difference between sublunary and celestial matter. The matter of the heavens, of the moon, the sun, the planets, and the stars, was thought to be crystalline perfect, immutable, and unchangeable. But Galileo's telescope had shown him that the

[4] Augustus De Morgan, *Essays on the Life and Work of Newton* (Chicago, The Open Court Publishing Company, 1914).

[5] The *Principia Mathematica* is available in a modern English edition prepared by the late Florian Cajori (Berkeley, University of California Press, 1934).

opposite was more truly the case. As a result, Galileo showed the essential uniformity of all matter and was thus led to the conviction that it is as "dignified" to study the laws governing the motion of a falling stone as those governing the movement of the celestial bodies. Further, since all matter is the same, the laws must certainly be the same laws. Nature, according to Galileo, is dominated by the word *necessity;* hence, its laws must be mathematical.

Newton's accomplishment was to give a formal statement of this credo of Galileo. He showed that the laws of motion apply equally to terrestrial and heavenly bodies, that the force which keeps the moon in her perpetual orbit is the same force which gives its curvature to the flight of a stone on the earth.

When Newton was at the height of his scientific career, he abandoned the pursuit of science to become a public servant. The third period of his life began when he was, at his own request, appointed

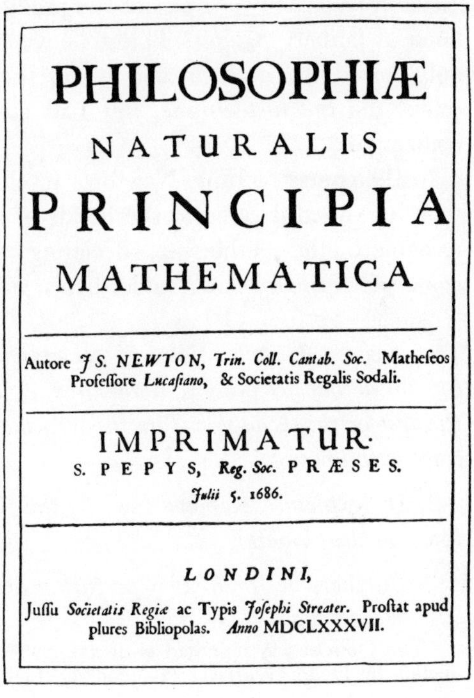

PHILOSOPHIÆ
NATURALIS
PRINCIPIA
MATHEMATICA

Autore *J S.* NEWTON, *Trin. Coll. Cantab. Soc.* Matheſeos Profeſſore *Lucaſiano*, & Societatis Regalis Sodali.

IMPRIMATUR·
S. PEPYS, *Reg. Soc.* PRÆSES.
*Julii* 5. 1686.

*LONDINI,*
Juſſu *Societatis Regiæ* ac Typis *Joſephi Streater*. Proſtat apud plures Bibliopolas. *Anno* MDCLXXXVII.

*Fig. 18.* Title page of the first edition of the *Principia.* Note the "Imprimatur" of Samuel Pepys, who, as president of the Royal Society, had to declare that he thought the book "fit to be printed."

Warden of the Mint. Under his supervision, the great undertaking of the total recoinage of English money was begun and completed. When this had been done, in 1699, Newton was promoted to be Master of the Mint. In 1703, he was elected president of the Royal Society, of which he had been a fellow since 1672.

He took his duties at the Mint very seriously, but this third period of his life was not wholly barren of scientific achievement. It not only witnessed the publication of the *Opticks* (1704),[6] but was marked by various discoveries. With one of these, there is associated a story which can never be too well known, and which illustrates the magnitude of Newton's creative ability better than any description could.

In the Leipzig *Acta* for June 1696, Johann Bernoulli, one of Europe's foremost mathematicians, published a challenge problem addressed "to the most acute mathematicians of Europe." The problem was to find the curve between two points not in the same vertical line along which a body falling by its own weight shall descend in the least possible time. Newton received two copies of the problem at four o'clock on the afternoon of January 26, 1697. Before he went to bed that night, he had not only solved the problem and found the curve in question to be one called the *brachistochrone*, but had completed the problem by generalizing it.

In the course of time, Newton's result was printed, although anonymously. When it came to the hands of the challenger, he immediately recognized the authorship, declaring with interjection, "*Ex ungue leonem!*" A mere "claw" sufficed to reveal the "kingly creature."

*The successful applications of Newton's theory of gravitation are far too numerous to present here; only a few examples will be given in the rest of this Chapter. The theory's major effects can be grouped usefully as follows:*

*1. It "explains" Kepler's laws as the result of the sun's gravitational force on the planets.*

*2. Further, it predicts "perturbations" (deviations from Kepler's*

[6] The *Opticks* was reprinted with a foreword by Albert Einstein and an introduction by E. T. Whittaker (London, G. Bell and Sons, Ltd., 1931).

*perfect ellipses when two planets pass close to each other); inversely, unexplained perturbations later led to the discovery of two planets, Neptune (p. 60) and Pluto (p. 65).*

*3. After the eighteenth-century English chemist and natural philosopher Henry Cavendish measured the gravitational force between two spheres of known mass, Newton's equations could be used to calculate the mass of the earth from measurements of falling weights at the surface or from the motion of the moon.*

*4. Likewise, the motion of planets around the sun yields the sun's mass (and the motions of double stars, their masses; the motions of galaxies, their masses).*

*5. Motions of moons around other planets, or the observed perturbations of planets or comets, give the masses of the planets.*

*6. The motions of artificial satellites and space probes can be predicted with high accuracy.*

*Note that Newton's mechanics made it possible to "weigh" astronomical bodies far from us. This always requires another mass that can be pulled by the gravitational force of the body to be weighed—Jupiter's moons by Jupiter, the planets by the sun. The second mass is not itself weighed unless it is large enough to pull the first body noticeably. For instance, the moon is large enough to wobble the earth as it goes around us each month, and this allows us to weigh the moon.*

*Finally, one often comes across the oversimplified statement "Einstein proved Newton wrong; General Relativity Theory has replaced Newton's mechanics." As a matter of basic philosophy this is true, but Newton's mechanical laws are still very much in use for predicting motions of planets, asteroids, comets, satellites, and space probes. It is only in the case of planets near the sun (Mercury and Venus) that a minute correction must be made to Newton's formulae.*

*Although Newton established the basis for precise prediction, a great deal of mathematical calculation is necessary in order to use his theory. As the following article shows, this time-consuming work can now be turned over to high-speed electronic machines, developed during the past fifteen to twenty years.*

TLP

# The Motions of the Five Outer Planets[1]

DIRK BROUWER AND G. M. CLEMENCE

(*Sky and Telescope*, February 1951)

The accurate measurement of the motions of the planets and the representations of these motions by a rigorous theory have played a basic role in the development of physical science, as well as in practical problems such as those of navigation. As the wealth of observational data accumulates over the years, the problem of adequately representing it by a consistent theory has become ever more difficult. The recent advent of the electronic calculator has at last made it feasible to perform the theoretical analysis with accuracy far greater than that of the accumulated observations. . . .

The Greek theories of the planetary motions culminated in the system constructed by Ptolemy some 1800 years ago. In this system, the motion of each planet is represented by superimposing one or more small circular motions in space upon a motion in a large circular orbit around the earth.

In the early seventeenth century, Kepler found the planetary orbits around the sun to be ellipses; and he then developed laws for the elliptic motions from which formulas and tables for computing the positions of the planets were prepared and published in 1627. However, Jupiter and Saturn departed from Kepler's theory also; and it was not until after Newton had formulated the theory of universal gravitation that a satisfactory explanation for the divergencies was advanced. Were a planet acted upon by only the gravitational attraction of the sun, the orbit would be an exact ellipse; the observed departures from elliptic motion may be attributed to the disturbing effects of the other planets. Assuming the correctness of Newton's simple law of gravitation, it becomes theoretically possible to solve what may be called the fundamental problem of celestial mechanics: Given the positions and direc-

[1] Published by courtesy of *Research Reviews*, Office of Naval Research.

tions of motion of several bodies (say Jupiter, Saturn, and the sun), together with their speeds and masses at a particular time, find their positions at any other time. But the simple statement of the problem gives no idea of the formidable character of its solution. Ever since Newton's time the most eminent mathematical astronomers have devoted their lives to devising practical methods for solving it, and in applying these methods to the actual planets. The difficulty is illustrated by the lapse of more than a century after the publication of Newton's theory before a mathematical representation of the motions of Jupiter and Saturn was obtained that came reasonably close to meeting the requirements of that time.

Two methods have proved successful in practice. In one, called the method of general perturbations, the coordinates of a planet in space are given by trigonometric series, in which the time remains an algebraic symbol. To find where the planet is at any time it is only necessary to substitute a number in the formulae; the number expresses the number of years and fractions thereof since some initial epoch, say 1900 January 1, Greenwich Mean noon. It is this method that has been most used for the principal planets. . . .

The other method is called the method of special perturbations.

*Fig. 19.* The IBM Selective Sequence Calculator which carried out over 12 million arithmetical operations in computing the orbits of the five outer planets. (International Business Machines)

Here the position of a planet is actually calculated step by step from the initial epoch, the steps being so close together that the planet does not move far enough from one step to the next to change the attractions of the other planets upon it very much. This method has two drawbacks. In order to find the position of a planet at any time it is necessary to calculate it for all the intervening times since the initial epoch; and if many steps are required it is necessary to use many significant figures [long decimals] in the calculations to avoid excessive accumulation of error in the end-figures. . . .

During the past three years, an application of the method of special perturbations has been made to the five outer planets of the solar system, Jupiter, Saturn, Uranus, Neptune, and Pluto, as a portion of a cooperative undertaking sponsored by the Office of Naval Research of the U.S. Naval Observatory, the Yale University Observatory, and the Watson Scientific Computing Laboratory. The paths of these five planets have been traced out for 407 years, from 1653 to 2060, by calculating their actual positions at forty-day intervals. These five planets were chosen because the first four are the controlling bodies of the solar system (except for the sun), each being far more massive than all the other planets and remaining material put together, while Pluto, the outermost, exerts appreciable effects on the others. The effects of Mercury, Venus, the earth, and Mars, are hardly appreciable and can best be worked in separately from the main problem.

The present application is the first in which the actions of the planets on one another have been calculated at each step, instead of assuming that the paths of all except one are known in advance. Thus, at each step, the attraction of each of the five planets on the other four was calculated, as well as the attraction of each on the sun. Each step of the integration involved 800 multiplications of large numbers, 100 divisions, 1200 additions and subtractions, and the recording of 3200 digits. The large number of steps made it necessary to use fourteen decimals in the calculations.

So large an amount of calculation could not have been accomplished in a reasonable length of time without an electronic calculator of high capacity. Fortunately, such a calculator was placed in operation in January 1948. This machine, the IBM Selective Sequence Electronic

Calculator, was able to make all the calculations, in duplicate, for a single forty-day step in less than three minutes. . . .

An operator with a desk machine, working forty hours a week, might have done the job in about eighty years, if he had made no mistakes. Experience shows that in work of this kind the occurrence of mistakes may double the time required. Furthermore, a mistake occurring at any step causes every subsequent step to be wrong. It is not certain that this work could have been successfully accomplished at all by ordinary methods.

As was mentioned earlier, the initial data required for solving the problem are the position, speed, and direction of motion for each planet at some initial epoch. Three numbers are needed to specify the position, one for the speed, and two for the direction, making a total of six numbers for each planet, or thirty numbers in all. These thirty numbers had to be determined by observing the planets with telescopes. When high accuracy is wanted it is necessary to have many observations, extending over a long period of time, and this is one reason why the calculations were extended so far into the past. The thirty constants of the orbits were known at the start with insufficient accuracy, and were improved by successive approximations. The first calculation extended for only thirty years. The resulting positions of the planets were compared with the observed positions, and the constants of the orbits were adjusted to bring about better agreement. A second calculation was then commenced, and carried for 180 years, after which a new comparison with observations was made, and the constants adjusted a second time. Another calculation was then made for the same 180 years, and another comparison with observations showed that the constants needed no further improvement. The final step was to extend the 180-year stretch to 400 years.

About 15,000 observations of Jupiter and Saturn were used in adjusting the constants of the orbits. For Uranus and Neptune fewer observations were available. Uranus was not discovered until 1781, and Neptune not until 1846. For Pluto the number of observations was comparatively small, as this planet was discovered in 1930. . . .

The observations of Neptune that were available when American astronomer Simon Newcomb constructed earlier tables covered only fifty years since its discovery in 1846. There are, however, two precious prediscovery observations by French astronomer J. J. Lalande in 1795, when the planet was recorded as a faint star. The curious situation with regard to Neptune is that the modern observations of this planet and the prediscovery observations of 1795 are compatible only if the attraction by Pluto with a mass comparable with the mass of the earth is included. . . .

In addition to the constants of the orbits, the masses of the planets must be known at the outset. Fortunately, reasonably good values of these were available from previous investigations. The results of the present work will, however, make further improvement possible. About a dozen observations of Uranus during the century preceding its discovery may be of particular worth for the evaluation of the mass of Pluto.

From the scientific point of view, the object of studying the motions of celestial bodies is to learn more about how the universe operates. For 200 years after Newton's formulation of his laws of motion it was thought that they would suffice to explain all of the celestial motions. French astronomer Urbain Jean Joseph Leverrier discovered, however, about a hundred years ago, after many years of study, that the planet Mercury did not move strictly in accordance with Newton's laws. The discrepancy remained unexplained until 1915, when Einstein formulated the general theory of relativity. Then it appeared that the discrepancy could be completely removed. But what is meant by complete removal? Only that the contradictions, if they exist, are smaller than the errors of the observations. As the observations continue to improve with the invention of new techniques, it is always possible that a discrepancy will arise where none was known before. Then attempts to explain it may lead to a fundamental advance in knowledge.

It is known that gravitation is not the only force acting within the solar system. For example, the presence of meteors and the zodiacal light [see Part 4] indicate something in the nature of a resisting medium. Whether this is dense enough to affect the motions of the planets appreciably is not known. The present work may help to provide an answer. And there may be other forces acting, at present unknown.

## Mass of Saturn

(*Sky and Telescope*, June 1960)

[In 1959] R. H. Krotkov and R. H. Dicke of Princeton University called attention to a small discrepancy between the observed and predicted motions of Jupiter. This has the form of a small oscillation in the orbital longitude of that planet, amounting at most to only 0.25 second of arc as seen from the sun, and with a period close to the twelve years of Jupiter's revolution.

This effect has now been explained by G. M. Clemence, of the U.S. Nautical Almanac Office, as due to a small error in the adopted value of the mass of Saturn, a body whose attraction greatly influences the motion of Jupiter. Dr. Clemence finds that the discrepancy is removed if Saturn's mass is 1/3499.7 that of the sun.

Previously, the most precise value of the mass of Saturn was 1/3497.6.

## Orbit of Venus

(*Sky and Telescope*, January 1961)

At the Nautical Almanac Office of the U.S. Naval Observatory in Washington, D.C., a major long-term program has been determination of more precise orbits for the principal planets. R. L. Duncombe has now published an exhaustive study of the motion of Venus from 1750 to 1949, the first major revision of Simon Newcomb's work of about seventy years ago.

Dr. Duncombe's orbit calculations are based upon approximately 24,000 observations of Venus made at seven observatories. Since the relative positions of the earth and Venus are nearly the same after a lapse of eight years, he divided all the observations into eight-year groups, and made a separate determination of the orbit for each interval.

While corrections to the old orbit are small, the elements of Venus are now much more precisely known. The relativistic shift in the perihelion point of the orbit was found to be 8.06 seconds of arc per century, very close to the amount predicted by Einstein's equation.

Dr. Duncombe was able to determine an improved value of the mass of Mercury from its perturbations of the motion of Venus. His result for the mass is 1/5,970,000 that of the sun, with a probable error of about ±8 per cent. . . .

Now underway at the Nautical Almanac Office is a thorough new investigation of the orbit of Mars.

*The precision of Newton's mechanics is well demonstrated by the remarkable agreement between computations and observations shown above. The difference (called a "residual" by Clemence and Brouwer) is seldom larger than 1″ (one second of arc)—smaller than a letter on this page would seem at a distance of a quarter of a mile from your eye.*

*When the observations do not agree with the predicted motion of a planet, as has happened at least twice since Newton's day, it is reasonable to look for a new mass that should be included in the calculations. In this way Neptune and Pluto were discovered.*

TLP

# The Discovery of Neptune

**LEO MATTERSDORF**

(*Sky and Telescope*, September 1946)

This is the story of a great triumph of mathematics, the story of the perseverance of two great minds until they finally had arrived at the solution of a mighty puzzle of nature. Besides the earth, which they did not suspect of being a planet, the ancients knew but five of these wanderers of the sky—the ones visible to the naked eye: Mercury, Venus, Mars, Jupiter, and Saturn. It was 172 years after Galileo used the telescope astronomically that man first knew another planet. In 1781, William Herschel, then an amateur astronomer in England, perceived an object which moved among the stars. He first thought it to be a comet, but later it was recognized as a new planet. He named it Georgium Sidus, after his sovereign, George III, but in time this planet came to be known as Uranus. It was soon discovered that Uranus had been seen before but that its planetary nature had not been recognized.

There were, in all, nineteen prediscovery observations of Uranus, so astronomers were able to compute an orbit for the new planet, and, under all the orthodox rules, the planet was to follow that orbit. But no matter how the computations were varied to allow for this and that, Uranus failed to keep to its predicted path. These errors were very small, it is true, but by 1844 the discrepancy had increased to two minutes of arc, or about 1/15 of the apparent diameter of the moon. Every allowance had been made in the orbit calculations for the pull of the known planets, and especially for the big ones, Saturn and Jupiter. It was generally believed that Newton's laws would hold well beyond the known limits of the solar system, although this was to be the first real test. If Uranus were behaving according to the law of gravitation, there should be no such deviation between its observed and predicted positions.

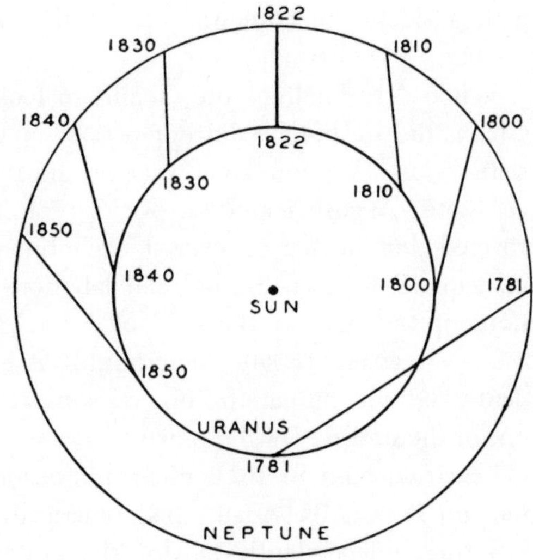


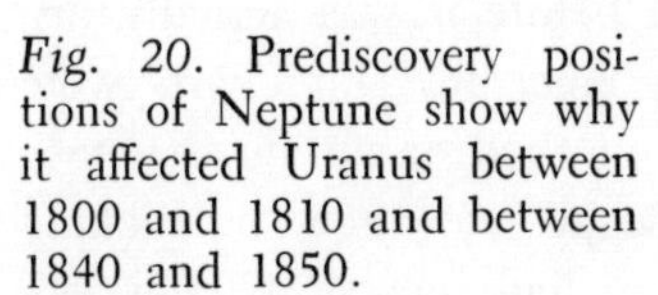
*Fig.* 20. Prediscovery positions of Neptune show why it affected Uranus between 1800 and 1810 and between 1840 and 1850.

Because Uranus seemed to accelerate in its orbit between the time of its discovery in 1781 and 1822 and thereafter seemed to be retarded, it began to appear that in the depths of space was another body, an unseen member of the sun's family, which was pulling Uranus from its normal path. According to Newton's universal law, every particle of matter in the universe attracts every other particle with a force that is directly proportional to the product of their masses and inversely proportional to the square of the distance between them. Thus, a body four times as massive as a second body but twice as far from Uranus would attract Uranus as much as the second would.

Only two men who undertook it had the skill and fortune to complete the problem. These were John Couch Adams, of England, and Urbain Jean Joseph Leverrier, of France. . . .

In 1841, when Adams was twenty-two years old and a student in St. John's College, Cambridge, he resolved to attack the problem of the irregularities in the motion of Uranus. He obtained his first solution in 1843; other solutions came later, and by the fall of 1845 he was ready to put his figures to the test. Although Cambridge itself had the best instrument for the search, Professor J. Challis of Cambridge sent Adams to see Sir George Airy, the Astronomer Royal, at Greenwich. Adams did go to Greenwich, but he did not see Airy, who did not care to be disturbed. Adams left a note for Airy and this Airy acknowledged, but with a sidetracking question about the error in the radius vector of Uranus.

When Airy finally wrote Challis to look for Neptune in July 1846, Challis did so, but he did not possess up-to-date charts of the stars in that region. We now know that he did see Neptune on two different occasions, August 4 and 12, over a month before it was actually discovered, but he passed over it each time. Since his star charts were inadequate, he used the old and laborious method of noting the positions of the stars in the field of his telescope and then, by looking again a few nights later, determining if any had moved. Challis evidently did not compare his observations with sufficient care to note that one of the stars he saw did move.

Leverrier, born in 1811, was a professional astronomer. In the summer of 1845, after Adams had practically finished his computations, Leverrier independently tackled the problem, and by the summer of

1846 had submitted three papers to the French Academy. In these he showed that only a planet beyond Uranus could be responsible for its perturbations. On August 31, 1846, in his third paper, he gave the position it should then have in the sky.

Public interest was growing by leaps and bounds and on September 16, 1846, Sir John Herschel (son of Sir William Herschel), in an address before the British Association stated with reference to the yet-undiscovered planet: "We see it as Columbus saw America from the shores of Spain. Its movements have been felt trembling along the far-reaching line of our analysis."

Knowing that the observatory at Berlin possessed a new chart of the stars in that region where the planet was expected to be found, Leverrier wrote to the chief assistant of the observatory, Johann Gottfried Galle (who lived until 1910), and asked him to look for the new planet at "a point on the ecliptic in the constellation of Aquarius, in longitude 326°." There, he said, Galle would find a new planet looking like a star of about the ninth magnitude [sixteen times fainter than stars visible to the naked eye], and having a perceptible disk." Galle received the letter on September 23, 1846, and lost no time in verifying the data sent to him.

That night Galle turned his telescope to the place in the heavens directed by Leverrier. No object in the field of view presented a disk. An assistant, H. L. d'Arrest, who had offered to aid in the search, checked on one of the new charts each of the stars which Galle reported seeing through the telescope. Of nine objects in Galle's field of view, eight were stars and the ninth was Neptune, within a degree of the spot computed by Leverrier. The next night the strange object was seen to have moved from its position of the previous evening. The new planet had been found! It was perhaps the greatest achievement of mathematics as applied to astronomy, and it was a substantial verification of the theory of universal gravitation.

As Adams' position was nearly as accurate as Leverrier's, these two mathematicians, a Frenchman and an Englishman, are today equally recognized as the discoverers of Neptune.

The orbit of Neptune is not that computed by either Adams or Leverrier, and many students have tried to show that it was a happy accident that the planet was found so close to the spot designated by

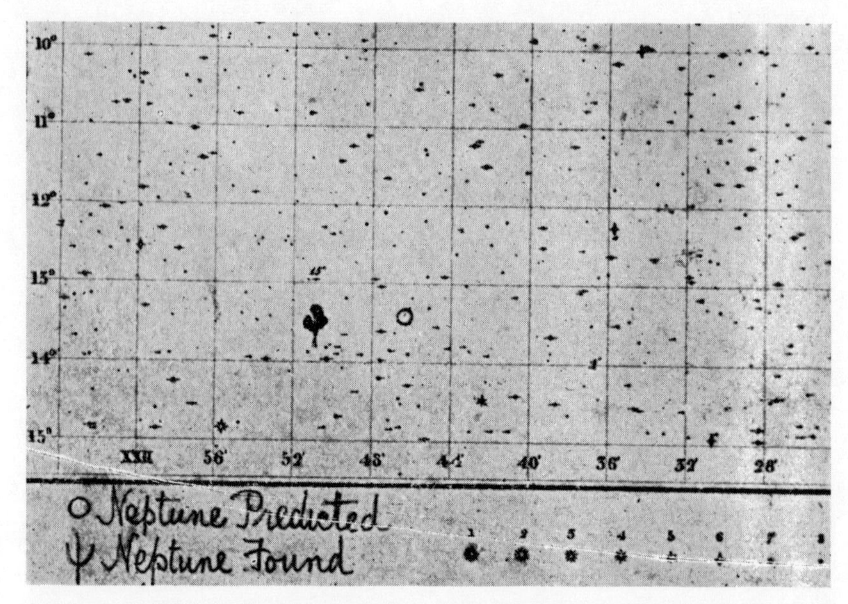


*Fig. 21.* A drawing based on a corner of the Berlin map used by Galle and D'Arrest in searching for Neptune on September 23, 1846.

these first predictions. Controversy on this matter is based on the fact that both computers used the wrong distance from the sun.

Neptune revolves around the sun in a nearly circular orbit in a period of slightly less than 164.8 years, whereas Leverrier had predicted the period as 217 years. Its mean distance from the sun is about 2,796,600,-000 miles. At this distance, sunlight is four hours old when it reaches the planet. On Neptune the sun's light has only 1/900 its brightness on the earth, but the planet appears to us as an object of magnitude 7.7, or [about three times] brighter than Leverrier had expected. . . .

Neptune, too, did not keep to its predicted orbit, and further unexplained differences developed in the positions of Uranus and some other planets. Although the differences were much smaller than Leverrier and Adams had to work with, the American astronomer Percival Lowell, in 1915, published the results of a detailed investigation and stated that he believed a trans-Neptunian planet existed at approximately forty-five times the distance from the sun that the earth is. In 1930, eighty-four years after Neptune's discovery, Pluto was discovered.

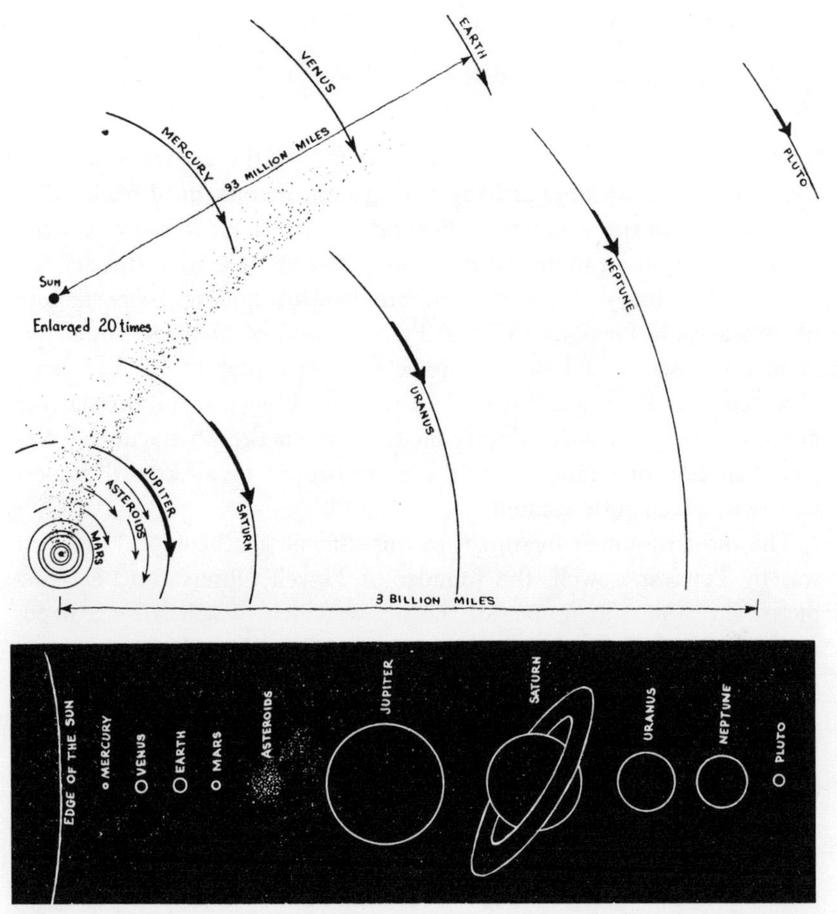


*Fig.* 22. Schematic diagram of the solar system drawn to scale. Sizes shown in lower part. (Yerkes Observatory)

# Reminiscences of the Discovery of Pluto

**CLYDE W. TOMBAUGH**

(*Sky and Telescope*, March 1960)

This year [1960] marks the thirtieth anniversary of the finding of Pluto, farthermost planet in the solar system. Yet for those who were at Lowell Observatory then, the impressions remain so vivid that it seems only yesterday. A number of people shared the many years of effort that led to this achievement. I came upon the scene on the eve of fruition of the enterprise. Only after arriving at Flagstaff, Arizona, did I realize that I was to join in the search for a new planet, and what it is like to work all night long in an unheated dome in winter at 7000 feet altitude. . . .

After Neptune's discovery, the problem of finding more remote planets became far more difficult. Perturbations of Neptune could not at first be used as a basis for prediction, since that planet had been observed over only a small part of its 165-year orbit. Instead, the starting point was the very small discrepancies between the observed and predicted motion of Uranus, after the perturbations by all known planets had been taken into account.

The most thorough treatment of this difficult mathematical problem was by Percival Lowell, the founder of Lowell Observatory. He predicted the approximate area of the sky in which to search for a hypothetical planet X. To account for the unexplained small perturbations of Uranus, he assigned a mass of seven earths and a mean distance of about 4 billion miles to the unknown object. If it were of low density and high reflecting power, like Jupiter and the other giant planets, its apparent magnitude should have been about 12 or 13.[1]

The observational problem thus proposed by Lowell was formidable, for the unknown planet could only be a faint, slow-moving body that would have to be singled out from hundreds of thousands of stars. No longer could one expect to recognize a new planet by visually checking a small sky field containing a few hundred stars.

Photography obviously provided the only efficient search technique. Lowell Observatory began a systematic photographic search in 1905. Each sky area was photographed twice, with exposures of about three

[1] Astronomers measure the brightness of stars by "magnitudes" on a logarithmic scale; the larger the magnitude, the fainter the star. The brightest stars in the sky are "first magnitude." The faintest visible to the naked eye are 100 times fainter, magnitude 6. With a small telescope one can see eleventh-magnitude stars, 100 times fainter than sixth magnitude, and so on—5 more magnitudes for each 100 times smaller brightness—to stars of magnitude 19 visible in the 200-inch telescope at Mount Palomar in California. A difference of one magnitude means a ratio of brightness about 2.5 to 1; 2 magnitudes, 6.3; 3 magnitudes, 16; 4 magnitudes, 40; 5 magnitudes, 100.

The number of stars increases rapidly with magnitude, as Tombaugh later implies; there are about 6000 stars of magnitude 6 or less in the whole sky, and over a billion of magnitude 16 or less.—TLP

hours in order to reach sixteenth magnitude. The plate centers were spaced about 5 degrees apart along the central plane [ecliptic] of the solar system.

This intensive search from 1905 to 1907 was unsuccessful. Next, an extensive series of photographs was made with the observatory's 42-inch reflecting telescope. Exposures of only a few minutes reached the seventeenth magnitude, but the telescope had a useful field of only one square degree and a great number of plates had to be taken to cover the search area.

The hunt was continued from 1914 to 1916 by Lowell and C. O. Lampland with a lens borrowed from Sproul Observatory, Swarthmore, Pennsylvania. Although this attempt did not result in the discovery of Pluto, it was later found that the plates actually contained weak images of the planet. . . .

In January 1929, I joined the Lowell Observatory staff. The 13-inch telescope lens made by Carl Lundin in Cleveland, Ohio, arrived soon after. It had a focal length of 66 inches, giving a plate scale of 30 millimeters per degree. . . .

The standard exposure was one hour. Such long exposures with a lens as fast as f/5.2 caused some background fogging of the plate from the light of the sky, even on dark nights. Fortunately, bright auroras are rare at Flagstaff, but even a crescent moon above the horizon could not be tolerated. Each month, then, a week on either side of new moon was used in making exposures at the telescope. The period from first-quarter moon to last quarter was spent in blinking the plates obtained during the previous two weeks.

Another precaution was of paramount importance. As the earth revolves around the sun, it passes each exterior planet and causes the latter for a time to appear to move westward in the sky. This retrogression arc depends on the distance, being greatest for nearby planets, such as Mars and the many small asteroids, and very small for objects as far away as Neptune or beyond. . . .

Near opposition, therefore, a typical asteroid is in apparent rapid westward motion and can readily be distinguished from a trans-Neptunian planet. These considerations limited the strip of sky to be searched each dark-moon period to 15 degrees either side of the point opposite to the sun. By adhering closely to this opposition point, the daily angular shift of each planet suspect served as a quick index of its distance. . . .

By April 1929, the actual observations began. Three good photographs were taken of each region of the sky within a few nights of each other (preferably all three in a week). The two best-matching plates were compared in the blink microscope, and the third was available as an immediate check on any suspected moving object.

This procedure made it practical to push a thorough search well into the seventeenth magnitude. Faint photographic defects gave rise to thousands of planet suspects over the years. Each had to be checked, for the risk could not be taken of letting the long-sought planet slip by. Other suspects turned out to be faint variable stars whose minimum brightnesses were fainter than the plate could detect. . . .

As the autumn of 1929 came, the perfected technique of observing and blink examinations had settled into routine. When the plates were well matched and reasonably clean of spurious images, I could carry out six or seven hours comparing pairs of plates each day. In the constellations Pisces and Aries, each plate recorded some 50,000 stars, and a pair could be examined in three days.

The number of star images gradually increased as the Milky Way was approached. The plates of eastern Taurus and western Gemini contained up to 400,000 stars each! The speed of examination decreased, and the work with the comparator began to fall behind schedule.

In February, 1930, after struggling through the Taurus plates, I skipped over to those in eastern Gemini, where the stars were less thickly packed. The entire length of the latter constellation had been photographed by the end of January that year. I chose three plates centered on the bright star Delta Geminorum, taken January 21, 23, and 29, respectively, but bad seeing made the first of these unacceptable for blinking.

While blinking a field two-thirds of a degree east of Delta, I suddenly spied a fifteenth-magnitude object popping in and out of the background. Just 3.5 millimeters away another fifteenth-magnitude image was doing the same thing, but appearing alternately with respect to the other, as first one plate and then the second was visible through the eyepiece.

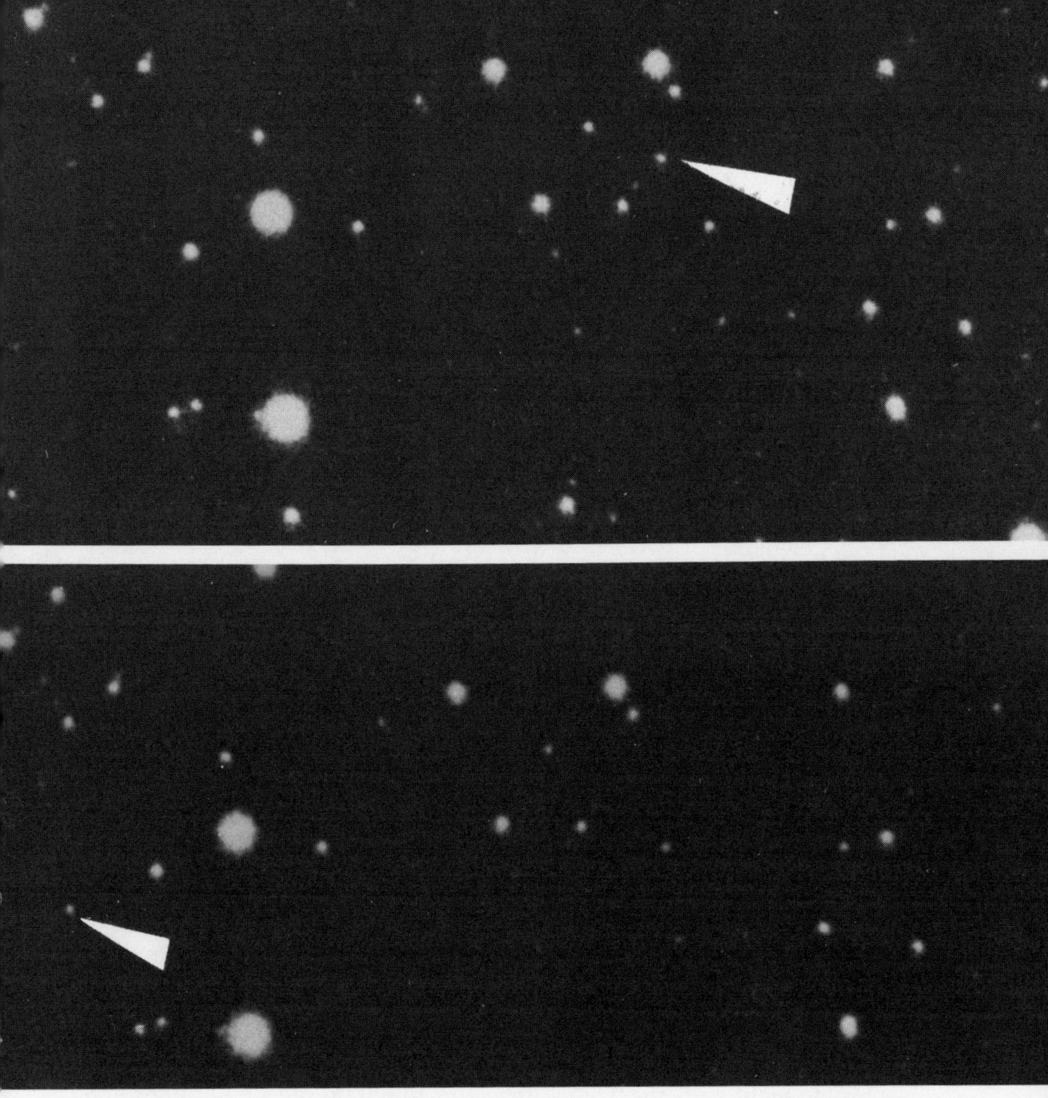

*Fig.* 23. Small parts of the plates that were blinked by Clyde Tombaugh on February 18, 1930. The discovery positions of Pluto are marked by arrows. Note the motion of the planet between January 23 (*top*) and January 29, 1930. (Lowell Observatory photograph)

"That's it!" I exclaimed to myself. The change in position—only three or four millimeters in six days—was much too slight for an ordinary asteroid near opposition. But were the images real or spurious? At once I laid out the 8-by-10-inch plates taken the same night with another telescope. Although nearly at its limit of visibility, there were the images in exactly the same respective positions!

There was the image displaced about a millimeter east of the January 23 position. Any possibility of the phenomenon being a pair of variable stars was now ruled out. Next, I measured the displacements approximately with a millimeter scale. The object was retrograding about seventy seconds of arc per day. This seemed to be it!

At 4:45 P.M. I told the other astronomers that I had found something. They repeated the same checks for their satisfaction.

The sky was very cloudy—no chance of getting a recovery plate that evening. Dr. Slipher stressed that no announcement should be made until observational confirmation was completed during the next few weeks. . . .

The next night, February 19, was clear, and another one-hour exposure of the Delta Geminorum region could be taken. Although three weeks had elapsed, the new image was quickly found about one centimeter west of the January 29 position.

From this plate, a contact film was made to serve in locating the planet visually with the 24-inch telescope. On the following evening, we gathered in the dome. The important question was whether the distant object would show a disk. The big telescope was turned to where the planet should be. There it was, a most unimportant-looking, dim, starlike object, which had moved perceptibly from its plate position of the night before. Each of the staff took a look. No disk could be made out, even though the seeing was fairly good. This caused some uneasiness, for Lowell had predicted a disk one second of arc in diameter and a stellar magnitude of 12.

For the next few weeks, the new planet was photographed every possible night with the 42-inch reflector[2] to obtain precise positions and in an unsuccessful search for possible satellites. . . .

As the weeks passed, the motion of the object conformed perfectly to that expected of a trans-Neptunian planet. It was decided to announce the discovery on March 13, 1930, which was the seventy-fifth anniversary of Percival Lowell's birth and the date of Uranus' discovery 149 years earlier. Observers at other institutions quickly confirmed the position and motion of the new planet.

[2] Two of the major types of optical telescope are the reflector, in which light is brought to a focus by reflection from a mirror, and the refractor, in which light is focused by passing through a lens.

In early May, the name *Pluto* was selected by Lowell Observatory and officially proposed to the American Astronomical Society and to the Royal Astronomical Society. For the planetary symbol, the interlocked letters *P* and *L* were chosen, being both the first two letters of the planet's name and Percival Lowell's initials.

Could the systematic search techniques by which Pluto was found lead to other discoveries of distant planets? Dr. V. M. Slipher encouraged me to continue the hunt with the 13-inch telescope entirely around the sky, and to a considerable distance from the ecliptic.

By 1943, a major part of the sky had been combed for planetary bodies down to the sixteenth and seventeenth magnitudes. No new planet suspects were found. The time interval between the plates of each pair was enough to reveal the motion of an object ten times as remote as Pluto. On the one-hour exposures, a planet like Jupiter could have been recognized at 40 billion miles from the sun, or one like Neptune at 25 billion miles.

In addition, during 1939 and 1940 a series of two-and-one-half hour plates was taken along the ecliptic to extend the planet search to magnitude 18. In the Milky Way, however, the stars were so numerous that the examination of the plates became prohibitively tedious. Three to four weeks of intensive work was required to blink a single pair. In Scorpius and Sagittarius even one-hour exposures recorded a million stars on each plate! . . .

During my share of Lowell Observatory's long-continued searching for trans-Neptunian planets, about 90 million star images were examined in 7000 hours at the blink comparator. Nearly 4000 asteroid images were marked on the plates, 40 per cent of them new, while 1807 vari-

*Fig. 24.* The motion of Pluto as seen on the sky is traced from 1930 to 1934. The bright star on the right is Delta Geminorum, and the star cluster NGC 2420 lies just below the starting point of the 1931–1932 observing period.

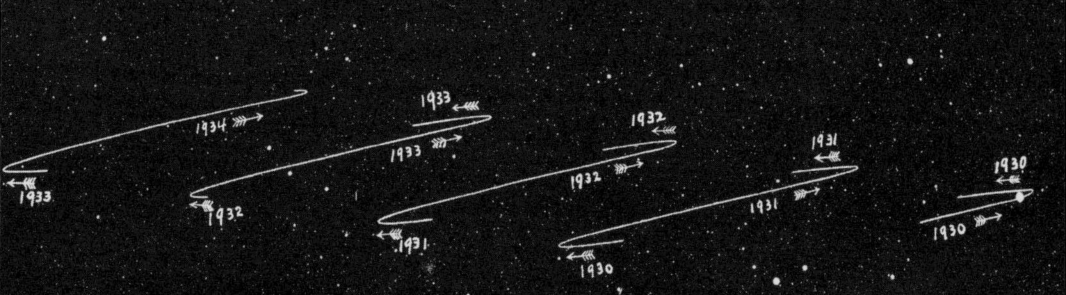

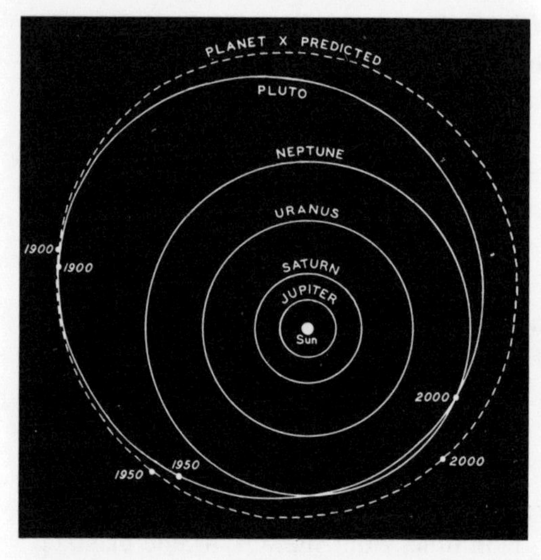


*Fig. 25.* Percival Lowell's predicted orbit of Planet X compared with the observed orbit of Pluto.

able stars were noted,[3] and 29,548 galaxies were counted. One new globular and six galactic star clusters were by-products of the search. Only one comet was found, on a pair of plates taken a year earlier.

It seems safe to conclude from the Lowell surveys that no unknown planet beyond Saturn exists that was brighter than magnitude 16½ at the time of search.

*It would be incorrect to think of the solar system simply as nine planets going around the sun, plus, perhaps, a few others as yet undiscovered beyond Pluto. Newton's mechanics allow for other stable orbits in which small satellites circle a planet circling the sun in a manner reminiscent of Ptolemy's epicycles.*

*Here is another field of discovery. Prediction is less important, and the necessary area of search far more limited.* Satellites *(moons) of the planets are always found near the planet they accompany, and the search for them becomes one of looking for faint moving objects near a bright one. Nevertheless, there are difficulties, as the following articles show.*

[3] Both variable stars that change in brightness and asteroids (small planets) that move showed changes between two photographs compared by Tombaugh. These, and the comets, star clusters, and galaxies he noted were by-products of his long search.—TLP

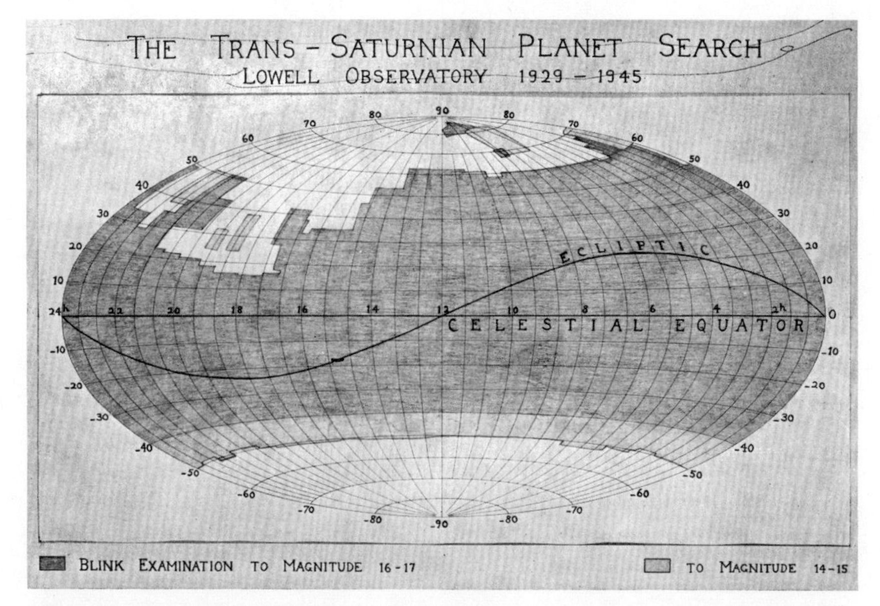


*Fig. 26.* Shaded areas indicate the regions of the sky covered by Lowell Observatory survey for faint distant planets.

*The small moons of Mars are an insignificant addition to the material of the solar system, but their motion allows an accurate determination of the mass of Mars, a quantity of considerable importance in current planning for space probes to land on Mars.*

TLP

# Asaph Hall and the Moons of Mars

JOHN T. KANE

(*Sky and Telescope*, September 1956)

As Mars pulls up to a neighborly 35,200,000 miles this month [September 1956], it is interesting to look back to the close opposition of the red planet in the late summer of 1877. Then the two satellites of Mars were discovered at the U.S. Naval Observatory by Asaph Hall, a carpenter who rose to be one of the most noted American astronomers of the nineteenth century.

The telescope Hall used, a 26-inch refractor which was one of the largest instruments of that time, is still in use at the Naval Observatory.

Born in Goshen, Connecticut, in 1829, young Asaph Hall saw his family fortunes deteriorate to the point where he could receive only a few years of elementary schooling before he was apprenticed out as a carpenter—a trade in which he became quite skilled. But at the age of twenty-four he heard of a tiny college with strong abolitionist sentiments in McGrawville, New York, that offered an education to just about anybody who wanted one.

Interest in astronomy and ability in mathematics led the former carpenter from McGrawville to the University of Michigan and thence to Harvard. He managed to obtain a position at the Naval Observatory,

*Fig.* 27. The 26-inch Clark refracting telescope at the U. S. Naval Observatory, used for ninety years of satellite observations. (Official U.S. Navy photograph)

beginning his career there in 1862—just when the city of Washington was an armed camp in the Civil War. . . .

Asaph Hall seems to have developed a skeptical turn of mind, even to questioning some of the astronomical statements common at that time. This is evident in the account of his discovery in a letter to a friend in England (*Monthly Notices* of the Royal Astronomical Society, Vol. 38, 1877–88):

The question whether Mars had a satellite or not, although at times occurring to me, I did not seriously consider until the spring of 1877. At that time several things had happened that brought this question prominently before me. Perhaps the principal of these was the discovery, in December 1876, of a white spot on the ball of Saturn, which gave me the means of determining the time of rotation of that planet, and taught me how untrustworthy may be the statements of the textbooks; this had made me ready to doubt the phrase one reads so often, "Mars has no Moon." Again, the favourable opposition of Mars in 1877 naturally attracted my attention. I then set to work to see what had been done in searching for satellites of this planet.

Beginning with the observations of Sir William Herschel in 1783, I found, of course, a great mass of observations of the planet; but since the time of Herschel, who appears to have looked for satellites of Mars, no serious search had been made except by one astronomer—Professor D'Arrest, of Copenhagen [with a 10-inch refractor]. . . . As D'Arrest was an accomplished astronomer and a skilful observer, the fact that he had found no moon on such a favourable occasion as the opposition of Mars in 1862 was discouraging.

The search was begun early in August, as soon as the geocentric motion of the planet made the detection of a satellite easy. At first my attention was directed to faint objects at some distance from Mars; but all these proving to be fixed stars, I began to examine the region close to the planet, and within the glare of light that surrounded it. This was done by keeping the planet just outside the field of view, and turning the eyepiece so as to pass completely around the planet. While making this examination on the night of August 11, I found a faint object on the following side and a little north of the planet, but had barely time to secure an observation of its position when fog from the Potomac River stopped the work. Cloudy weather intervened for several days.

The search was resumed on August 15. On August 16 the object was found again on the following side of the planet, and the observation of that night showed that it was moving with the planet.

On August 17, while waiting and watching for the outer satellite, the inner one was discovered. The observations made on the seventeenth and eighteenth put beyond doubt the character of these objects, and their discovery was publicly announced by Admiral [John] Rodgers [then superintendent of the Naval Observatory] on the eighteenth. For several days the inner moon was a puzzle. It would appear on different sides of the planet in the same night, and at first I thought there were two or three inner moons, since it seemed very improbable to me, at that time, that a satellite should revolve around its primary in less time than that in which the primary rotates. To settle this point I watched this moon throughout the nights of August 20 and 21, and saw that there was, in fact, but one inner moon, which made its revolution around the primary in less than one-third the time of the primary's rotation, a case unique in our solar system.

Hall observed the Martian satellites until October 31, and the Washington observations by themselves gave sufficient data for accurate determinations of the orbits.

Newspaper editors of that day were quite impressed by the discovery. In a lead editorial on August 27, 1877, the Washington *Evening Star* declared: ". . . to the scientist the discovery is one of great interest and importance, more than compensating for the cost of the great equatorial telescope which brought the two satellites within human vision." . . .

Hall's findings agree closely with the modern data: The inner satellite revolves some 5800 miles from the center of the planet, so its average distance from Mars' surface is only about 3700 miles. Its period of revolution is 7 hours, 39 minutes, while the planet takes 24 hours, 37 minutes, 23 seconds to rotate once. Therefore, to an observer on Mars, this moon would appear to rise in the west and set in the east.

The outer satellite has a period of 30 hours, 18 minutes, at some 14,600 miles from the center of Mars. It is about one third as bright as the inner moon. . . .

Finally, concerning the names of these companions of Mars, the mythological attendants of the god of war, Panic and Fear, seemed quite suitable to the satellites' discoverer, who concludes, "Of the various names that have been proposed for these satellites I like best those suggested from Homer by Mr. Madan, of Eton, *viz.* Deimos for the outer satellite, and Phobos for the inner one."

*The persistence of a dedicated visual observer shines through the words of Asaph Hall. But there is a strange side to this story of Phobos and Deimos. In* Gulliver's Travels, *first published in 1726—over 150 years*

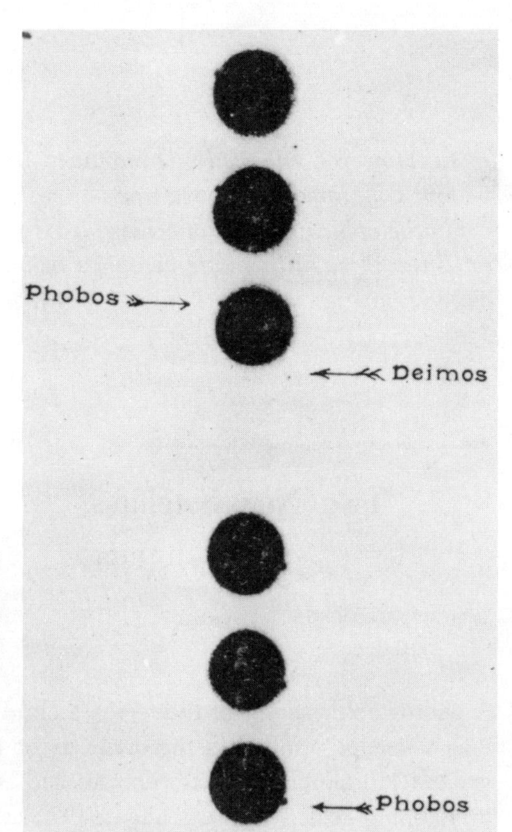


*Fig.* 28. The satellites of Mars photographed on September 16–17, 1909, with the 13-inch refracting telescope at Poulkovo Observatory in Russia.

*before Hall's discovery of Mars' moons—Jonathan Swift lampoons mankind as he tells of the imaginary lands that Gulliver visits (among them the countries of the miniature Lilliputians and the giant Brobdingnagians). In what may have been intended as a take-off on the march of science, Swift credits the astronomers of "Laputa" with having discovered "two lesser stars or satellites, which revolve about Mars, the inner one distant 3 diameters, the outer 5 diameters from the planet's center." He goes on to specify that the periods (10 hours and 21½ hours) obey Kepler's Third "Harmonic" Law (see p. 34). This remarkable coincidence between fact and fantasy (or evidence of some unknown astronomer who had seen Phobos and Deimos before anyone else) has long intrigued and awed astronomers. How did Swift guess so well?*

*Recently it has been suggested, just as speculatively, that Phobos and Deimos might be* artificial *satellites, launched by living beings on Mars. The evidence is sketchy: These two satellites are closer than any others to the planet they accompany; they are faint and therefore presumed small. However, the reader is reminded that such wild conjectures are seldom confirmed twice in a row!*

*Photographic observations have led to several other discoveries of satellites; three of them are described below in the course of more complete summaries.*

TLP

## Two New Satellites of Jupiter

SETH B. NICHOLSON

(*The Sky*, November 1938)

A photographic survey of the region around Jupiter made with the 100-inch telescope resulted in the discovery of two new satellites. The survey covered about 10 square degrees and consisted of sixteen partially overlapping fields which extended 3 degrees east and west and a degree and a quarter to the north and south of Jupiter. The exposures were one hour each on 8-by-10-inch plates (covering about one square degree) and reached magnitude 20 over most of that area. The survey was completed from July 27 to August 1, 1938, except for two fields which were photographed on August 25, and six additional fields, three on each side of Jupiter, which were photographed on July 5 and 6 to record any satellites that would have been hidden in the glare near Jupiter when the principal survey was made three weeks later. Jupiter's motion was allowed for in guiding the telescope, so that the images of its satellites were nearly circular, while those of the stars were elongated.

On these plates images of about forty moving objects were found, most of which could easily be distinguished from satellites because their motions were so different from that of Jupiter. The images of known satellites J VI and J VII were found about two days and fourteen days respectively, ahead of their predicted positions. The image of J VIII was identified and found to be about eight minutes of arc from its predicted position. No position of J IX was computed until after the survey had been completed so that the rediscovery of that satellite, which had not been observed for ten years, served as a check on the completeness of the survey.

In addition to the satellites for which positions were available, six other objects were found, moving with approximately the same rate and direction as Jupiter. These were followed until their accelerations identified three of them as satellites of Jupiter and three as asteroids in orbit around the sun.

One of the three satellites was readily identified as J IX fifteen days ahead of its ephemeris position. J VIII was about forty days ahead of its position computed from similar mean elements.

One of the new satellites, J X, was first photographed on July 6; the other, J XI, on July 30. . . .

The new satellites are about nineteenth magnitude, approximately the same brightness as J IX. Perhaps the most surprising result of the survey was that no fainter satellites were found since satellites a magnitude fainter should have been recorded in the central region of the plates. The period of J X is apparently about 270 days, like the periods of J VI and J VII. The period of J XI is not obvious from an inspection of the observations, and no orbit is yet available.

## Twenty-nine Satellites[1]

**CLARENCE A. ATWELL**

(*Sky and Telescope*, April 1948)

Who discovered the moon? That is about the same as asking, "Who discovered the planet earth?" The answers to these questions are obvious. No one who ever lived on earth could rightly claim such a discovery. The earth's satellite without doubt is the object most commonly gazed at in the entire list of heavenly bodies, and until 338 years ago held the distinction of being the only known satellite.

When Galileo, in January 1610, turned his telescope to the planet Jupiter, he saw for the first time its four brightest satellites.

[1] The title and some of the material in this article were revised in press to conform with the discovery of a fifth satellite of Uranus at the McDonald Observatory of the University of Texas in April 1948.

*Fig. 29.* Venus (*above*) and Jupiter with its four bright moons, photographed with the 10-inch telescope at Yerkes Observatory. (Yerkes Observatory photograph)

Then it was that an era of discovery began which has brought the total number of known satellites in the solar system to twenty-nine. There must have been thrills connected with each new discovery, but probably none greater than Galileo's. He saw in Jupiter's system a confirmation of the Copernican idea of the mechanism of the solar system, and his observations aroused the desire of astronomers to find more heavenly bodies then unknown. Discoveries of the other satellites came in groups: 1655 to 1684, 1787 to 1789, 1846 to 1851, and 1877 to 1948. New planets, new telescopes, the advent of photography, and better observing methods were among the causes that suddenly opened up the opportunities to make these groups of discoveries. . . .

TABLE 2. SATELLITES OF THE SOLAR SYSTEM*

| Name | Stellar Mag. | Mean Dist. from Planet ("†) | (mi) | Revolution Period (d) | (h) | (m) | Diameter (mi) | Discoverer |
|---|---|---|---|---|---|---|---|---|
| SATELLITE OF THE EARTH | | | | | | | | |
| Moon | —12.6 | 530 | 238,857 | 27 | 07 | 43 | 2160 | |
| SATELLITES OF MARS | | | | | | | | |
| Phobos | 12 | 8 | 5,800 | 0 | 07 | 39 | 10? | Hall, 1877 |
| Deimos | 13 | 21 | 14,600 | 1 | 06 | 18 | 5? | Hall, 1877 |
| SATELLITES OF JUPITER | | | | | | | | |
| V | 13 | 48 | 112,600 | 0 | 11 | 57 | 100? | Barnard, 1892 |
| Io | 5 | 112 | 261,800 | 1 | 18 | 28 | 2300 | Galileo, 1610 |
| Europa | 6 | 178 | 416,600 | 3 | 13 | 14 | 2000 | Galileo, 1610 |
| Ganymede | 5 | 284 | 664,200 | 7 | 03 | 43 | 3200 | Galileo, 1610 |
| Callisto | 6 | 499 | 1,169,000 | 16 | 16 | 32 | 3200 | Galileo, 1610 |
| VI | 14 | 3037 | 7,114,000 | 250 | 16 | | 100? | Perrine, 1904 |
| VII | 16 | 3113 | 7,292,000 | 260 | 01 | | 40? | Perrine, 1905 |
| X | 18 | 3116 | 7,300,000 | 260 | | | 15? | Nicholson, 1938 |
| XI | 18 | 5990 | 14,000,000 | 692 | | | 15? | Nicholson, 1938 |
| VIII | 16 | 6240 | 14,600,000 | 739 | | | 40? | Melotte, 1908 |
| IX | 17 | 6360 | 14,900,000 | 758 | | | 20? | Nicholson, 1914 |
| SATELLITES OF SATURN | | | | | | | | |
| Mimas | 12 | 27 | 115,000 | 0 | 22 | 37 | 400? | W. Herschel, 1789 |
| Enceladus | 12 | 34 | 148,000 | 1 | 08 | 53 | 500? | W. Herschel, 1789 |
| Tethys | 11 | 43 | 183,000 | 1 | 21 | 18 | 800? | G. Cassini, 1684 |
| Dione | 11 | 55 | 234,000 | 2 | 17 | 41 | 700? | G. Cassini, 1684 |
| Rhea | 10 | 76 | 327,000 | 4 | 12 | 25 | 1100? | G. Cassini, 1672 |
| Titan | 8 | 177 | 759,000 | 15 | 22 | 41 | 2600? | Huygens, 1655 |
| Hyperion | 13 | 214 | 920,000 | 21 | 06 | 38 | 300? | G. Bond, 1848 |
| Iapetus | 11 | 515 | 2,210,000 | 79 | 07 | 56 | 1000? | G. Cassini, 1671 |
| Phoebe | 14 | 1870 | 8,034,000 | 550 | | | 200? | W. Pickering, 1898 |
| SATELLITES OF URANUS | | | | | | | | |
| Ariel | 16 | 14 | 119,000 | 2 | 12 | 29 | 600? | Lassell, 1851 |
| Umbriel | 16 | 19 | 166,000 | 4 | 03 | 28 | 400? | Lassell, 1851 |
| Titania | 14 | 32 | 272,000 | 8 | 16 | 56 | 1000? | W. Herschel, 1787 |
| Oberon | 14 | 42 | 364,000 | 13 | 11 | 07 | 900? | W. Herschel, 1787 |
| SATELLITE OF NEPTUNE | | | | | | | | |
| Triton | 13 | 16 | 220,000 | 5 | 21 | 03 | 3000? | Lassell, 1846 |

† Seconds of arc, as seen from the sun.

* Reproduced from the *Observer's Handbook* of the Royal Astronomical Society of Canada. Periods are given in days, hours and minutes. [Three more satellites have been discovered: Jupiter XII, farthest from Jupiter, by Nicholson in 1952; Miranda, closest to Uranus, by Kuiper in 1948; and Nereid, farther from Neptune than Triton, by Kuiper in 1949. All are very faint.]

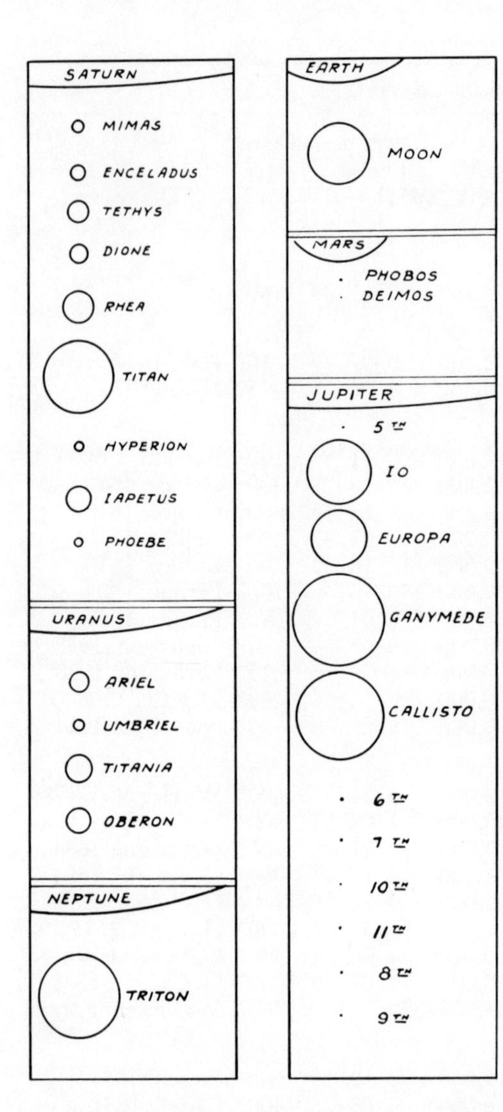


*Fig. 30.* Twenty-eight of the satellites of the solar system and segments of their parent planets are shown at a scale of 1″ = 14,500 miles. Distances are not to scale. (Diagram by Clarence Atwell)

Since we started with mention of the earth's moon, and Mercury and Venus have none, let us proceed outward from the sun, planet by planet rather than in the order of discovery. Until as recently as 1877, authors and poets often wrote about "moonless Mars." Sir William Herschel had searched for Martian satellites before this date but had been unable to find any. In 1877, Asaph Hall made use of the new 26-inch refractor at the U.S. Naval Observatory to locate the two satellites which he called Phobos and Deimos (Fear and Panic).

The innermost, Phobos, moves at the fearsome rate of one revolution in 7 hours 39 minutes, less than one third the time it takes Mars to rotate on its axis. This gives the curious result of Phobos rising in the west and setting in the east, as seen from the surface of Mars. Deimos is farther away from the planet and revolves once every 30 hours 18 minutes. Since this is comparatively so near the 24-hour 37-minute rotational period of the planet, Deimos has a very slow apparent motion through the Martian sky, remaining in the sky over two days between rising in the east and setting. Phobos is estimated to be 10 miles in diameter, and Deimos, 5.

After Galileo saw Io, Europa, Ganymede, and Callisto, Jupiter's four bright satellites, 282 years passed before another of the present total of eleven was seen. Then at Lick Observatory near San Jose, California, E. E. Barnard discovered the fifth, faint and nearer Jupiter than the first four. This satellite is next to Phobos in shortness of its period of revolution, but it is like Deimos in being a slow-motion object in the sky of Jupiter, as the planet rotates in about one sixth less time than the fifth satellite revolves.

After Jupiter V, all the remaining six satellites were discovered photographically in the twentieth century. C. D. Perrine located VI and VII at Lick in 1904 and 1905, and P. J. Melotte found VIII at Greenwich Observatory in 1908. S. B. Nicholson discovered IX on a photograph plate taken at Lick in 1914. These last two have the largest orbits of all the satellites, nearly 15 million miles from Jupiter, and their periods are measured in years. They have the added distinction of retrograde motion, revolving from east to west in their orbits.

Finally, in 1938, Nicholson discovered two more Jovian satellites by making long photographic exposures with the 100-inch telescope at Mount Wilson Observatory. XI has an orbit similar to VIII and IX, and retrograde motion. All except the Galilean satellites of Jupiter are fainter than the twelfth magnitude.

As a possessor of satellites, Saturn is almost equal to Jupiter, having a total of nine. Huygens discovered the brightest one, Titan, in 1655. The French astronomer Jean Dominique Cassini found a second in 1671, another in 1672, and then, in 1684, two more. Herschel found the next two, and the Bonds and W. H. Pickering at Harvard found the eighth and ninth respectively. Phoebe is some 200 miles in diameter, and has a retrograde motion. . . .

For Uranus, we find a surprising variation not yet noted, for the orbits of its four named satellites are almost at right angles to the plane of the ecliptic. This gives a peculiar effect as viewed from the earth. At two places in the orbit of Uranus about the sun, the orbits of these satellites appear almost circular to us; at intermediate positions, they appear almost on edge, and the satellites seem to move up and down on a line through the planet. At present, the orbital plane is nearly flatwise to us. The orbits will be edgewise again in 1966.

In order of distance from Uranus, the named moons are Ariel, Umbriel, Titania, and Oberon. The outer two were found by Herschel in 1787, after which he thought he could see four others. Inasmuch as it requires considerable skill to get a good photograph of the satellites of Uranus even with modern large telescopes, it is little wonder that Herschel was not certain of what he saw visually.

Soon after the planet Neptune was discovered in 1846, astronomers of all the great observatories made observations of it. In that same year the English astronomer William Lassell found that Neptune has one satellite, Triton, with a period of five days, 21 hours, and retrograde motion.

Some have proposed the capture theory, whereby it is thought that the three retrograde satellites of Jupiter and one of Saturn may once have been asteroids that strayed too close to one of these large planets and were actually taken out of their paths around the sun. The English astronomer R. A. Lyttleton has advanced a different theory for Triton. He suggests that the planet Pluto, comparable in size with Triton, once may have been a second Neptunian satellite. Gradual changes in the diameters of their orbits may have caused them to come near enough to each other to cause extremely disturbing results to both. The result he suggests is that Pluto was driven away from Neptune to begin an independent orbit around the sun, and that Triton's motion about Neptune was reversed from its original normal direction.

Satellites have helped unfold other mysteries of the universe. Observing the apparent periods of Jupiter's four bright satellites led Roemer in 1675 to demonstrate the speed of light traveling across the spaces of the solar system. It is necessary to measure only the period of a satellite and its distance from the planet to have the data for calculating the mass of the planet and satellite combined. Satellites also provide a means of measuring the oblateness, or equatorial bulge, of

Fig. 31. Uranus and its five satellites. Oberon is uppermost, Ariel is below at left center, Umbriel and Titania are at the right. Miranda, discovered by Gerard Kuiper in 1948, is nearest the overexposed image of the planet. Photograph taken with the 82-inch reflecting telescope at McDonald Observatory, Fort Davis, Texas. (Yerkes Observatory photograph)

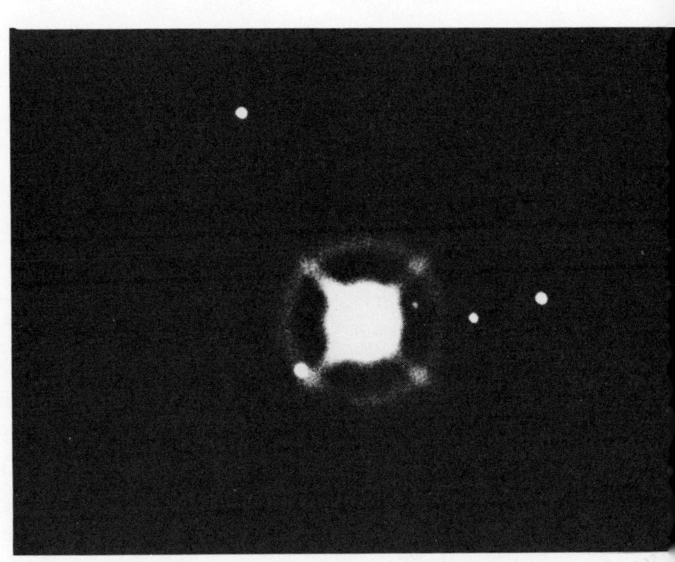

a planet. Triton's orbit is inclined 20 degrees to Neptune's equator, and in a 600-year period the axis of this orbit describes a nearly conical motion with respect to Neptune's axis. This motion is caused by the attraction of the planet's equatorial bulge. . . .

The study of satellites is by no means a cold and lifeless subject. The title of this article will no doubt some day be out of date as astronomers continue to examine photographic plates for additional small elements of the solar system.

*Fig.* 32. Neptune and its two satellites. *Left:* Prime focus, May 29, 1949, 5:05 UT, exp. 30 min., 103a-F, showing both Triton and Nereid (*arrow*). Fuzzy spots are galaxies. *Right:* Cassegrain focus, February 24, 1949, 8:55 and 9:06 UT, showing Triton. (McDonald Observatory)

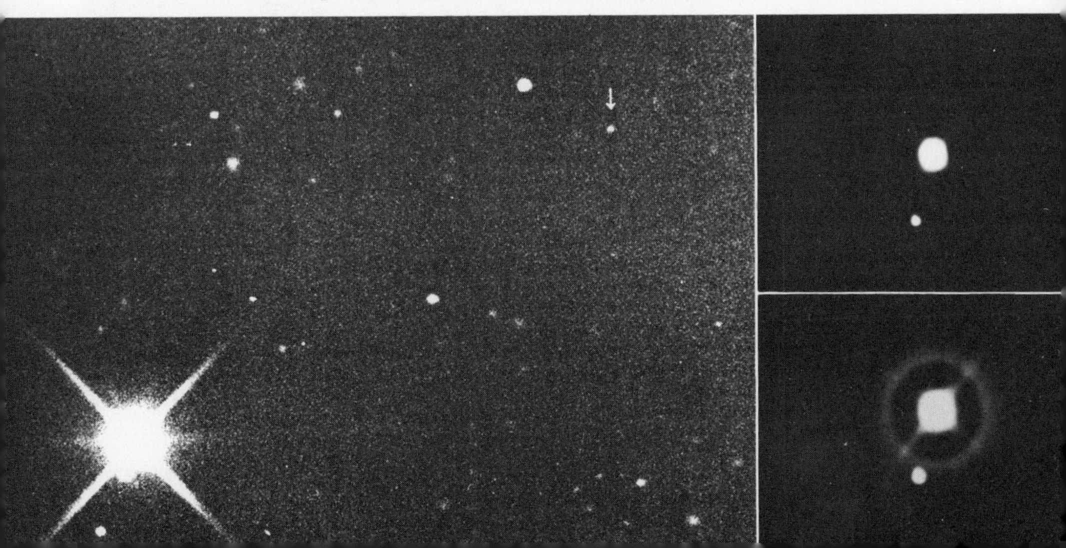

# Neptune Satellite Nereid Confirmed

(*Sky and Telescope*, June 1949 and January 1950)

Dr. G. P. Kuiper, Yerkes and McDonald observatories, confirmed his discovery of a second satellite to the planet Neptune.

The angular distance between the new moon and its primary planet is 410 seconds of arc, corresponding to a radius for the new satellite's orbit of 5 million miles, whereas that of Triton, Neptune's thirteenth-magnitude satellite, is only about 220,000 miles. The period of the satellite is about two years, and its diameter is about 200 miles, as estimated from its photographic magnitude of 19.5.

In addition to the discovery plates on May 1, 1949, and three more plates on May 29, photographs of the new satellite were procured at McDonald Observatory during the second half of June. Three or more positions of the satellite thus became available, making possible complete computation of the orbit.

In describing the discovery in the *Publications* of the Astronomical Society of the Pacific for August 1949, Dr. Kuiper states that we would therefore expect Nereid to be about 1/16 the diameter of Triton, or about 300 kilometers.

*As in the case of the planets, we surely cannot assume that we have yet discovered* all *the satellites of the solar system. For instance, it is easy to see that if Phobos or Deimos were one tenth as large, or nearly black, Asaph Hall would have missed them. Small faint satellites could be in orbit around Jupiter without having yet been detected. A good place to look is near the earth itself.*

TLP

# Meteoric Satellites of the Earth

JOSEPH ASHBROOK

(*Sky and Telescope,* June 1955 and July 1961)

One of the most famous meteoric phenomena on record happened on February 9, 1913. This was long believed to have been a procession of about fifty fireballs, moving very slowly from horizon to horizon in nearly the same path, seen from western Canada, across Minnesota, Ohio, New Jersey, and Bermuda to the equator—a distance of over 5600 miles.

It was, however, established by C. C. Wylie in 1939 that these widely spaced observers had not viewed the same meteors, so what really occurred was an intense but ordinary meteor shower rather than a true meteoric procession.

Even so, there are some interesting consequences of the original idea of a procession of meteors. For if the course and velocity with which such bodies approach the earth were favorable, they could be captured as satellites, circling far enough above the earth's surface to avoid destruction by the atmosphere—the fate of all ordinary meteors. They would then be the type of body looked for in C. W. Tombaugh's intensive photographic search [now] under way at the Lowell Observatory. His is the first sustained effort, with modern optics and careful programming, to discover additional satellites of the earth.

How a hypothetical satellite would appear to an observer was discussed in detail by W. H. Pickering in 1923. He showed that a meteorite one foot in diameter, revolving in an orbit 200 miles above the earth's surface, could be as bright as tenth magnitude at times, shining by reflected sunlight. It would resemble an unusually slow-moving telescopic meteor. Objects of this sort may well be picked up in Tombaugh's search. . . .

Is it possible that a meteoric satellite has already been observed? There is a classic case where the discovery was reported by a prominent professional astronomer in a leading scientific journal, together with full details and a complete orbit computation. The man was F. Petit (1810–65), director of the Toulouse Observatory, whose communication to the French Academy of Sciences was printed in its *Comptes Rendus* of October 12, 1846.

Three observers saw the body, Lebon and Dassier at Toulouse, and Larivière at Artenac, 26 miles away, on March 21 of that year, at 6:45 P.M. When Larivière first noted this luminous object, it was low in the south, near Sirius; it moved slowly past Orion and into the northwestern sky, where it vanished behind a low cloud bank. It stayed in sight for 10 seconds, and its apparent diameter was half that of the moon.

First supposing this object to be a meteor, Petit calculated its track, and found to his surprise that the observations indicated an elliptical orbit around the earth with a period of revolution of 2 hours 44 minutes and 59 seconds. The mean distance from the center of the earth came out 6180.1 miles, and the orbital eccentricity 0.36007. Therefore, at closest approach—during the time of observation—the body would have missed the earth's surface by only 7.1 miles.

In the audience at the French Academy when this paper was read sat the great Leverrier, co-discoverer of Neptune. He commented that the orbit calculation should be revised to take air resistance into account.

Hindsight is easy, when an additional century of experience by meteor astronomers is available to us. In 1846 the calculation of meteor heights and paths was still a novelty, and Petit had not realized that the observations were too rough to support such an elaborate superstructure of computation. His orbit depends very critically upon the uncertain estimates of the duration of visibility. The 10-second duration reported by Larivière leads to an elliptic orbit that intersects the earth's surface twice; the six seconds of the Toulouse observers makes the orbit around the earth a hyperbola. Petit had arbitrarily averaged these durations for his calculations with seven-place logarithms!

Petit's similar discovery of a second supposed earth satellite on July 23, 1846, also appears invalid, from uncertainty in the all-important estimates of duration. There can now be hardly any doubt that both these objects were merely ordinary fireballs. Clyde Tombaugh need not fear having been anticipated 109 years ago, if he finds a satellite of the earth.

The discovery of two faint, cloudlike objects circling the earth at the same distance as the moon has been reported by the Polish astronomer K. Kordylewski, at Krakow Observatory.

His find is the result of many years of searching, based upon the idea that the most likely locations for additional natural satellites are the Lagrangian points of the earth-moon system. These places have the property that small bodies located near them will persist in stable orbital motion. Two of these points, known as $L_4$ and $L_5$, are at the same distance from the earth as the moon, the first 60 degrees ahead of the moon in its orbit, the other 60 degrees behind.

Very few details are available concerning Dr. Kordylewski's discovery. His two libration clouds are both near the $L_5$ point, several degrees apart, and were recorded on four photographs taken on March 6 and April 6, 1961. He suggests that similar objects may be found near the $L_4$ point, 60 degrees east of the moon.

As this issue goes to press [mid-1961], no observations of Dr. Kordylewski's clouds by other astronomers have been received.

*The discussion of meteors is continued in Chapter 4, and the problems of man-made satellites are reserved for Chapter 3. It must suffice for the moment to say that there may be a number of small natural satellites of the earth, ranging from perhaps a mile in diameter down to fractions of an inch or less. Note the differences implied in the terms* satellite, passing meteoroid, cloud of meteoric matter, *and* atomic particle con-

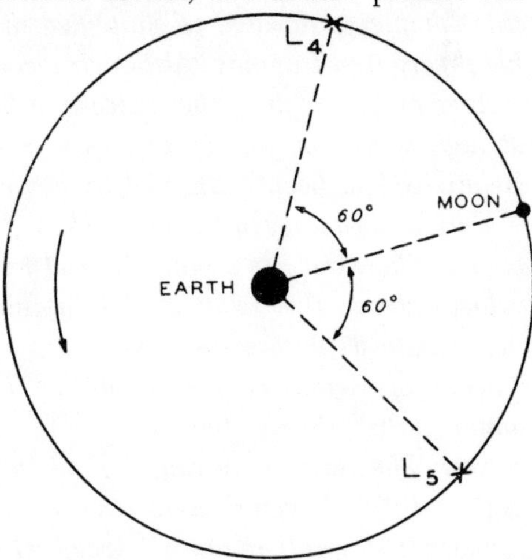


*Fig.* 33. As the moon travels around the earth, these Lagrangian points (*L*) form equilateral triangles with the earth and moon. *K*: Kordylewski's two clouds are in the vicinity of the $L_5$ point.

trolled by the earth's magnetic field. All of these offer considerable hazard to space probes, and the space engineers must learn more about them before manned vehicles can reach the moon safely.

So far, this portion of the book has shown the extraordinary versatility and accuracy of Newton's mechanics, and the extensive system moving in a predictable manner. His simple laws of motion and gravitation (p. 44), relating the acceleration of a mass to the proximity of other masses, brought order to a wide variety of motions—from the falling apple to the moon in its orbit, from small satellites to large planets. The errors and unsettled problems described in these related articles are not to be considered defects in Newton's mechanics, but rather the result of misapplications or errors in observation. Kepler's laws of elliptical orbits (p. 32) described only the motions of planets around the sun; Newton explained them, modified them (perturbations, p. 52), and extended them to satellites. What is more, Newton's equations gave consistent results from a variety of observations. (For instance, the mass of Jupiter determined from satellite motions agrees with the mass determined from perturbations.)

However, before leaving Newton's theory, something should be said about what is wrong with it. We skip the realm of small-particle physics, where the laws of quantum mechanics are quite different, and turn to relativity theory. In what way does Einstein's theory differ from Newton's? After a brief description of Einstein the man, the remainder of this Chapter is devoted to simplified discussions of the applications of his theory in astronomy. Although recent laboratory physics has added further proofs (such as the increase in mass of atomic particles moving at high speed), it was properly said for several decades that General Relativity had been confirmed by astronomical observations.

Various meanings of the word relativity should be distinguished at the outset. The word has a philosophical meaning that concerns ethics and value systems; this relativity has nothing to do with the theories of mathematical physics discussed here, except by analogy. The Special Theory of Relativity first published by Einstein in 1905 concerns, among other things, the velocity of light measured by moving observers. The earth is moving around the sun at almost 19 miles a second, and it had been assumed that light from a star would pass us at a somewhat slower-than-normal speed when the earth was moving away *from the star—somewhat faster when the earth was moving toward the star six months later. In 1887 an accurate laboratory measurement by two Americans, Albert A. Michelson and Edward W. Morley, had established, however, that light moved at precisely the same speed (about 186,000 miles per second) in both directions—with the earth's motion or against it. In order to explain this, Einstein assumed that an observer's constant velocity cannot make a difference in his physics. That is, he cannot tell whether he is moving and other objects are "at rest," or whether they are moving and he is "at rest." One should only speak of* relative *motion, not assume an absolute standard of rest, as Newton did. The consequence of Einstein's assumption is that the length and mass of a physical body, and duration of a time interval, are* different *for two observers, one moving relative to the other. Neither observer could be said to be more right or wrong in his measurements than the other, since it is impossible to say which one is in motion and which at rest—the two observers are in "equivalent reference frames" if their relative motion is constant.*

*In 1916 Einstein published his General Theory of Relativity, in which he "explained" Newton's force of gravitation by another principle of equivalence. This was another broad assumption: that the effect of gravitational force is the same as an acceleration of all the surroundings in the opposite direction. That is, a man sitting on a chair far out in space would feel his "weight" against the chair if it were being accelerated toward him, even if there were no gravitational force. In order to replace Newton's simple gravitational force with this equivalent acceleration, Einstein had to assume that space-time is curved near large masses. In effect, he replaced Newton's assumption of gravitational force* ($F = G\, m_1\, m_2/r^2$, *as explained on p. 50) by a change in* geometry. *The succeeding articles show that the results are practically the same, except for the motion of light, which is unaffected by forces in Newton's theory. In Einstein's theory, the motion of light is different in regions of curved space-time, such as near the sun or near any concentrated mass. The motions of planets close to the sun are also predicted by Einstein's theory to be slightly different than by Newton's, and there are other differences concerning the high speeds of very distant galaxies.*

TLP

## The Founder of Relativity

(*Sky and Telescope*, June 1955)

On April 18 [1955], Albert Einstein died in his sleep at the age of seventy-six. This was the passing of a man who had contributed more to the deep foundations of physics and astronomy than anyone else since the days of Newton. During more than fifty years of work at Zürich, Prague, Berlin, and after 1933 at the Institute for Advanced Study at Princeton, Albert Einstein's original genius illuminated both the exceedingly small and the exceedingly large. Our understanding of the atomic nucleus and the realm of the galaxies depends to a considerable extent on his work on relativity and quantum theory. . . .

One of those who knew Einstein best is Professor Philipp Frank, lecturer emeritus in physics and mathematics at Harvard University, who wrote a biography of Einstein and had been a friend of his since 1910.

The remainder of this article is based on Dr. Frank's remarks.

*Fig.* 34. Albert Einstein (1879–1955). (Yerkes Observatory photograph)

Einstein often said he was basically interested in philosophy, Dr. Frank recalls, and regarded physics as a part of philosophy. He felt that an interest in philosophy made one a better scientist by turning attention to the really basic problems involved in our investigation of nature. Einstein habitually tried to develop his ideas in a very general way. The equivalence of mass, $m$, and energy, $E$: $E=mc^2$, providing the basis for possible release of atomic energy first occurred to him as a logical consequence arising from the principle of relativity.

In his later years he was much occupied with seeking a general theory that would be valid for all the "forces" of nature—gravitational, electrical, magnetic, nuclear, and so on. Those who came to speak to him about relativity found that he wanted instead to talk about the broader problems.

The feature of Einstein's thinking that set him above his contemporaries was his unsurpassed ability to trace *all* the consequences of an idea. For instance, he might ask a student in the laboratory for details of an experiment. On being told, he would immediately be able to express all the inferences to be drawn from the results of the experiment. This ability was of obvious value to his students and to scientists in general. To him, in return, their work was of interest because all scientific activity and experimentation were associated parts of the general pattern of thought.

Einstein did much of his work on relativity before he was twenty-six, the age at which he announced the special theory. . . .

He had a certain antipathy to being paid for research, thinking that a paid scientist might feel pressed to produce results that would not be his best work. We have his oft-quoted statement to the effect that he would rather earn his living with his hands, at a plumber's or shoemaker's job, and do his thinking on his own time. When his first great work was being done, he was employed in the Swiss patent office. . . .

When he first visited New York in the 20s, he was already at the peak of his fame. Reporters came on board ship and asked him to explain the theory of relativity in a few sentences. Einstein said that if the words themselves were not taken too seriously, he would suggest the following:

"Before the theory of relativity, people believed that if all material bodies were to disappear from the universe, men and stones and everything, then nonetheless time and space would still exist. But relativity theory says that this is not true. If all material objects were to disappear, time and space would disappear too, and that is the essence of relativity."

## Relativity and Its Astronomical Implications

**PHILIPP FRANK**

(*Sky and Telescope*, October, November, and December 1942)

The heroic period in the struggle for the laws governing the orbits of our planetary system was the period of three men: Copernicus, Galileo, Newton. To have a rough idea about the duration of that struggle, we may say that Copernicus worked around 1500, Galileo around 1600, and Newton around 1700. Copernicus laid the foundation to the *pattern of description* of those orbits which (with Kepler's corrections) are used by astronomers today.

However, the ambition of men like Galileo and Newton was a much deeper one than Copernicus'. They wanted to set up a pattern of description which covered not only the orbits of planets, but which would enable us to describe any motion in the universe, such as the motion of balls pushed by the direct impact of our muscle force or the motion of the particles which produce optical sensations. This general pattern of description was started by Galileo and reached its climax with Newton's "laws of motion."

In the period from Newton (around 1700) to Einstein (around 1900), these laws have never been seriously challenged. Einstein's work was the first radical progress beyond Galileo and Newton in the field of the general laws of motion. Observe that the period from Newton to Einstein was nearly as long as that from Copernicus to Newton—about two centuries each.

Einstein's laws of motion have the reputation of being much harder to understand than Newton's. This reputation results primarily from *underrating* the difficulties implied by the Newtonian laws. Two centuries of triumphs of those laws have produced the illusion that they are not merely physical hypotheses, but necessary results of reasonable thinking or of good sense. The first step toward understanding Einstein has to be, therefore, the destruction of a sort of complacency. If we succeed in understanding how sweeping and daring Newton's hypotheses have been, we are not likely to cherish the illusion that Newton's laws of motion have been the last word in the history of human knowledge. To understand Newton will set the green light for understanding Einstein.

## 1. The role of "inertia" and "force" in Newton's pattern of description

The Galileo-Newton way to approach the phenomena of motion was to describe them by describing the accelerations of the moving bodies concerned. By *acceleration* we mean not only a change in speed but also a change in the direction of the velocity. In this sense, a body traversing a circular orbit with constant speed has an acceleration. Galileo discovered that the acceleration of a stone falling to the earth is constant. Newton advanced the hypothesis that the acceleration of a planet in its orbit round the sun is proportional to the mass of the sun and inversely proportional to the square of the distance of the planet from the sun.

It was the great success of this hypothesis which encouraged Newton to venture a pattern of description which could cover every sort of motion in the universe.

If we denote the mass of the body by $m$, the acceleration by $a$, and the "force" exerted upon the body by its environment by $f$, we can express the Newtonian principle by

$$m \times a = f \quad \text{or} \quad a = f/m.$$

The meaning of these formulae, which are well known in all problems of physics, is easy to grasp if the motion is rectilinear (in a straight line). But the formulae also remain valid if the body is deflected.

Obviously, from the formula, the motion becomes particularly simple if the mass $m$ becomes very great. Multiplied together, $m$ and $a$ must equal $f$, so that as $m$ approaches an infinitely large value, $a$ shrinks toward zero. . . .

Therefore, the paths of great masses can be simply described—they move along straight lines with constant speed. The important result of this conclusion is that the paths of such great masses can be described in a purely *geometrical* way, without introducing any dynamical concept such as mass or force. This property of matter, to keep on moving along a straight line with constant speed, is called its *inertia*. . . .

## 2. The system of fixed stars[1] and the law of inertia

The geometrical (inertial) component of motion seems to be particularly simple because it is exactly a straight line. However, this matter is not as simple as it may appear.

If we say that a body traverses a straight line "on the earth," we mean that it moves parallel to an edge of a room (for instance) which is rigidly connected with the earth.

But a body which has rectilinear motion with respect to the earth obviously does not have rectilinear motion with respect to the system of fixed stars. A ball may move parallel to the edge of the room, but this edge is attached to the earth and is describing a rotational motion with respect to the stars. So the ball rolling along the edge is describing a kind of spiral curve with respect to the stars.

The statement "The geometrical component of every motion is a rectilinear motion" has no meaning at all, unless we add "with respect to the earth," or "with respect to the fixed stars," or "relative to a definite system of bodies of reference." It is also evident that only with a particular one of these additions can the statement be true. For if a body of great mass describes a straight line with respect to the earth, it cannot describe a straight line with respect to the fixed stars at the same time. . . .

A system of reference with respect to which the inertial (geometrical) component of the actual motion of bodies is rectilinear is usually called an *inertial system*. We can easily understand that our earth is not such an inertial system. This is well known from the observation of projectiles and the circulation of air currents. The inertial component of the motion of projectiles with respect to the earth is a curved line, even if we neglect the effect of gravity and of the curvature of the earth. . . .

[1] The term *fixed stars* is used in a general sense to define a set of fixed directions. This concept was used, in effect, to establish the rotation of the earth. Some of the stars are moving slowly relative to others, but this need not concern us here.

### 3. Newton's general pattern of description fails to work in the case of "gravity"

A falling stone falls with a certain acceleration which remains constant during its fall. If we replace it by another stone of greater mass, its acceleration remains the same no matter how large its mass becomes! Even the greatest mass fails to "resist" the influence of "gravity." In this case, then, we are unable to separate a dynamical component of motion from the geometrical one.

*The whole motion behaves like the geometrical component and there is no dynamical component at all!*

As we know from every elementary textbook, Newton assumed that the force of gravity acting upon a stone of mass $m$ is proportional to $m$. The greater the mass, the greater is the gravitational force attracting it. Since the mass cancels from both terms of the equation, the result is that the acceleration becomes independent of the mass. This means that a mass in the field of gravity behaves as if it were *not* subjected to a force but only to inertia. Furthermore, since the mass does not move in a straight line with constant speed (a projectile follows a parabolic path), it behaves like a body following the law of inertia relative to a system which is *not* an inertial system (which has, for example, an acceleration relative to the fixed stars). . . .

For two centuries, the whole period between Newton and Einstein, this fact, the proportionality of mass and gravity, was regarded as a remarkable coincidence, and finally came to be taken so much as a matter of course that it was no longer discussed at all. . . .

Einstein was the first to advance the hypothesis that one essential point in Newton's theory was the proportionality between gravity and mass, which implied the cancellation of the mass $m$ from the equation of motion in the gravitational field.

### Summary of Sections 1 to 3

Newton's laws of motion are correctly considered in terms of acceleration and mass. Lack of acceleration is shown by constant speed in a constant direction. Newton's basic principle is that acceleration is inversely proportional to mass, with "force" a proportionality factor; as the mass increases, the acceleration becomes smaller in a constant field of force.

If the force is zero or the mass infinite, the acceleration is zero. This means the motion is rectilinear with constant speed. The geometrical form of the orbit is independent of the value of the mass (provided the mass is sufficiently great).

This *geometrical* path of an infinite mass is a straight line and of uniform speed only if referred to a certain system of reference, which is called the *inertial* system. This system is in a first approximation the system of fixed stars. In some other system, the geometrical path may appear curved, or it may appear that the mass has an acceleration. (This thought is directly applied to gravity by Einstein, but not by Newton.)

When "forces" act on a mass which is not infinite, a dynamical component is added to its geometrical motion, but increasing the mass to infinity will make its motion purely geometrical.

Galileo had looked for the dynamical component in falling bodies, by changing their masses, but he obtained the peculiar result that the acceleration of a falling body is 32 feet per second each second regardless of its mass. This did not fit well with the ideas of the relation of mass and acceleration, for if a *constant* force were acting on the masses, the heavy ones should be accelerated more slowly, and take longer to fall from a given height.

Newton accounted for this apparent disagreement by assuming that the force of gravity must be variable—that it must increase with the mass, and so massive bodies, pulled down by a greater force, fell as fast as light ones.

Einstein regarded this "inseparability" of the inertial and dynamical components as the essential feature of the gravitational motion.

### 4. The homogeneous field of gravity and Einstein's principle of equivalence

Einstein's theory of gravity can be explained with very little mathematics, and it leads directly to the curvature of light past the sun and the "Einstein-shift", reddening in the spectrum of certain stars.

The field of gravity is homogeneous in a room on the surface of the earth. (The difference in the distances from the top and bottom of the room to the center of the earth may be ignored.) The force of gravity may therefore be considered as directed vertically downward and producing in all points of the room the same acceleration of gravity (nearly 32.2 feet per second each second). . . .

For the purposes of argument and illustration, let us neglect the motion of the earth with respect to the fixed stars—its rotation and revolution are considered to have ceased for the moment. The earth is now an inertial system, and the room, also: with respect to the room the geometrical component of every motion is rectilinear and with constant speed. Relative to the room, a stone is observed to fall with a constant acceleration $g$. A launched projectile describes a parabola which is composed of the same downward acceleration, and a rectilinear motion with constant speed in the direction of the initial velocity (see Fig. 35).

These facts are described in our traditional Newtonian mechanics by saying that the action of a force called gravity produces the acceleration of falling bodies and the curvature of the path of a projectile. But the facts observable in this room do not enable us to separate from the inertial motion the motion due to the gravitational field—regardless of the mass, the downward acceleration observed is always the same.

Why not describe the observed facts by saying that the room *is not an inertial system,* but is moving "upward" with a constant acceleration $g$ with respect to some *real* inertial system which we call $J$. . . .

With this simple thought—that the room is not an inertial system—we can describe in quite a different way all the phenomena in the room traditionally ascribed to gravity. Thus, a falling stone does not fall with respect to $J$, for $J$ has the same acceleration relative to the room as the stone—the stone and $J$ fall together, and the stone is fixed with respect to $J$. The projectile, similarly, does not fall with respect to $J$, but it does travel along a straight line in accordance with its initial velocity. Briefly, with respect to $J$, all bodies in the room travel along straight lines with constant speed. That is, they all have purely geometrical paths. No dynamical "gravity" exists relative to $J$. However, since the room is accelerating upward with respect to $J$, the stone appears to strike the floor of the room, exerting a pressure. In the new description, the impact is not due to the falling of the stone, but to the acceleration of the floor with respect to the inertial system $J$. . . .

Therefore, all our experience about bodies moving in the homogeneous field of gravity in a room can be described in two ways, one according to Newton, the other according to Einstein, . . . possible because the gravitational motion cannot be separated from the inertial one. We can now easily understand how Einstein formulated his famous *principle of equivalence* in 1912 when he was teaching at the University of Prague. He stated that a homogeneous field of gravitation is "equivalent" to an accelerated motion of the room with respect to the inertial

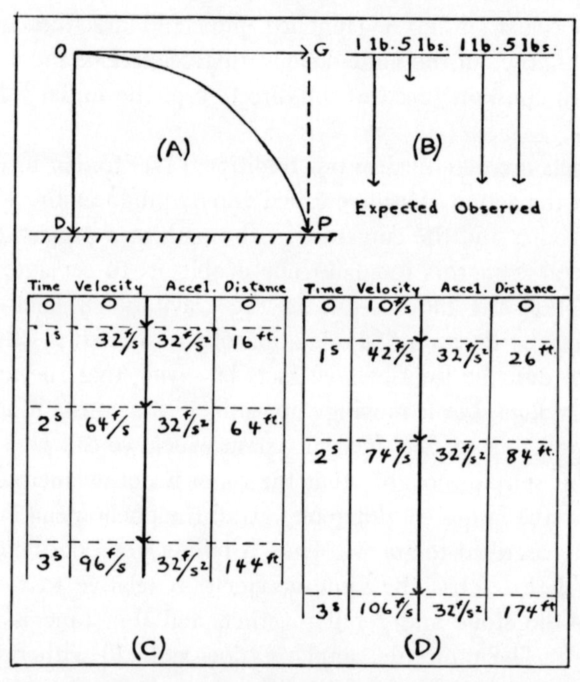


*Fig.* 35. The action of gravity on falling bodies. *a.* A projectile shot in the direction *OG* will follow the path *OP* reaching *P* in the time that a body dropped from *O* falls to *D*. *OG* represents the geometrical component and *OD* the dynamical, if we consider gravity as a force. *b.* A one-pound body might be expected to "fall" five times as fast as a five-pound body if they are subjected to the same force, but they are observed to fall together. *c.* The course of a freely falling body—time is in seconds from the start; velocity is in feet per second; acceleration is in feet per second; and distance is in feet from the start. *d.* Like *c*, with an initial downward velocity of 10 feet per second.

system. This is evident in the case we have just considered, for there it is only a reformulation of the Newtonian laws of motion of masses.

Einstein, moreover, ventured the hypothesis that the equivalence also applies to all optical and electromagnetic events in this room. Since no influence of gravity upon optical phenomena had been discovered before Einstein, this hypothesis opened the way for a new type of prediction about the action of gravity upon light rays and light waves that can be tested by astronomical observations.

## 5. The deflection of light rays by gravity

Let us consider our room as having an acceleration of $g$ upward with respect to the inertial system $J$. There may be a small hole in the wall through which a beam of light enters in a horizontal direction (parallel to the floor). The light ray would remain parallel to the floor of the room if the room were at rest, and would strike the opposite wall at the same height as it entered. But while the light was traversing the room the latter has moved upward relative to $J$.

The angle by which the ray is deflected is easy to calculate[2] because of the immense speed of light.

The value of $a$ under the most favorable conditions which can be found on earth is about 1/5000 of a second of arc, which could not be measured by terrestrial experiment. Einstein suggested that we investigate the possible deflection of light rays by the gravitation of the much more massive sun. To estimate this deflection, we apply Newton's formula for gravitation to get the acceleration of gravity at the surface of the sun. Allowing for the long distance in which the passing light ray is close to the sun's surface, . . . we obtain the deflection $a = 0''.87$ [.87 seconds of arc]. The rays are, roughly, deflected by one second of arc in passing the sun.

This value of the deflection is the result of two basic hypotheses: (1) The equivalence or inseparability of the effect of gravity from the effect

[2] The mathematical derivation has been deleted. The light moving at speed $c$ takes $t = L/c$ seconds to go the distance $L$ across the room. In that time, the room, with acceleration $g$ upward, moves up a distance $D = gt^2/2 = gL^2/2c^2$. The small apparent deflection of the light as it hits the far wall is $\alpha = 2D/L = gL/c^2$ radians. One radian (about 57°) = 206265 seconds of arc. If the light beam enters at angle $\phi$ to the horizontal, $\alpha = (gL/c^2) \cos \phi$.—TLP

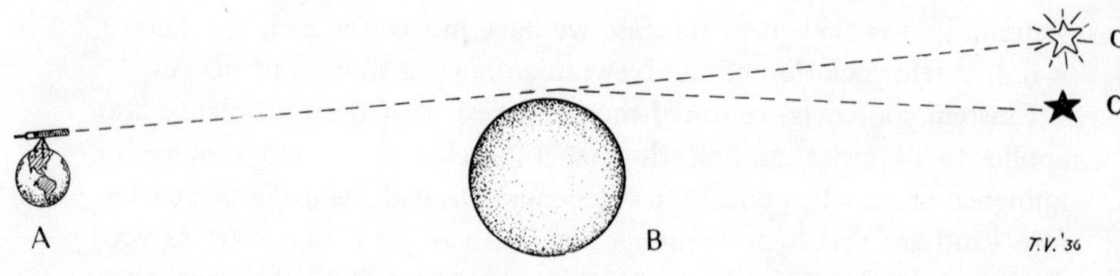


*Fig.* 36. Because of the deflection of light in a gravitational field, starlight passing the sun is bent toward it. Therefore, we observe stars near the sun (*B*) to be displaced outward from *C* to *C'*.

of inertia. (2) Newton's law of gravitational attraction. However, Einstein found that the consequences of his hypothesis of equivalence turned out to be incompatible with Newton's law according to which the action of gravity varies inversely as the square of the distance. Einstein concluded that in close proximity to the attracting body, that is, in a very strong field of "gravity," there must be some departure from the Newtonian law. His whole argument is beyond the scope of this article, so I shall restrict myself to a few words which will suffice for our further purposes. In a perfunctory way, then, Einstein's idea is as follows:

The path traversed by a mass following its inertia or moving in a field of gravitation must be described according to Einstein in a purely geometrical (not a dynamical) way. In the close proximity of a gravitating mass (for instance, the sun), space has such geometrical properties that no rectilinear motion in the traditional sense is even geometrically possible. The curve which a mass traverses by its own inertia or in a field of gravitation is rather "as rectilinear as possible."

These straight-as-possible curves are, in a weak field of gravitation, identical with the orbits of the planets derived from Newton's law of attraction. In the close proximity of large "attracting" masses there is a change in a geometrical property of space which is called, in modern geometry, curvature of space. Einstein finds a second deflection of light rays is produced in addition to and exactly equal to the first deflection. There results, then, a total deflection of 1″.75, or roughly two seconds of arc.

Still speaking perfunctorily, one may say that the "weight of light" produces a deflection of one second, and the "curvature of space," a deflection of another second. If the observed deflection is zero, then

Einstein is entirely wrong—light does not behave like a falling body nor does it follow the principle of equivalence. If the deflection is nearly one second, light would have "weight" but space would not be curved, and even in the sun's proximity "gravitation" would follow the inverse-square law. If, however, the observed deflection is nearly two seconds, Einstein's theory would be confirmed to its whole extent.

The test was made at a total solar eclipse in 1919 when stars could be photographed close to the edge of the eclipsed sun.

In its issue of November 7, 1919, the London *Times* carried the headlines: REVOLUTION IN SCIENCE. NEWTONIAN IDEAS OVERTHROWN.

At a joint meeting of the Royal Society and the Royal Astronomical Society held in London, results of observations obtained at the solar eclipse on May 29, 1919, by two expeditions were announced. A few photographs were obtained from which the deflection at the sun's limb was found to be 1″.64. . . .

### Summary of Sections 4 and 5

An alternate explanation for the observed phenomena of "gravity" is furnished by Einstein's principle of equivalence. He proposes that a homogeneous field of gravitation is equivalent to acceleration on the part of the reference system itself with respect to another system which is an inertial system. No concept of force is involved in this new kind of gravitation—it is merely the result of geometry of motion and matter.

If true, Einstein's new principle should apply to light waves as well as to more tangible matter. The resultant deflection of a beam of light in a gravitational field may be calculated, but it proves to be exceedingly small in the case of phenomena on the surface of the earth. Applied to starlight passing the sun, it is thousands of times larger—specifically, 0.87 seconds of arc for a star appearing just at the sun's edge.

However, the consequences of the principle of equivalence are tied in with the concept of the curvature of space, which is again insignificant in terrestrial cases. But for starlight passing the sun, the "straight-line" path is actually curved by another 0″.87, so the entire Einstein "bending of light" is expected to be 1¾ seconds of arc, an observable quantity.

Confirmation of the complete theory of Einstein resulting from his equivalence principle came with the total eclipse of the sun of May 29, 1919, at which astronomers obtained an observed shift of the position of a star close to the sun amounting to $1''.64$, close to the predicted value of $1''.75$.

## 6. The primary Doppler effect and starlight

In all astronomy texts, elementary and advanced, the importance of the Doppler shift in stellar spectra is discussed in detail, for it is upon this phenomenon that much of our information regarding celestial bodies depends.

The traditional statement usually runs: If a star which emits light of a frequency of $n$ oscillations [waves] per second is approaching our earth with a radical velocity $v$, the light from the star seems to have a frequency $n' = n\ (1 + v/c)$ for an observer on the earth, where $c$ is the velocity of light in a vacuum. . . .

The ratio of $n$ to $n'$ is usually made photographically by comparing the positions of lines on spectra from laboratory sources with those from the stars. The laboratory sources are at rest relative to the receiving instrument—the photographic plate—while the star is in motion. Of course, the "motion" of the star may be partly due to a motion of the earth, as, for instance, the result of the earth's revolution around the sun.

## 7. The secondary Doppler effect

We consider now the case of a star which emits light and is at rest relative to the inertial system $J$. The telescope on earth, according to the alternative explanation of gravity, may be considered uniformly accelerated with respect to $J$ (as on p. 99), with acceleration $g$, parallel to the light ray coming from a star directly overhead.

The effect of this equivalent acceleration, $g$, is to speed up the lower end of the telescope during the time $t = L/c$ while the light is passing down the tube of length $L$. The frequency of the starlight at the upper end of the telescope is $n$ waves per second, but when the light reaches the lower end where the receiver is located, the receiver is moving upward at velocity $v=gt = gL/c$, faster than when the light first entered the telescope. . . .

Therefore, according to the Doppler principle, $n'$ vibrations per second are received, and

$$n' = n(1 + v/c) = n(1 + gL/c^2).$$

We notice that the frequency of starlight received and recorded is different at different distances, $L$, from where it was first received; that is it is different at various points in the telescope, or observatory, or elsewhere on the earth. This is called the secondary Doppler effect.

While the primary effect comes from the *velocity* of our earth relative to the star, and has the same value at all points in the observer's system, the secondary effect comes from the *acceleration*, and has a value changing from point to point. The farther we go "downward," the greater is the increase in the frequency. It we proceed inversely to the acceleration upward, the frequency decreases. . . . However, the effect of the earth's gravity is very small, well beyond the limits of any possible astronomical observation.

The secondary Doppler effect is the starting point of Einstein's theory of the effect of gravity upon the frequency of light.

### 8. The secondary Doppler shift and the Einstein shift

Christian Doppler advanced his principle in 1842, when he was professor at the University of Prague. Seventy years later, in 1912, Albert Einstein held the same position in the same university and advanced the generalization of Doppler's principle which led him to the prediction of the effect of gravity upon the frequency of light. This has since become known as the Einstein shift.

As discussed in the preceding section, if we make investigations in an observatory on earth which has an acceleration $g$ relative to $J$, we notice that light traveling in the direction of the acceleration has different frequencies, $n'$, at different points of our system.

But, according to Einstein's principle of equivalence, the same effect which is produced by the acceleration $g$ can be produced also by a force of gravity which is an attraction *toward the star*. That is, the frequency *decreases* as light moves away from the star.

The potential energy difference along the vertical length $L$ is $\Delta\phi = gL$, and the change in frequency caused by gravity, the so-called Einstein shift, is then given by the formula:

$$n' = n\,(1 - \Delta\phi/c^2).$$

All this means, then, that if light travels through a potential difference $\Delta\phi$, in a field of gravity, then a shift in the frequency of the spectral lines should be observed amounting to $-n\Delta\phi/c^2$. Since the gravity of the sun and stars is much greater than that of the earth, we can neglect the latter. Therefore $\Delta\phi$ is always positive and the change in frequency is negative—toward the red. . . .

In the case of the sun, the effect is still very difficult to observe, but for some stars with larger mass and smaller radius than the sun's, the Einstein shift should be observable.

W. S. Adams, using the 100-inch telescope at Mount Wilson Observatory, succeeded in obtaining a spectrum of a star known to be very dense (the companion of Sirius). He measured the Einstein shift in its lines, and the average value he obtained was almost in exact agreement with the prediction.

This, then, is another proof of Einstein's principle of equivalence and of general relativity principles.

## 9. The advance of Mercury's perihelion

The observations of the deflection of starlight by the gravity of the sun prove that the field of gravity must be different from the field ascribed by Newton's law of attraction. The conclusions drawn from Newtonian laws have been in marvelous agreement with astronomical observations of the orbits of the planets. But for at least a century there have been some flaws, particularly concerning the orbit of Mercury, which is nearest to the sun, and therefore in the most intense field of gravity.

If a planet is attracted by a center of mass in exact accordance with Newtonian law, its orbit is an ellipse which keeps its location in space. We observe that the orbits of all planets gradually change their positions in space—that is, the major axis of each elliptical orbit performs a slow rotation in the plane of the orbit. This results in a slow change in the location of perihelion (the point in the orbit nearest the sun)—the advance of perihelion.

The advance was ascribed by Newton and his successors to the attraction of a planet by its fellow planets. The effect of the other planets is just a perturbation, which is noticed as the advance of the perihelion. If we calculate from Newton's law of universal attraction the value of this effect for each planet in turn, we obtain values which are, generally, in exact agreement with observation.

But Mercury is a conspicuous exception, as its perihelion advances 574 seconds of arc per century, which is about 43 seconds of arc *more rapidly* than can be accounted for by perturbations of the other planets. Astronomers looked for an explanation of this "flaw" in universal gravitation for over a century, until Einstein was able to show that the same "curvature of space" which accounts for the doubling of the deflection of light passing the sun also applies to the motion of Mercury. This is the third proof of Einstein's principles of equivalence and general relativity.

### 10. Conclusion

It is seen that relativity is one of the most amazing achievements of the scientific mind in this century—three different phenomena, the deflection of light rays in a gravitational field, the change of frequency of light in a gravitational field, and the additional advance of the perihelion of Mercury, were derived from one and the same hypothesis. This was Einstein's "equivalence of gravity and inertia." This achievement is the more astonishing, as the effect of gravity upon light had not been predicted before, even qualitatively. . . .

## The Motion of Mercury

**G. M. CLEMENCE**

(*Sky and Telescope*, December 1947)

To the student of motions in the solar system Mercury is of special interest. It is the nearest to the sun of all the planets and the most quickly moving, completing a circuit around the sun in less than three months. It is the least massive of the nine major planets. The mass is known with low accuracy, but it is approximately 1/20 that of the earth, or four times that of the moon. It is not this characteristic that is of particular interest, however; perhaps the most interesting fact about the planet is that it furnishes the most accurate observational confirmation of the theory of general relativity.

To get a clear picture of the problem, and of the accuracy of the measurements involved, it is useful to make a scale drawing of Mercury's orbit, its path around the sun. Draw a circle five inches in diameter, and draw any diameter of the circle. Although the orbit of Mercury is not really a circle but an ellipse, the deviation from a circle is hardly noticeable on this scale. Place the sun on the diameter of the circle, ½ inch from the center; it should be a dot about 1/16 inch in diameter. The point where the diameter intersects the circle nearer to the sun is the *perihelion* of Mercury. This Greek word means "near the sun." On the same scale the orbit of the earth may be represented by a circle 13 inches in diameter with the center at the sun.

The orbit of Mercury is not stationary in space but is slowly rotating. Measure off along the orbit from the perihelion a distance of 1/100 inch. This is the amount of motion of the perihelion during the past 180 years, that is, since accurate observations of Mercury were commenced. It is due to two causes: the effect of the gravitational influence of all the other planets, and that (about 1/1000 inch on the diagram) is due to relativity. It is remarkable that this small quantity can be detected at all, but it has actually been measured with an accuracy of 1/50 of its amount, or 1/50,000 inch on the diagram. This feat is all the more remarkable when the peculiar difficulties of observation are considered.

In the first place, the perihelion is not a visible point in the sky whose motion among the stars can be directly measured. Instead, the position of the perihelion has to be deduced by observing the position of Mercury itself; the perihelion is the point of the orbit where Mercury is moving most rapidly. Therefore, numerous observations must be made, the motion of the planet deduced from these, and the position of the perihelion found from the deduced motion of the planet.

Another difficulty is that the observer has to stand on the earth, which is a poor observing platform to use for this purpose; the sun would be much better. From the earth the orbit of Mercury is seen

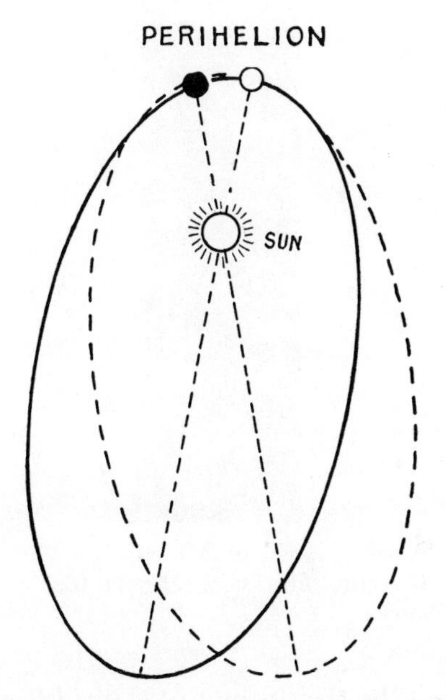


*Fig.* 37. The advance in Mercury's perihelion.

nearly edge on, with the sun in the middle. The planet never gets very far away from the sun in the sky, and it has to be observed in the daytime, usually between 11 A.M. and 1 P.M., under about the worst observing conditions. . . .

The orbit of Mercury is seen nearly edge on, but not quite. Actually it is inclined at an angle of 7 degrees, but there are two times every year when the earth is so situated that the orbit is seen exactly edge on, about May 8 and November 10. At these times, if Mercury is on the near side of its orbit it passes between us and the sun, and may be easily seen as a small, round, intensely black spot, moving across the sun's disk. If it passes near the center of the disk, the duration of the transit is from five to eight hours. There will be eight transits during the remainder of this century, two in May and six in November. The most recent one occurred on November 7, 1960, after which there will be no more until 1970.

Observations of the exact time at which Mercury is seen internally tangent to the sun's disk are of some value for determining the motion of Mercury and the position of its perihelion. Such observations have been made at most transits since 1677, and, indeed, it was the observa-

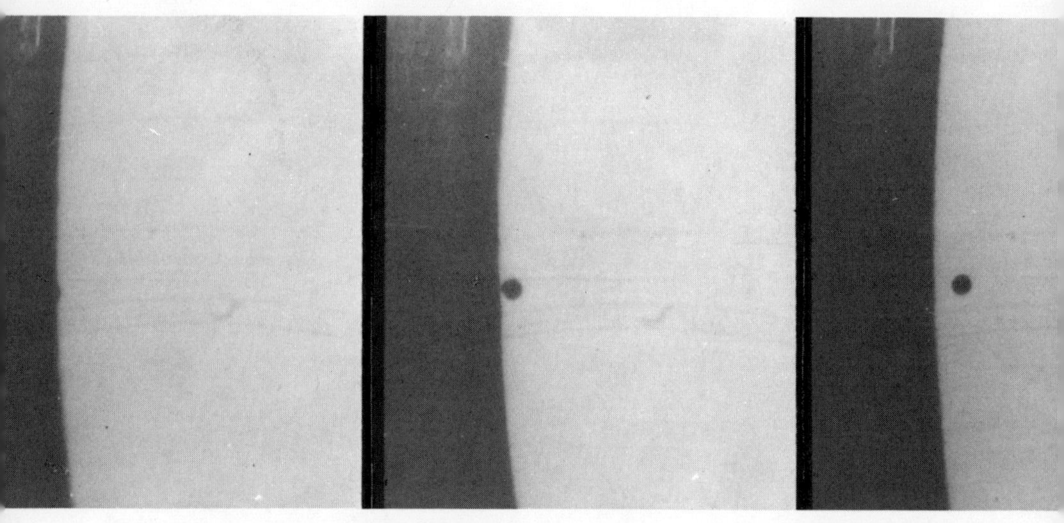

*Fig.* 38. The transit of Mercury on November 11, 1940, photographed on motion-picture film with the 60-foot tower telescope at Mount Wilson Observatory.

tions of the transits up to 1848 which permitted the French astronomer Leverrier to detect the discrepancy between observation and theory which nearly sixty years later was explained by relativity. In modern times, however, the meridian observations are more useful than the observations of the transits, due primarily to their greater number. . . .

When Einstein first announced the General Theory of Relativity many astronomers and physicists found themselves intuitively opposed to such a concept, and the confirmation of the theory given by the motion of Mercury helped greatly to convince many doubting persons that the theory was valid. Now the position is somewhat changed; most scientists have adopted more sophisticated methods of thought, and no doubt would continue to believe in relativity even if the motion of Mercury disagreed with it. In this case the discrepancy would be ascribed to some other cause as yet unknown. The perihelion of Mercury has therefore lost some of its interest, but Mercury has recently assumed a position of peculiar importance in connection with timekeeping; it is the most accurate clock in the solar system, at least the most accurate one that is accessible to astronomers at the present time.

Since time immemorial the earth has been our standard clock; the period of the rotation of the earth has been regarded as invariable, and until perhaps twenty-five years ago this assumption worked sufficiently well. But it has now been established that the earth does not rotate uniformly. In addition to the very gradual slowing down caused by the friction of the tides, there are rather abrupt changes from time to time, due to unknown causes, which cannot be predicted. These changes are too small to be detected by any man-made clocks (at least as yet), but they can be detected by astronomical observation. . . .

In addition to the confirmation of general relativity and its aid in precise timekeeping, Mercury is very useful for weighing the planet Venus.

If a planet has satellites they may be used to determine its mass, but no satellite of Venus has ever been seen, and it is necessary to weigh Venus by measuring its gravitational influence on some other planet. The effect of Venus is to pull Mercury out of an exact ellipse; the actual orbit of Mercury is a very complicated curve in space, but the departures from an ellipse are very small, only a little more than the apparent diameter of the planet. These departures can be calculated very exactly, once the mass of Venus is known. What is done is to calculate them on the basis of an *assumed* mass of Venus. The actual departures are then measured and compared with the calculated ones. If, for example, they turn out to be twice as large, this means that the mass of Venus is twice as great as was assumed, and the assumed mass can be corrected to the right value.

Venus disturbs the earth and Mars as well as Mercury, and therefore we do not depend on Mercury exclusively, but on a combination of all the information that can be obtained from different sources. The different planets are weighed from time to time, as more accurate observations and more refined methods become available. The last time that Venus was weighed was by the writer a few years ago when he analyzed all existing observations of Mercury, about 10,000 in number, extending from 1765 to 1937. The result came out 1/409,000 of the sun's mass. Shortly before that H. R. Morgan and F. P. Scott at the U.S. Naval Observatory had obtained 1/407,000 from the action of Venus on the earth. The true mass, therefore, cannot be very far from 1/408,000.

## Relativity and Planetary Motions

(*Sky and Telescope*, May 1956)

The motions of the inner planets afford an important test of the General Theory of Relativity. For each orbit, the longest diameter is slowly turning counterclockwise, but relativity theory predicts a slightly faster shift than Newtonian gravitation calls for. This difference, expressed in shift of the perihelion per century, amounts to 43.03 seconds of arc for Mercury, 8.6 for Venus, and 3.8 for the earth.

At the U.S. Naval Observatory, R. L. Duncombe has made a detailed examination of the observational evidence for the relativity effect in these three planets. He finds that the observed motion of the perihelion per century slightly exceeds the gravitationally predicted values, being 43.11, 8.4, and 5.0 seconds, respectively. The close agreement between these two sets of numbers is a fresh verification of the correctness of relativity theory. . . .

*This recent work on accurate description of the motions of planets provides an intentional contrast with the earlier observations discussed in Chapter 1. The sun, planets, satellites, asteroids, comets, and meteoroids all move in a way that can be explained and predicted with high precision using Newton's laws of mechanics. Slight, systematic discrepancies between prediction and observation have been discovered, however, and these provide a basis for an entirely different theory, Einstein's General Relativity, which makes no use of Newton's force of gravitation.*

*Nevertheless, Newtonian mechanics is still very much in use, corrected for small relativisitic effects where necessary, and is of great importance in Chapter 3.*

TLP

# 3

# Recent Probing of Space

*Perhaps no development of the past thirty years has caught the public imagination so vividly as the beginnings of space exploration. Man's frontier has been enlarged a millionfold and new dimensions have been added to astronomy.*

*The astronomical profession can claim little credit for the engineering advances that made possible the launching of artificial satellites and space probes. The rocket vehicles that carry them were developed primarily in Germany and were exploited there in the development of ballistic missiles for military purposes. The astronomical aspects of Newton's mechanics are involved in many ways, but the difficulties in launching the first satellites were mainly practical ones. The upward force required to lift the space vehicle off the ground and into a stable orbit around the earth can be calculated from Newton's formulae, as can the energy required for complete escape from the earth on a trip to the moon or to another planet. The difficulty lay in the magnitude of the necessary force—which must be greater than the total vehicle* weight—and the long time over which it must be applied. Rocket engines that produced large thrust were designed without too much trouble (see p. 182), but all of them required vast amounts of fuel. The weight of this fuel is then added to the weight of the vehicle. The problem early became one of finding a fuel that, when used in an efficient rocket engine, could lift itself plus the extra weight of the vehicle and the "payload."

A rocket engine consists of a heat-resistant nozzle into which fuel and oxidizer can be pumped, burned, and exhausted as a jet, firing to the rear. The push on the jet gases that fires them rearward produces (according to Newton) an equal reaction forward—hence the rocket motor is often called a reaction motor. A good one produces a fairly constant thrust—a force of many thousands of pounds—and uses fuel at a rate of hundreds of pounds per second. A simple index of the fuel and motor quality is therefore the number of pounds of thrust produced per pound of fuel used per second. It can be shown that this performance quality, the "specific impulse," is improved by increasing the fuel-burning temperature and hence the speed of jet exhaust. Still, there is a limit to the specific impulse of any one fuel; this limit depends, in essence, on how much chemical energy is in each pound of fuel. For instance, kerosene and oxygen can give over 300 pounds of thrust per pound burned per second; hydrogen and oxygen can give over 500.

Another broad design problem is the control of a rocket vehicle. In this the astronomer can be of some practical help. The proper aiming and timing of a launch are computed from the same Newtonian theory that applies to the orbits of planets, and the stars provide an excellent frame of reference. (The astronaut truly fixes his sights on the stars.) Again, however, the practical "steering" of the rocket is probably as serious a problem as calculating the proper orbit or determining the necessary corrections in direction and speed.

At the end of World War II the U.S. and the U.S.S.R. both started developing high-thrust reaction motors for long-range missiles, using as much of the German experience and as many expert German engineers as possible. It is a little-known fact that the U.S. shot several rockets up above the atmosphere to obtain astronomical data in the *early '50s, and in this way learned about the far ultraviolet light from sun and stars. Engineers and scientists in the U.S.S.R., however, pressed ahead with the design of very high-thrust rocket motors, while the U.S. effort was delayed by indecision in the Department of Defense. The U.S.S.R. launched the first artificial satellite, Sputnik I, on October 4, 1957. This was followed in early November by another, Sputnik II, which carried a dog, before the U.S. launched its first, in January 1958. In this way the space race started, and it developed rapidly into a major international contest.*

*Although there are military implications, it should be made clear that artificial satellites and space probes are primarily concerned with scientific advance—and it is in this aspect that they enhance national prestige. Of course, many of the engineering achievements necessary for success in space probing can be applied to military purposes, but no more so than can the past developments of telescopes, explosives, airplanes, radio, radar, and TV. Space-probe technology goes far beyond present military requirements. Launch rockets are larger than the rocket motors required for long-range missiles and antimissiles, just as the 200-inch telescope at Palomar is larger than telescopes used in battleship gunsights. The development of space probes and the fruition of the present U.S. plan to reach the moon are by no means military goals.*

*In this Chapter it is first necessary to establish the* astronomical *purposes of satellites and space probes. The chronology of early satellite launchings follows, and finally some examination of the plans and efforts toward deeper probing—to the moon, Venus, and other planets. (These plans are proceeding at such a pace that no book today can remain up-to-date for very long.)*

*It may seem obvious at first that astronomers should be interested in space probes, because by this means they can get a closer look at what they have been studying from a distance. But a little reflection demonstrates this reasoning to be weak. A large part of astronomy is concerned with stars and galaxies so far away that their light takes hundreds, thousands, or millions of years to reach us. Returns from a space-probe visit would take at least twice as long. The moon, Mars, and Venus are exceptional; the sun is scarcely an object to visit, and it will be shown later that conditions for a visit are also unattractive on the outer planets.*

*The major advantage space probes offer astronomers is that they get* outside the earth's atmosphere. *If medium-sized optical telescopes can be operated efficiently from the probes, improved astronomical observations will result, for two reasons. First, the earth's atmosphere is opaque to a large fraction of the light from outside: all X rays, most ultraviolet rays, and most infrared light from planets, stars, galaxies, and all other outside sources are unobservable by instruments on the earth's surface. Second, the earth's atmosphere is unsteady. No photograph taken from an earthly observatory is as clear as it could be. Moving currents of air cause the picture to "wobble" during the exposure. In addition, the sky is not entirely dark, even at midnight, and skylight fogs photographs of faint objects. Not all of the night-sky light comes from the earth's atmosphere, however, and the extra-atmospheric telescope will still be troubled with "sky fog," though less so than in terrestrial photography.*

*Another major astronomical advantage will accrue when radiotelescopes can be placed "out of sight" of the earth (on the back side of the moon, for instance). Then the true radio noise of the universe can be measured without the side effects of "static" and amateur radio broadcasting. Other, more specific advantages will emerge in the course of the articles that follow immediately. An attempt has been made to contrast the changing hopes and interests of astronomers as rocket capabilities have developed. Note, first, the uncomplicated approach as early as 1943.*

TLP

## Celestial Target Practice?

**DORRIT HOFFLEIT**

(*Sky and Telescope*, April 1943)

How to get to the moon or Mars? That problem will never rest. Wartime, especially when ordnance departments are seeking farther range firing equipment, recalls this much farther range problem. It would be easy to get to Mars if our earth had neither gravitational force nor an atmosphere. Then, by carefully planning departure times, and cooperating with nature so as to reduce effort to a minimum, we would have to send a projectile off with an initial speed of only 0.78 miles per second—less than artillery shells. The projectile would travel the longest path between the two planets, taking 237 days to Mars' aphelion.

However, because of the restraining influence of our earth's own gravitational field, the projectile would have to move at least 6.95 miles a second to escape from the earth. This is formidable, but not discouraging in view of recent technological progress.

But in addition we must take the atmosphere into account. We know that, to our own advantage, the atmosphere acts like a stone wall to high-speed meteors, succeeding in destroying practically all of them before they can pound upon the surface of the earth. The resisting force increases as the square of the velocity. Getting through the atmosphere is thus the chief obstacle to interplanetary missiles.

# Attack on the Third Dimension[1]

**WILLY LEY**

(*Sky and Telescope*, January 1953)

It was for symbolic reasons that Columbus Day was chosen for the dates of the First and Second Symposiums on Space Travel held at the Hayden Planetarium. I said in 1952 that Columbus, when he set out on his trip to the West, had the wrong conception about the size of the earth [see p. 9].

We can compare his situation with that in which the proponents of space travel find themselves now. We are thinking of reaching and exploring the moon, and compared to Columbus we simply know "all about it." I wish to emphasize, however, that I put quotation marks around this "all about it." When we calculate a space-ship flight track

[1] From a talk given at the Second Symposium on Space Travel at the Hayden Planetarium, American Museum of Natural History, October 13, 1952.

to the moon we know that it will end in the place where the moon will be when the presumed space-ship reaches it and that it will not lead us elsewhere. Once such a flight track has been calculated, we also know with great precision where the space-ship would be after, say, ten hours of elapsed time. We know how fast it would move at that instant and we can devise ways and means of checking whether the actual flight track lives up to calculation or not. Of course, we know the distance and size of our goal, and even though nobody has been there yet, our astronomers have fairly definite ideas about the nature of the moon and the conditions we would encounter on its surface. In many respects we are immeasurably better equipped for a trip into space than Columbus was for his trip across the Atlantic, except for one point: he had a ship that could make the trip and we do not.

The difference between a trip into space and all other trips man has ever made is that all the earlier trips were essentially two-dimensional, while a trip into space would be essentially along the third dimension. Even airplanes are, for practical purposes, tied to the two dimensions of the flat map, for a flight altitude of four or even eight miles counts little when compared to the 7900-mile diameter of our globe. The older trips were West and South or a combination of the two, but when it comes to space travel the paramount dimension is the length of the radius vector [or distance outward]. Where earlier forms of travel had the firm support of the ground, of the seas, or of the airflow around wings, the space-ship is supported, in a manner of speaking, by its cut-off velocity and its inertia, and the helping or opposing forces are not winds or currents but gravitational fields. . . .

People began crossing the ocean just as soon as they had ships for doing so. The will to go out into space exists, and the machine for doing so is in the process of being shaped.

I do not need to elaborate on the historical fact that five centuries ago there were also people who insisted that it couldn't be done and that it was dangerous besides. Nobody, to my knowledge, ever said that space travel would be easy. But more and more people, after having studied the problem, say that it can be done.

# Astronomy from the Space Station[1]

FRED L. WHIPPLE

(*Sky and Telescope*, April 1953)

My discussion will be limited to the purely astronomical problems that will face the astronomer when he begins an observational program from an observatory located above the earth's atmosphere. I am going to omit intentionally the exceedingly important observations of the earth, particularly those meteorological and geophysical in character.

The astronomer must first design and locate an observatory that can be operated by men in an accompanying vehicle under the extremely unusual conditions in empty space. The only really practical location is in the precise orbit of the manned satellite vehicle, ahead or behind; otherwise the observatory will drift away from the satellite vehicle. In twenty-four hours the drift is nearly forty times the difference in distance of observatory and vehicle from the earth.

There are a number of technological problems with regard to setting up and operating a telescope in space. Coating the mirror with a metal reflecting surface, however, will be easy—because of the complete vacuum in space. Furthermore, much electronic equipment will operate without the complication of vacuum seals needed in our atmosphere. Pointing the telescope, holding its position accurately, and so forth, are of great interest in technological design. Shielding surfaces from rapid temperature changes produced by the sun and earth is of extreme importance. The observer will not be able to touch the telescope or be within it, because of the precise directional control required for most problems. Hence all operation must be by remote control. The changing of film and plates requires storage units being transferrable to the telescope from the satellite station.

The spectroscopic techniques used in the satellite station will be

[1] From a talk given at the Second Symposium on Space Travel at the Hayden Planetarium, American Museum of Natural History, October 13, 1952.

adaptations of laboratory vacuum methods now used for ultraviolet and X rays. Large regions in the radio spectrum will be opened up by having the observatory above the ionosphere, and we may expect an active new branch of radioastronomy to develop. Furthermore, there exists the possibility of constructing huge antennas in space, so that the accuracy of radioastronomy may be greatly increased.

On the earth's surface, radioastronomy has already opened up the spectrum from about one millimeter to 30 meters wavelength, but the most interesting parts in the ultraviolet, X-ray, and shorter wave regions are completely invisible from the earth's surface. The entire spectrum, from less than one angstrom unit [10-millionth of a millimeter] up to radio-type waves comparable to the dimensions of the earth, can be observed from the satellite station.

The over all astronomical fields of research to be covered will include solar problems, the planets and smaller bodies in the solar system, the stars, the galaxies, and the interstellar medium of gas and dust.

The solar research will undoubtedly be handled by small, specialized equipment of several varieties, each designed to attack a special problem of solar structure and activity. The present rocket program in the United States will give us preliminary information on solar radiation in the far ultraviolet and X-ray region, and direct measurement of corpuscular radiation from the sun. It is possible also that, from space, radar observations of passing corpuscular streams can be observed by reflection.

The planetary work will make use of a large telescope with, say, a 100- or 200-inch mirror. In observing Mars, for example, a resolving power of approximately 10 miles should be possible with a 100-inch instrument. Of equal interest will be a study of the complete chemical composition of all planetary atmospheres. Vital clues as to life processes are presented by atmospheric constituents.

Stellar spectroscopy in the far ultraviolet and X-ray region will provide any large telescope, or even several of them, with programs for generations, including problems of the composition and evolution of stars, the processes going on in their atmospheres, particularly the loss of material, and possibly in some cases the accretion of matter from the interstellar medium. . . .

Beyond the earth's atmosphere, it will be possible to determine the percentage of almost all trace elements in the interstellar medium; through the earth's atmosphere, even with radioastronomy techniques, only a very few of them can be isolated. The importance of this problem becomes apparent when we realize that many of the great gas and dust clouds of the Milky Way are stellar incubators in which new stars are, indeed, at the present time being born.

The observatory in space may well reveal the secrets of the origin of the universe itself. The most important problems for the space astronomer will probably be new ones, beyond the horizons of our science today.

## Astronomical Uses for Artificial Satellites

(*Sky and Telescope,* March 1959)

"Many years ago Henry Norris Russell remarked that all good astronomers go to the moon after they die so that they can see the heavens freed from the complications produced by the earth's atmosphere." Thus did Lawrence H. Aller begin his summary of the research applications of artificial satellites in astronomy. . . .

Already contemplated are the sending of 50-pound probes to the vicinities of Mars and Venus, and the landing of a 250-pound payload on the moon. Probably ten such initial explorations could be carried out in the next two years. Later plans include space stations and, eventually, a lunar observatory. In the very earliest experiments, however, weight limitations will impose severe restrictions. . . .

Among the experiments proposed by the Space Science Board, several offer possibilities of major advances in astronomy, and will be described briefly.

*General Theory of Relativity.* . . . The rates at which two identical atomic clocks operated by atomic vibrations keep time, if they are placed at points with unequal gravitational potentials, should disagree by an amount equal to the potential difference divided by the square of the velocity of light. (See p. 106, where the frequency, *n*, now applies to atomic vibrations in the clock.) If an atomic clock is flown in a suitable satellite, calculations show that its rate should diverge from that of a terrestrial counterpart by several units in 10 billion ($10^{10}$). The relative motions of the two clocks will superimpose differences of about the same size, but their amount can be allowed for. Thus, the major practical problem involves only a choice of a frequency standard—an accurate atomic clock.

In Boulder, Colorado, National Bureau of Standards scientists have proposed using an ammonia maser (one type of accurate oscillator for an atomic clock) which has a frequency stability of one part in $10^{11}$.

The frequency standard is used as the "pendulum" or escapement of the clock. The difficult task, in practice, is to compress the clock in both size and weight to fit into a satellite and to make sure that it can survive the rigors of the launching. For satellite orbits of a suitable size, the relativistic effect would amount to about three parts in $10^{10}$, or 30 millionths of a second per day. Since the transmission time for signals from the satellite to the ground may be uncertain by about five microseconds, a clock with an accuracy of one part in $10^{11}$ would have to run over a period of several weeks in order to measure the gravitational relativistic effects accurately. . . .

The moon is the most favorable natural gravitational clock, as time may be deduced with high accuracy from measurements of the moon's position in the sky. But its orbital motion is slow, and a rapidly moving artificial satellite would be an even more accurate gravitational timekeeper, taking perhaps one tenth as long as the moon to give a satisfactory result.

In consultation with Princeton University Observatory astronomers, Dr. Clemence has formulated the following specifications for such a satellite's orbit: a distance from the center of the earth of at least 16,000 miles to minimize atmospheric drag, yet not more than 24,000 miles, to keep lunar perturbations small; an orbital eccentricity of less than 0.05 if possible; and an orbital inclination to the equator of about 40 degrees for ease in tracking and to avoid certain computational difficulties. The satellite is to be spherical with as small a cross section as possible; it may carry a flashing light to facilitate observations. Finally, since atmospheric drag even at such great heights is not negligible, two satellites would be needed to give a measure of the effect of drag.

Launched from the final stage of the same vehicle, these would be identical in every respect except for a weight placed in the center of one to make it ten times as massive as the other.

In theory, these satellites should permit the determination of gravitational time with a precision of one part in 10 thousand million ($10^{10}$) in about two months. Actually, Dr. Aller pointed out, the experiment should be run for about two years. For lunar observations to give the same result, up to twenty years would be required.

*Astrophysical Problems.* The possibility of exploring the far ultraviolet region of the spectra of the sun, stars, and nebulae is very inviting to the astrophysicist. Heretofore, our information has been obtained slowly and laboriously by means of high-altitude rockets giving only momentary snapshots. . . .

Tracking of stars, planets, or nebulae from a satellite requires special apparatus and a payload of a thousand pounds or more. Dr. Aller said that studies of individual faint stars and nebulae will probably require putting a man in space, as he doubts that a foolproof tracking mechanism can be devised for these elusive objects in the difficult observing conditions of outer space.

The first observations of the far ultraviolet spectra of stars, made with rockets by Naval Research Laboratory scientists, provide a valuable check on theories of stellar atmospheres. The results from current rocket work are difficult to interpret, and much further effort is needed.

For instance, the star Spica, for which the line spectrum suggests an excitation temperature of 28,000 degrees, should be about thirty times brighter than it is observed to be in the ultraviolet region as measured by photon counters [accurate photoelectric cells] carried aloft in rockets. At the same time, a large nebulosity has been observed around Spica at far-ultraviolet wavelengths, yet in this part of the sky there is no visible nebulosity at all.

*The program of the National Aeronautics and Space Administration (NASA) covers many projects. Among the largest of these is the one best known to the public—manned satellites and space probes. Many of the observations needed by astronomers, however, do not require a man aboard; in fact, the presence of any living creature on a space vehicle designed for astronomical observations is generally a disadvan-*

*tage. This view, to which some may take exception, does not diminish the importance of* NASA *man-in-space projects that have other purposes.*

*These unmanned satellites require reliable remote control and telemetering. Assuming for the moment that a telescope and other observing equipment in a satellite can be pointed and operated as needed (by radio from the earth, automatic devices, or tape-recorded* "orders" *aboard), and that the observations can be returned to earth (by* TV, *radio, or landing and recovering parts of the satellite), no man is necessary in the vehicle, provided that no breakdowns occur.*

*There are two main disadvantages to carrying a man along in the satellites designed for astronomical observation: added* weight *and disturbing* motions. *In addition to the astronaut's body weight of 150 pounds or more, shielding, food, air, water, and other necessities of life must be provided; and extra equipment is needed to return him to the earth. Modern miniaturized equipment used in space flights undertaken for specific purposes can save weight by substituting automatic equipment in place of a man as well as cutting down the size and weight of the instrument package.* And, *more important for astronomical observations, such inert electronic equipment will not jiggle the vehicle, whereas a man or any living animal, by breathing and other body motions, would make accurate pointing of the telescope impossible. This accuracy is essential to most astronomical observations, important among them the taking of high-quality photographs.*

*The matter has been given a good deal of thought by designers of both manned and unmanned vehicles during the past five years. It is possible that more efficient and advanced design will allow new techniques not yet considered fully—such as a telescope that can be separated from a manned vehicle and recovered while in orbit. Such vehicles may later become more suitable for astronomical observation.*

*One of the two major* NASA *projects affecting astronomical research, the* Orbiting Solar Observatory (OSO), *is already functioning, as described below. The other,* OAO, *the* Orbiting Astronomical Observatory, *for study of planets, stars, and galaxies, is still in the planning stage.*

**TLP**

## Space Observations of Sun and Earth

(*Sky and Telescope*, May 1962)

The sun is now being observed by a complex 450-pound artificial satellite that was launched from Cape Canaveral on March 7 by a three-stage Delta vehicle. The Orbiting Solar Observatory (OSO) moves in a nearly circular track some 350 miles above the earth's surface. It is the first in a series of satellites intended to study the sun throughout an entire eleven-year sunspot cycle, and carries an array of thirteen experiments to measure solar radiation at ultraviolet, X-ray, and gamma-ray wavelengths.

OSO consists of two major sections: a wheel-like base and a fan-shaped sail. They are connected by a shaft so that the sail may face the sun while the base spins 30 times per minute for gyroscopic stability. Two servomotors, controlled by sun sensors and working at right angles to each other, point the sail-carried instruments directly at the sun. The pointing accuracy is presumably of the order of one or two minutes of arc.

The over all orientation of the observatory is controlled by nitrogen jets. The gas supply, which limits the useful life of the satellite, was expected to last about six months. However, according to project manager J. C. Lindsay, the gas is being used at a lower rate than anticipated and the observatory's lifetime may be somewhat extended. Initially, the pitch of the satellite was shifting one quarter of a degree per day, and a correction was needed only once every twelve days, when the error had grown to 3 degrees.

The sail is always within 3 degrees of being broadside to the sun. It carries 1860 solar cells covering an area of nearly 3¾ square feet. These charge nickel-cadmium batteries that in turn supply about seven watts of power to the telemetry, data, and control systems, and nine watts to the various experiments.

Observational data are stored on a continuous-loop tape that records at ¾ inch per second. Upon command from the ground, the tape is

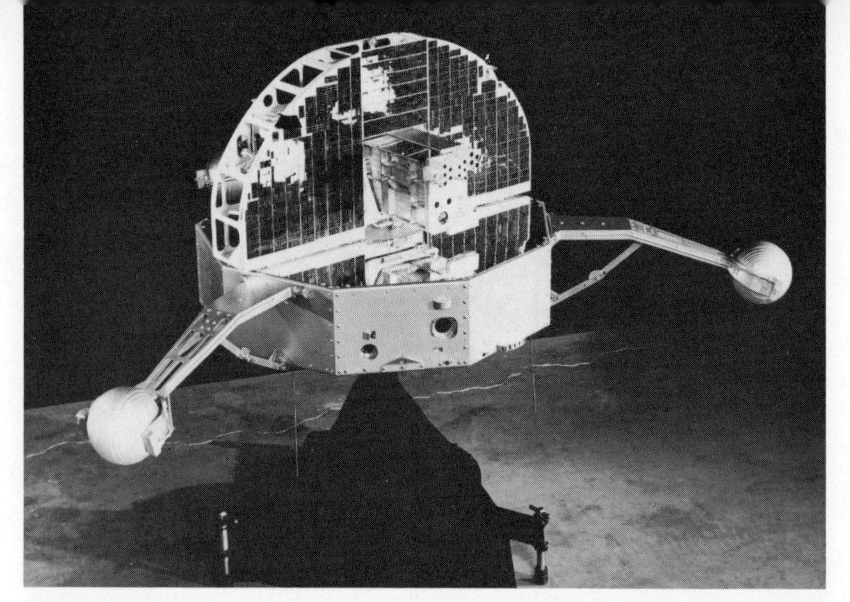

*Fig. 39.* Well above the earth's atmosphere, this 37-inch-high Orbiting Solar Observatory is studying solar radiation. While the nine-sided base spins for stability, the semicircular sail continuously faces the sun, which illuminates the solar power cells, visible in the photograph as tiny black rectangles. Protruding from the sail is the stabilized package containing instruments that are always pointed directly at the sun. (NASA photograph)

*Fig. 40.* The Orbiting Solar Observatory, with its wide array of sensing and correcting mechanisms, is an extremely complex satellite. (NASA photograph)

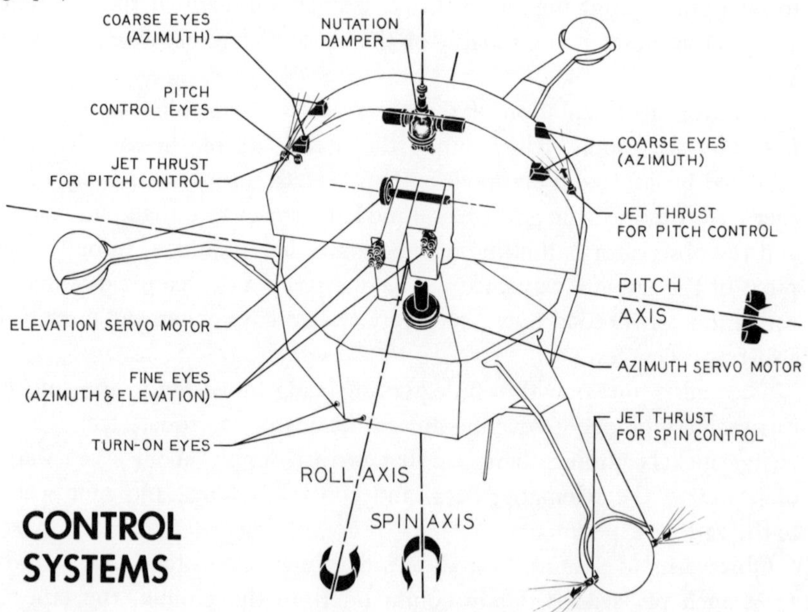

played back eighteen times faster, delivering ninety minutes of observations during the five minutes that the satellite remains within range of a receiving station. To conserve power, the spacecraft automatically turns itself off when entering the earth's shadow and on again when leaving it.

In the nine-sided wheel section are mounted eight experiments. As the wheel spins, the different sensors look first at the sky, then at the sun, comparing radiations from different directions. A special photodiode [photo cell] with a colored filter records ultraviolet, violet, and blue light between 3800 and 4800 angstroms. An ion chamber is used to measure ultraviolet radiation of 1100 to 1250 angstroms, including the Lyman-alpha line of hydrogen, which in the sun's spectrum is an emission feature.

Gamma-ray intensity is being recorded in three experiments, covering the energy ranges from 0.05 to three million, 0.2 to 1.5 million, and 100 to 500 million electron volts. One study includes an unshielded detector to measure any gamma radiation generated in the vehicle itself when it encounters high-energy particles.

The first major neutron experiment to be made in space will count the particles that leak out of the earth's atmosphere. These are believed to be produced by cosmic rays striking oxygen and nitrogen nuclei. Previous measurements have been made by rocket-borne devices that were limited in the length of observing time.

Two nonsolar studies are being performed. One is a test of several surface materials for changes during prolonged exposure to conditions in space. The other is a probing of the lower regions of the Van Allen belt [of charged particles in motion around the earth] by a detector that can distinguish between proton and electron ionizations.

A small stabilized platform supported by the sail carries instruments that point continuously at the sun. They include equipment for monitoring gamma rays, X rays, and interplanetary particles.

A detector and photomultiplier tube [a sensitive photoelectric cell] are used to measure the gamma rays. Incoming rays produce in the scintillator light flashes that are detected by the photomultiplier, which signals each flash electrically. The device is intended to detect radiation of 0.024-angstrom wavelength produced by the mutual annihilation of an electron and positron, with complete conversion of their mass into energy.

The X-ray experiments cover the wavelength intervals 0.1–0.6, 1–8, and 100–400 angstroms.

To determine the rate of incoming meteoric particles, their momenta, and their energy of motion, OSO carries a photomultiplier covered with a very thin layer of aluminum. The tube records the luminous energy generated by the impact of a particle, while a microphone mounted on the tube measures the mechanical impulse delivered.

The National Aeronautics and Space Administration has described OSO as the first of its more sophisticated "second-generation" scientific satellites. This application of an artificial satellite to astrophysical problems of prime importance is especially welcome to astronomers.

*While the value of telescopic observations* entirely *outside the earth's atmosphere is obvious, another possibility now being exploited is the less difficult one of carrying a telescope above* most *of the atmosphere by means of a high-altitude balloon. There are several advantages; among them are easy recovery of the equipment, photographs, or stored data, and the lower cost for a telescope of given size. Both manned and unmanned balloon flights have been carried out, and the results tend to confirm the general conclusion reached for space vehicles: unmanned, remote-controlled instruments are more effective for astronomical observations.*

TLP

## Project Stratoscope— Solar Photographs from 80,000 Feet

JOHN B. ROGERSON, JR.

(*Sky and Telescope*, January 1958)

Our planet's atmosphere continually tantalizes the astronomical photographer. At best it is only semitransparent, and most of the time its motions blur his pictures. And in solar photography, where we are interested in recording small details on the sun's surface, poor seeing conditions are a most important limitation.

It is no wonder that astronomers have long wanted some stable observing platform placed well above the swirling murk of the lower atmosphere, so their telescopes could be used to full advantage. A major advance toward this goal was achieved on September 25, 1957, when a 12-inch reflecting telescope was carried aloft by an unmanned Skyhook balloon to a height of more than 80,000 feet over Minnesota, and solar photographs of unprecedented definition were secured.

This flight was part of Project Stratoscope, on which the writer has been working under the leadership of Princeton astronomer Martin Schwarzschild, with the support of the Office of Naval Research and the Air Force Cambridge Research Center.

For over a decade, Dr. Schwarzschild has been studying the problem

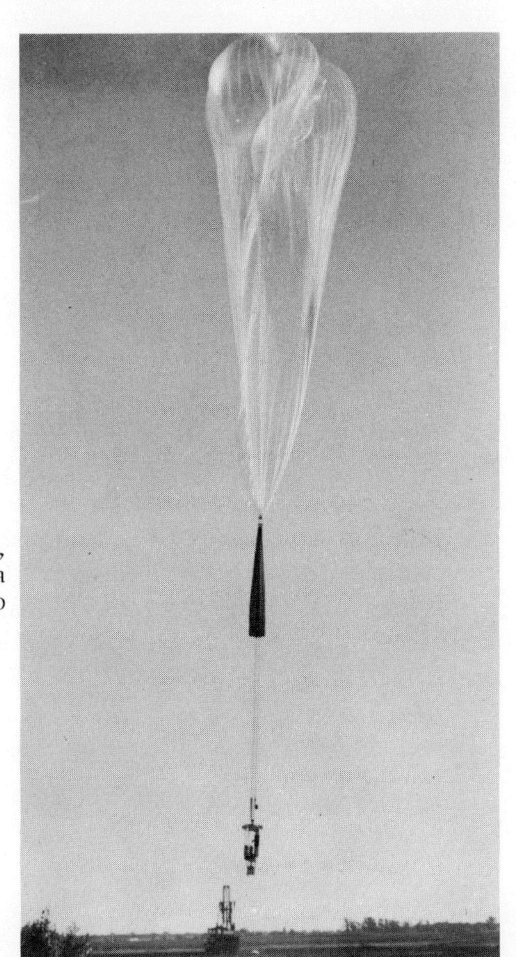

*Fig. 41.* A Skyhook balloon, with Stratoscope camera hanging beneath, rises into the sky.

of the solar granules, which are seen as tiny bright specks densely spread over the sun's surface in very great numbers. The granules are so minute that they are difficult to observe effectively. Individual grains are short-lived, forming and vanishing within a few minutes. They are thought to be rising currents of turbulent gas that play an important part in the transport of energy from the hot solar interior outward into space.

More than sixty years ago, excellent photographs of solar granulation were obtained by J. Janssen at the Meudon Observatory in France, but they show effects of turbulence in the earth's atmosphere on photographs of the sun. On the basis of such pictures, the granules were long supposed to be some 1000 miles in diameter. . . .

Recently, from Mount Wilson Observatory photographs, R. S. Richardson and Schwarzschild inferred that some solar granules are only 150 miles in diameter.

Granules of this size would be too small to be photographed by ordinary techniques. In November 1956, and later in April 1957, photographs of the solar granulation had been taken at altitudes of 20,000 and 25,000 feet from a manned balloon. An 11-inch telescope matched the best ground-based photographs to date.

The current project consisted of three balloon ascents from the General Mills Flight Center, New Brighton, Minnesota. The first of these, on August 22, 1957, carried a dummy telescope, plus a special instrument to test the quality of the guiding provided by the pointing mechanism.

The second flight was launched at 6:15 A.M. Central standard time on September 25. While the balloon hovered at a predetermined altitude of about 82,500 feet for 4¾ hours, the photoelectric tracking device kept the camera pointed toward the center of the sun. At intervals of one second, 35-mm. photographs were taken continuously until some 8000 frames had been secured. Then the telescope, with its accessory instruments and exposed film, was automatically separated from the balloon and parachuted to earth, landing near Athens, Wisconsin, at 1:14 P.M.

A third successful flight was carried out on October 17. The 12-inch telescope, which with its accessory equipment weighed 1400 pounds, was lifted to a maximum height of over 84,000 feet. For this flight, the pointing control was modified in such a way as to cause the telescope to scan slowly back and forth across the limb of the sun. Five such scans were made during the nearly 2½ hours of camera operation. As with the first two flights, the instruments were recovered very nearly intact. The repairs of the landing damage averaged about 5 per cent of the construction costs for each flight.

The special reflecting telescope has an effective focal length of 200 feet. Only a small portion of the nearly two-foot image of the sun can be photographed on one frame of the 35-mm. movie camera. The telescope itself is 9½ feet long, and weighs about 300 pounds.

Solar heating and temperature variations at such great altitudes influenced the design and operation of the telescope. Its walls were made of perforated Invar steel to minimize thermal expansion and contraction. The aluminized quartz secondary mirror was arranged to rotate so that it would face the heat of the sun only 2 per cent of the time, reflecting the image into the enlarging system only at times of picture-taking. . . .

In pointing the telescope, pairs of photodiodes [photoelectric cells] were employed to find the sun and to center the instrument on it. These "photoelectric eyes" were arranged so that both eyes of a pair saw the same amount of sunlight when the telescope was pointing directly at the sun in one coordinate. Thus, if the telescope were not pointing correctly, one eye would see more sunlight than the other, and this switched on a motor to move the telescope.

By using several pairs of eyes, the telescope was pointed correctly both horizontally (in azimuth) and vertically (in elevation). The horizontal motion was obtained by reacting against a heavy flywheel, the main mass of which was provided by the heavy storage batteries necessary as a power source. The telescope was tilted vertically against the pendulum action of the gimbal structure in which it was mounted.

In these ascents, unmanned flight had another important advantage besides increased payload; small motions, even breathing, by a human observer would cause intolerable amounts of telescope motion. Upper-air winds were not expected to swing the equipment through more than a fraction of a degree.

From the thousands of exposures made on these flights, several pictures were obtained with sharper resolution than ever achieved before. They include both the center of the solar disk and the limb [edge], and show that the solar granulation has a cellular, though highly irregular, character. The bright cells appear to be separated from each other by dark, often very sharp lines. Thus, there appear to be only thin lines of descending gas separating the rising columns. The sizes range from 900 down to about 150 miles on the sun's surface.

The results of Project Stratoscope are so promising that plans are under way for further ascents in which the 12-inch telescope will be used with a television pickup tube. The image would be relayed to the earth's surface for reproduction on a television screen, giving the ground observer the possibility of selecting interesting regions of the solar surface or improving the focus by remote control. . . .

*The value of these remarkable photographs in learning more about the complex structure and motions of the sun's surface is obvious. For all daytime astronomical observations, balloons offer similar improvements, since the earth's atmosphere is generally at its worst in sunlight.*

*Not all of the many types of astronomical observations to be made outside the earth's atmosphere can be discussed here. One that is a*

*Fig.* 42. Photograph of the sun's surface taken by the Stratoscope camera from above 80,000 feet, showing granulation near the center of the solar disk at a scale of 1 millimeter = about 190 miles. (Official U.S. Navy photograph)

*matter of much concern in space-probing is the* refinement of the dynamics of the solar system. *More accurate measurement of distances and motions governed by Newton's mechanics can determine more accurate constants in the present theory, thus paving the way for accurate "space navigation" in the future.*

*First among the constants to be improved is the distance from sun to earth, the so-called "astronomical unit" that sets the scale of virtually all other distances measured by astronomers. From earth-based observations with optical telescopes, this distance appears to be about 92,925,000 miles, with an uncertainty of 10,000 miles. This determination results primarily from triangulating—measuring the distance from the earth to a nearby planet or asteroid by means of the difference in the planet's direction as seen from two places on earth separated by a known distance. The accuracy of such measurements is limited by the unsteady atmosphere of the earth.*

*A new method of measurement recently became practical with the development of high-power radar, and the distance to Venus has been measured by timing radio pulses reflected back from that planet. Other schemes are described below. It should be recognized that an accurate determination of the earth's speed in its orbit around the sun (in miles per second) can be used to determine the sun-earth distance. Similarly, the ratio of the sun's mass to the earth's mass is related, by Newtonian mechanics, to the astronomical unit and to the length of the year. The earth-sun distance can be expressed in miles or kilometers, or as the angle formed at the sun by the earth's radius, the "solar parallax," amounting to about 8″.80 (8.8 seconds of arc).*

TLP

## Distance of the Sun

(*Sky and Telescope*, November 1959)

An extremely precise radio method of finding the sun's distance has been proposed by A. E. Lilley, Harvard Observatory, and Dirk Brouwer, Yale Observatory. It uses the same principle—Doppler shifts caused by the earth's motion around the sun—employed by an older optical technique involving observations of stellar spectra. When the earth moves toward a star, there is a shift of stellar spectrum lines toward shorter wavelengths, while for a receding earth the displacement is to longer wavelengths. In practice, the optical procedure did not give the accuracy that its radio counterpart now offers.

If a radio source is located behind a cloud of interstellar hydrogen, the 21-centimeter line of neutral hydrogen can be observed as a very sharp absorption feature. [That is, the frequency 1430 megacycles would be missing.] It is planned to measure the frequency of such an absorption line (for a source near the ecliptic) at different times of the year for several years. Because of the earth's revolution, the observed frequency of the absorption line will vary back and forth during the year. Thus it will be possible to ascertain the orbital velocity of the earth, and hence the precise size of its orbit and the distance to the sun.

Dr. Brouwer's computations show that the method should be capable of fixing the sun's distance to one part in 300,000—a precision hitherto promised only by radar observations of Venus. The main limitation to the accuracy attainable is the rotation of the earth, which may change the observed frequency of the 21-centimeter line by one cycle in the course of 20 seconds, and thus limit the time that can be profitably spent on any single measurement.

Actual observations will start early in 1960, at the Naval Research Laboratory and at the Agassiz station of the Harvard Observatory. For recording the hydrogen line, a new radiotelescope has been developed with financial support from the National Aeronautics and Space Administration.

*Radiotelescopes are sensitive radio receivers fitted with directional antennas, often paraboloid "dishes" or of helical shape. They detect radio "static" from various regions of the sky (called "sources"). One frequency—1430 megacycles, or the 21-centimeter wavelength—comes from clouds of hydrogen atoms between the stars and provides a standard of known frequency.*

TLP

# Pioneer V and the Scale of the Solar System

MARSHALL MELIN

(*Sky and Telescope*, December 1960)

The interplanetary probe launched March 11, 1960, under the auspices of the National Aeronautics and Space Administration, has turned out to be of unusual astronomical significance, for observations of this object, 1960$\alpha$, have been used to test a novel and promising method of calibrating the solar-system distance scale. The first results were reported to the American Astronomical Society in August by J. B. McGuire, D. D. Morrison, and L. Wong of Space Technology Laboratories.

Communication with Pioneer V was maintained for 107 days while the probe traveled more than 170 million miles along its orbit, between those of the earth and Venus. It was a detailed study of this motion that gave the means of a re-evaluation of the astronomical unit—the mean distance of the earth from the sun.

Early in its trajectory, the probe was tracked by helical antennas at Cape Canaveral and at Singapore, and by more powerful parabolic antennas at Hilo, Hawaii, and Jodrell Bank, England. The probe quickly outdistanced the helical antennas, and from March 13 onward was tracked only by the paraboloids.

Between May 8 and 21, the 150-watt transmitter of 1960$\alpha$ was operated by ground command on several occasions, but deterioration of the nickel-cadmium storage batteries that accumulated energy from the solar cells brought these transmissions to an end, and only the five-watt transmitter could be used.

Jodrell Bank maintained contact until June 26, the final transmission leaving Pioneer V at 11:31:20 Universal time, at a distance of about 22,462,115 miles, according to Space Technology Laboratories scientists.

The tracking program was aimed at precision measurements of the line-of-sight velocity of Pioneer V, by means of the Doppler shift in radio frequency. . . .

The probe rebroadcast signals at exactly 16/17 the received frequency. This offset in frequency permitted probe and earth station to communicate with a single antenna each without being swamped by the transmitter attached to the same antenna.

In this way the Doppler shift could be measured—the change in frequency resulting from the relative velocity of Pioneer V and the ground station. The shift could be obtained with a precision of about one cycle per second—better than had been anticipated. At the end of 107 days, the weak returning signals were taking four minutes for their long round trip through interplanetary space.

The observed relative velocity decreased gradually to a low of 2.4 kilometers per second on April 6, but had risen to 8.3 when the signals ended.

The observed frequency shift was first corrected for the daily motion of the antenna around the earth's axis and for the monthly motion of the earth, around the center of gravity of the earth-moon system.

Next, the probe's motion was computed from step to step by taking into account the gravitational attractions of the sun and all the planets from Mercury to Jupiter. Then the observed and predicted radial velocities were compared, and the ratio of mass of sun to mass of earth were adjusted to give the best fit to the observations. From this ratio the length of the astronomical unit could be deduced. This study gave it as $92.9251 \pm 0.0085$ million miles. . . .

This new value agrees well with the mass of the sun as found by optical observations of Eros, an asteroid that passes close to the earth in its motion around the sun. However, it disagrees strongly with the results obtained from radar observations of Venus in 1958.

It is disconcerting that these and other determinations should differ. For astronautical applications, especially space navigation, the astronomical unit must be known much more accurately.

When contact between Pioneer V and the earth was lost, the probe had completed only about a third of one revolution around the sun. This method for evaluating the sun's distance would give a greatly improved result if, for a future interplanetary probe, the Doppler observations could be extended over a larger part of a complete revolution.

**Artificial Satellites.** *Having discussed the engineering problems of launching space vehicles and some of the goals of astronomical observation from above the earth's atmosphere, it is now appropriate to trace the progress of space exploration, starting with the earliest and simplest artificial satellites.*

Some of the public's excitement over these first ventures outside the earth's atmosphere is reflected in the articles written hastily at the time. A much better understanding is possible if the basic requirements for satellite launching are first reviewed briefly and the new, space-age terms redefined.

In order to put a satellite into a stable orbit about the earth it is necessary to give it at least two "pushes" or "impulses," the first an upward push to get it above the atmosphere, and the second a sidewise push to start it around the earth. Once it is in orbit above the atmosphere, no further rocket power is needed to keep it up (just as no power is needed to keep the moon in its orbit). Without the second impulse, however, the rocket would generally fall back to earth.

If, after the "burn-out" of the second rocket impulse, the satellite is moving at the correct speed parallel to the earth's surface, it will have a circular orbit and remain at constant height. The higher it is, the slower it must move in order to have a circular orbit and the longer it will take to go around once (Kepler's third law, p. 34). During the satellite's period of revolution, the earth rotates while the satellite's orbit remains roughly fixed in space. Thus on its second time around, the satellite generally passes over points farther west on a map of the earth. The satellite's path is determined by the compass direction of the original launch: for a "polar orbit," the shot is due north or south; an "equatorial orbit" can only be launched from the earth's equator due east or west. The "inclination" of the orbit is roughly the angle at which it crosses the equator; more accurately, it is the greatest latitude reached.

If the final burn-out velocity (speed and direction) is not equal to the circular velocity, the satellite will go into an elliptical orbit, at one point (perigee) closest to the earth, and half a period later (at apogee) farthest. In early launchings this often resulted in the satellite dipping into the earth's atmosphere at perigee; the resulting air drag then grad-

*ually brought the satellite lower and lower until it overheated and burned up. It was then said to have had a "lifetime" of so many revolutions or of so many months. Several satellites have been put into elliptical orbits intentionally in order to make measurements at various heights above the earth. At a speed of about 7 miles per second the vehicle will leave the earth in an open (parabolic) orbit, never to return. That is, it will escape from the gravitational attraction of the earth. The speed in elliptical or circular orbits is always less than this "escape velocity."*

*Most launched satellites have had two or three "stages"; the first stage is a large rocket that lifts the whole combination off the ground and gets it moving at a fair speed upward before first-stage burn-out, when the main fuel supply is used up. On the front end of the first-stage rocket is a smaller second-stage rocket, which is then fired, leaving the empty first-stage hulk to fall back to earth. After second-stage burn-out, this process may be repeated with a third-stage rocket carrying the final satellite payload in its nose.*

*During each impulse the direction of the thrust must be carefully controlled, often by heat-resistant vanes in the rocket exhaust. In order to get the horizontal thrust of the second or third stage, the vehicle is usually turned (aimed in a new direction) between stages by small sidewise jets located fore and aft. The accuracy with which the intended orbit is achieved is dependent on the control of the direction and of the timing of each impulse. The launching is generally tracked by radar and at least partly controlled by radio. After final burn-out, the orbit is determined by radar or optical observation; it is possible to correct this orbit by pointing the rocket properly and reigniting it at the proper time for a computed interval, but this requires a good deal of control equipment.*

TLP

## Artificial Satellite No. 1

(*Sky and Telescope*, November 1957)

The artificial satellite age began on October 4, 1957, when a Russian test vehicle started to circle the earth fifteen times a day.

According to a preliminary analysis by German astronomers at Bonn Observatory using early observations, the new moonlet was launched that day about $20^h$ Universal time[1] from a point somewhere in Central Asia.

In *Soviet Aviation*, Professor Y. A. Pobedonostsev stated that the three-stage launching rocket attained a speed of about 4500 miles per hour in the first two minutes. When the first stage dropped away, the vehicle was moving upward at a 45-degree angle. At second-stage burn-out, the speed was nearly 12,000 miles an hour. Unpowered flight lasted until horizontal motion was achieved about 625 miles from the launching site; then the third-stage motor took over to boost the speed to approximately 18,000 miles per hour before ejection of the artificial moonlet.

During the first days of the satellite, conflicting reports and speculation were mingled with facts, but we know, for instance, that the satellite is a sphere 22.8 inches in diameter, with the surprisingly large total weight of 184 pounds. According to Radio Moscow on October 5, the period of orbital revolution was 96.2 minutes, implying an average height of 370 miles.

As soon as the existence of the moonlet was revealed, *Moonwatch* teams [groups of astronomical observers, see p. 144] were alerted; then it was learned that no favorable passages over the United States would occur for a number of days. Like the projected American satellites, the Soviet one presumably can be seen only during or near morning and evening twilight, when it may be viewed as a sunlit speck against a fairly dark sky; it would be invisible at other times.

American observations, at least initially, were limited to the radio

[1] Universal time (UT) is the time of day at Greenwich, England, longitude 0°—a "standard time" used by astronomers to avoid confusion between different local times.

signals transmitted from the satellite, the continuous beeping audible over a range of thousands of miles because of the great altitude of the satellite. The transmitters, which consumed one watt of power, radiated pulses of 0.3-second duration, followed by an equal interval of silence, at 20.005 and 40.002 megacycles (wavelengths of about 15 and 7.5 meters). The pulses at one frequency occurred simultaneously with the pauses on the other. By October 8, these transmissions appeared to be growing weaker.

The great early strength of the signals made them easily detectable by amateur operators, and they were received by many members of the American Radio Relay League. The ten Minitrack stations organized by The Naval Research Laboratory to monitor American satellites at 108 megacycles required hasty conversion of antennas and receivers to pick up the Russian frequencies.

During a passage of the satellite, the steady beeping could be followed for twenty-five to thirty-five minutes. At one crossing over the New

*Fig.* 43. Photographs of 20.005-megacycle radio pulses from Sputnik I during the night of October 5, 1957. (Photograph by Robert Slavin and G. R. Miczaika, Geophysics Research Directorate, Air Force Cambridge Research Center, Bedford, Massachusetts)

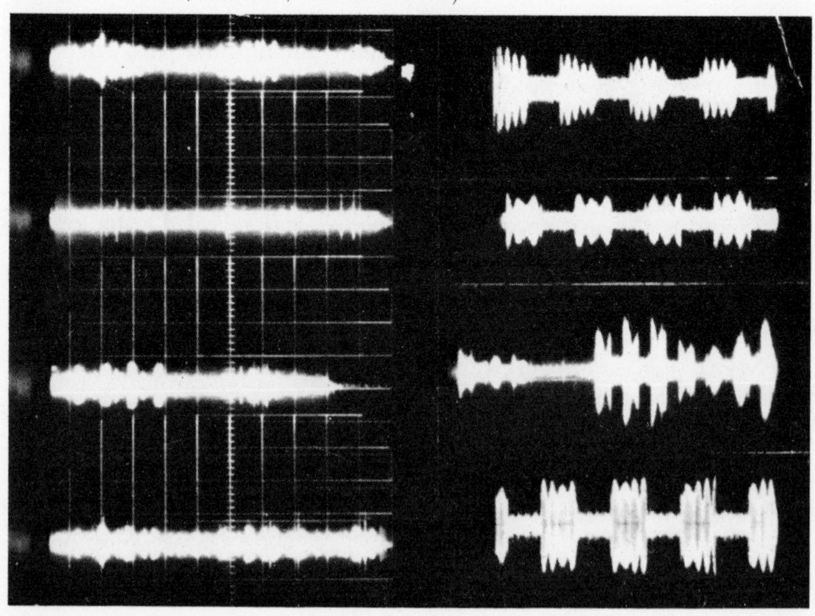

York City area, at 7:52 A.M. EST on October 5, the receiving station of RCA Communications, Inc., at Riverhead, Long Island, measured the change in frequency of the carrier wave as the satellite approached and then receded, an example of the Doppler effect. From this the orbital velocity was deduced to be 4.92 miles per second.

Several monitoring stations picked up other strong 20-megacycle signals, probably originating from a ground station in the Moscow area, which apparently triggered the telemetering system in the satellite.

The earliest reports of visual sightings were contradictory. Later, apparently reliable optical observations of a bright object were obtained on October 6 and 8 at Mount Stromlo Observatory, Australia, and at the University of Alaska. On the morning of October 9, it was seen as a fifth-magnitude object from the University Observatory, Vienna, Austria.

Astronomers at Harvard computed a preliminary orbit on October 9, . . . based on a radio observation at Boulder, Colorado, and sightings in Alaska and Australia. Later computations gave a perigee distance of 143 miles and an apogee of 583 miles.

Actually, three pieces of "hardware" were moving in closely similar orbits: the satellite itself, the discarded third stage, and the empty nose cone of the rocket. Probably most authenticated visual observations refer to the third stage which, much larger than the 22.8-inch sphere, may well appear brighter. Because of its greater air drag, the third stage should be moving below and *ahead of* the satellite, a seeming paradox predicted by celestial mechanics. This fits a report from Hobart, Tasmania, of the passage of a bright body followed by a fainter one. . . .

Other satellites, both American and Russian, are expected during the remainder of the International Geophysical Year. The first American launching is to be in December, according to President Eisenhower's statement of October 9.

## The First Man-Made Satellite

(*Sky and Telescope*, December 1957)

Sputnik, first Russian artificial satellite, was launched on October 4 [1957] in secrecy, and its early career was marked by an almost complete lack of information as to its physical characteristics.

It is a sphere with a diameter of 58 centimeters (nearly 23 inches), weighing 83.6 kilograms (about 184 pounds). It has a hermetically sealed casing of aluminum, its surface polished and specially treated. Before being launched, the sphere was filled with gaseous nitrogen, according to a news release from *Pravda* on October 9.

*Fig. 44.* Earth's natural satellite, the moon, shares the predawn sky on October 5, 1957, with the easily seen trail of the third stage of Sputnik I. (Photograph by Paul Donaldson)

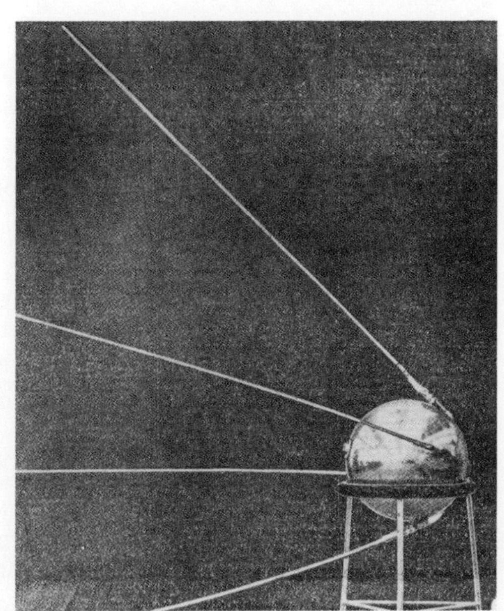

*Fig. 45.* A Soviet wirephoto shows the 23-inch Sputnik I on a support, with the antenna rods that were folded against the rocket body.

Four metal rods, 2.4 to 2.9 meters long, are attached to the outer surface of the casing. When Sputnik was being carried to its orbit by a three-stage vehicle, the antenna rods were folded against the body of the rocket. When the protective nose cone was jettisoned, and the satellite began its independent motion, the antenna rods opened out on swivels.

As it moves around the earth, the satellite is periodically subjected to sharp variations of temperature, being heated by the sun's rays while over the daytime side, yet cooled by radiation while on the nighttime side. It is an independent celestial body exchanging heat with surrounding space, and forced circulation of the nitrogen within the sphere plays an important part in maintaining its temperature equilibrium. . . .

An important part of the satellite's scientific mission was to broadcast, over a considerable length of time, signals that would have to penetrate the layers of the earth's ionosphere from above. In fact, we do not know at present the heights of the uppermost layers; Sputnik was, however, above the layers of maximum ionization, and perhaps above the entire ionosphere. Future satellites will thus undoubtedly add to our knowledge of the propagation of radio energy through the atmosphere. . . .

The visual satellite-tracking program in the Soviet Union is closely patterned after the American *Moonwatch* organization.

At the time of the Sputnik I launching, there were in the U.S.S.R. 66 satellite-observing stations, about 30 of them connected with colleges and three with observatories. The 25 or 30 members of each team are volunteer observers. . . .

Radio observations of Sputnik were carried on in Russia at 26 special radio clubs that assist the armed forces there, each one lavishly supplied with radio equipment. In addition, thousands of radio amateurs in the U.S.S.R. recorded the messages from the satellite.

For photographic observing in the United States, the first Smithsonian satellite-tracking camera was set up for testing in South Pasadena, California, the only instrument of such power designed specifically for satellite observing. This program calls for a dozen instruments of the same kind to be set up at stations widely spaced over the earth.

As the drawing in Fig. 47 shows, the trajectory of the satellite carries it over practically all of the earth except the regions within the

*Fig. 46.* On the roof of the Fort Worth Children's Museum, eleven telescope tandems, each manned by a child-parent team, at work in 1957.

Arctic and Antarctic Circles. Owing to the earth's rotation, the angle of the trajectory to the equator differs from the 65-degree inclination of the plane of the orbit. When the satellite crosses into the Northern Hemisphere, the trajectory passes the equator at an angle of 71½ degrees in a northeasterly direction. Then it gradually turns to the east and on reaching latitude 65° north begins to move southward, crossing the equator in a southeasterly direction at an angle of 59 degrees. In the Southern Hemisphere a latitude of 65° south is reached.

Since the time between the jettisoning of the nose cone and the detachment of the satellite from the third-stage rocket was not very great, the rocket and the cone were comparatively near the satellite for some time. They circled the earth along orbits very close to that of Sputnik.

Dr. Paul Herget, director of the Cincinnati Observatory and one of the astronomers who has been calculating the orbit of the satellite at the Vanguard Computing Center in Washington, calls attention to [a statement on p. 141], saying:

"The empty rocket shell is, in a manner of speaking, *always* ahead of the actual satellite, even if there is no drag. The state of affairs arises from the fact that after burn-out the two are 'sprung' apart. When the

*Fig. 47.* Consecutive revolutions of Sputnik I beginning with a passage over Moscow. All parts of the earth, except the polar regions, were covered by the satellite's flight.

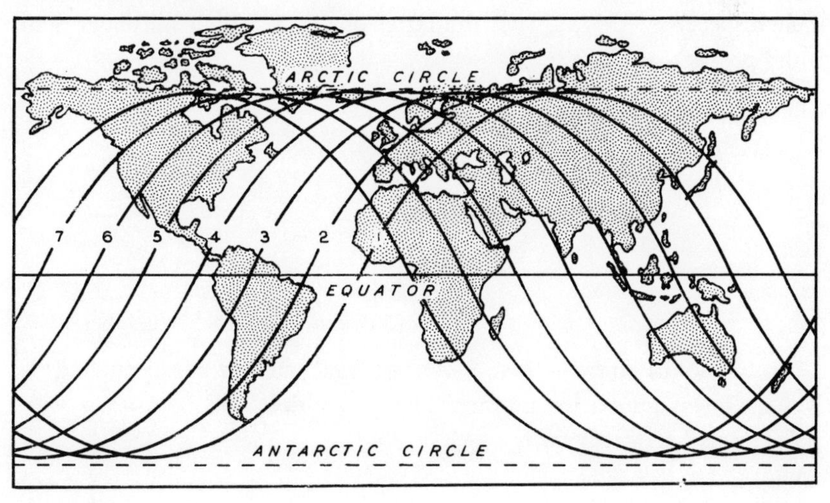

two bodies are sprung apart, the satellite [pushed forward] attains a slightly larger velocity than it had before, and it will now be moving in an orbit that is larger than the initial one. Therefore, by Kepler's third law [p. 34], the period of the satellite is increased while that of the rocket is decreased, and the rocket will complete its first revolution around the earth before the satellite does. The earliest observations of the two bodies showed that the satellite had been 'sprung' with a velocity of 2.1 feet per second relative to the rocket." . . .

Meanwhile, at Cambridge, Massachusetts, Smithsonian astronomers have been analyzing optical observations with the aid of an IBM 704 at Massachusetts Institute of Technology. These observations have so far been almost entirely of the rocket, which is bright enough to be easily seen without optical aid. To derive the orbital elements the IBM 704 required 21 seconds, making 40,000 calculations per second.

As the earth's upper atmosphere begins to be populated with man-made astronomical objects, some simple and generally understood nomenclature is needed. A proposal, later accepted, was made to name each satellite by the year of its launching, followed by a lower-case letter of the Greek alphabet to indicate the order during the year. If more than one object is observable from a single launching, an Arabic number will be added to indicate the decreasing order of brightness among the components of that launching.

According to this scheme, the bright and easily seen third stage of the October 4 rocket will be called 1957$\alpha$1, while the faint 23-inch sphere becomes 1957$\alpha$2. It is the latter object to which the label Sputnik I properly applies.

## Another Russian Satellite

(*Sky and Telescope*, December 1957)

A scant month after the first Soviet artificial satellite began circling the earth, it was joined by another. The new object will be known scientifically as Satellite 1957$\beta$.

Popularly known as Sputnik II, the satellite initially completed a circuit of the globe every hour and 43.7 minutes, about 7½ minutes slower than did its predecessor, Satellite 1957$\alpha$. At apogee the new object reached a height of about 1050 miles above the earth's surface, and at perigee dipped to about 100 miles high. The orbit is inclined approximately 65 degrees to the earth's equator, like that of the first satellite. The initial plane of the second launching did not coincide, however, with the plane of the first satellite's orbit on November 3.

According to the official Soviet announcement of the launching, the new satellite had the remarkable weight of 1120 pounds. It became evident within a few days, however, that this figure includes the weight of the last stage of the carrier rocket. (The 184 pounds for 1957$\alpha$ referred only to the 23-inch sphere.)

This half-ton includes the weight of the shell and of several interior compartments containing instruments. One instrument is for the study of primary cosmic rays, the fast-moving atomic nuclei that are stopped by the denser layers of the atmosphere and produce the secondary cosmic rays recorded at the earth's surface. Other equipment is intended to record the sun's radiation in the ultraviolet and X-ray regions of the spectrum.

Inside an airtight container was a dog who captured headlines throughout the world. This was a laika, a small-boned breed of Eskimo dog. The animal was provided with food, liquid, and air; its heartbeat, breathing, blood pressure, and temperature were being telemetered to radio receivers on the ground.

On the initial revolutions around the earth, 1957$\beta$ was tracked by American observers by its 40- and 20-megacycle radio transmissions. While these are the same frequencies as for the first moonlet, the latter had been silent for over a week.

The earliest American sighting seems to have been that by the Tucson, Arizona, *Moonwatch* team on the morning of November 5. Viewers generally called the fast-moving speck of light first magnitude or brighter, but with rapid fluctuations in brightness, a result of changing reflections of sunlight as the shiny conical satellite rotates.

# Orbit of Sputnik II

(*Sky and Telescope*, January 1958)

Earth's new family of artificial moonlets was increased by two on November 3, 1957, at 4:40 Universal time, through another successful Soviet launching. Satellite 1957$\beta$ consisted of a third-stage rocket and a discarded nose cone. As 1957$\alpha$ had three parts (23-inch sphere, rocket, and nose cone), there were five small independent bodies circling the earth in November.

According to the first Russian announcements, the new satellite's period was 103.7 minutes, so it was making 14 circuits of the earth per day, instead of the 15 of 1957$\alpha$.

From observations extending over about three days, George Veis, Smithsonian Institution Astrophysical Observatory, calculated the following orbital elements:

The average distance, $a$, of the satellite from the earth's center was 1.14604 equatorial radii of the earth. Since the eccentricity, $e$, was 0.0965, the apogee height of the satellite was 1017 miles above the earth's surface, and the perigee height was 140 miles. The period was 103.66 minutes on November 4, shortening at the rate of 0.024 minute or 1.4 seconds per day.

The inclination, $i$, of 1957$\beta$ was 63.4 degrees to the earth's equatorial plane. On November 4, at 0:50.7 UT, the satellite passed northward through the plane, and at that time, the satellite's right ascension as seen from the center of the earth was 112°.4. This quantity, the right ascension of the ascending node, was decreasing by 3.1 degrees each day. Lastly, $\omega$, the angle in the orbit plane between the ascending node and the perigee point, was 39 degrees. Sputnik II is itself the final stage of a rocket. Fixed to a special frame within it are instruments for studying solar radiation in the far ultraviolet and X-ray regions of the spectrum, a spherical container with radio transmitters and other instruments, and a hermetically sealed chamber to carry the test animal, a dog. The apparatus for cosmic-ray observations was fixed to the rocket's body. Russian scientists have released details of this equipment.

A nose cone, made of a ceramic containing cobalt, shielded the instruments from the aerodynamic heating effects of the rocket's upward passage through the dense lower layers of the atmosphere. After the final stage was placed in its orbit, the protecting cone was separated from the rocket, but continued in an orbit around the earth. The radio transmitters and equipment for telemetering observational data from Sputnik II were designed to operate for the first seven days only; since then the satellite has been tracked optically and by radar.

The solar-radiation apparatus carried three photomultiplier cells, set at 120 degrees from one another, and each equipped with a filter wheel. By means of the optical filters, the Lyman-alpha line at 1216 angstroms and selected regions of the X-ray solar spectrum could be isolated, these being observed in succession as a motor turned the filter wheel. The electrical energy from the photomultiplier tube, proportional to the intensity of the sun's radiation at each of the selected wavelengths, was amplified and telemetered to monitoring stations on the ground.

Owing to the continual change in the satellite's orientation with respect to the sun, and also to the fact that part of its orbit was on the nighttime side of the earth, the electric circuits were switched on only when the sun came within the range of vision of any of the three light receptors. This was done automatically by means of photoresistors lit by the sun at the same time as the photomultipliers.

In structure, the spherical container in Sputnik II resembles the 23-inch ball of Satellite 1957$\alpha$2. It contains the radio transmitters, the storage batteries, the heat-regulating controls, and sensitive elements for recording temperature and other physical quantities.

The hermetically sealed chamber is cylindrical in shape. It contained air-conditioning equipment and a stock of food for the laika dog. There was equipment for recording the animal's pulse beat, breathing, and blood pressure; also, apparatus for taking electrocardiograms and measuring temperature and pressure within the chamber. The heat controls inside both the spherical and cylindrical chambers maintained a set temperature, transferring excess heat into the rocket hull by forced-gas circulation. . . .

## First American Satellite

(*Sky and Telescope*, March 1958)

Earth gained a new artificial satellite on January 31 [1958], as a large modified Jupiter-C missile rose in a great burst of flame from its launching pad at Cape Canaveral, Florida, at 10:48 P.M. Eastern standard time [3:48 A.M., Feb. 1, Universal Time]. Seven minutes later, a pencil-shaped moonlet 80 inches long was in orbit, traveling around the earth in a period just a few minutes short of two hours.

The path of Satellite 1958$\alpha$ is inclined about 34 degrees to the earth's equator. Early calculations at the Naval Research Laboratory placed its perigee over the Northern Hemisphere about 230 miles above the earth's surface, and apogee at 1600 miles high. Thus, initially "Explorer" had a considerably more elongated orbit than its predecessors, Sputnik I and II, and on each revolution did not penetrate as deeply into the atmosphere. Its lifetime is estimated to be at least a year or two and perhaps as long as ten years.

When Soviet scientists launched Sputnik II early in November, the U.S. Army was directed to modify the Jupiter-C vehicle to carry aloft a satellite. Most of the development program was carried on by the Army Ballistic Missile Agency, Huntsville, Alabama, and the Jet Propulsion Laboratory at California Institute of Technology. The Explorer success is largely due to the Army's missile expert, Dr. Werner von Braun, famous for his part in developing the German V-2 rocket.

The four-stage vehicle, nearly 69 feet long over all, had a first stage 56 feet long and nearly six feet in diameter. The liquid-propellant motor developed some 83,000 pounds of thrust; the missile rose 53 miles before burn-out, 150 seconds after take-off. Then the first stage dropped off, the remaining assembly coasting upward to the apex of its trajectory, attaining level flight about 400 seconds after take-off. At that time the vehicle was some 400 or 500 miles downrange, southeasterly from Cape Canaveral, and about 200 miles high. The solid-propellant second stage, consisting of a cluster of scaled-down Army tactical Sergeant rockets, was then fired, followed by the third stage of similar units.

As these rockets fired, they were spinning some 1000 times a minute around the assembly's longitudinal axis, so that failure of any one of them would not cause the direction of flight to change.

The fourth stage, another Sergeant, was fired after the others had burned out and dropped away, leaving the 31-pound satellite (exhausted fourth stage rocket and instrument casing). The total acceleration was great enough to carry it to a maximum distance roughly two fifths the earth's radius out into space. If the perigee is at 230 miles and apogee at 1600, the semimajor axis of the orbit was some 4880 miles and the eccentricity about 14 per cent. For a revolution period of 115 minutes, the average orbital velocity was nearly 16,000 miles an hour, changing from about 18,500 at perigee to about 14,000 at apogee.

In the 7½-pound steel instrument case is a payload of about 11 pounds of instruments designed to gather information on micrometeorite impacts, cosmic rays, skin temperature, and internal temperature of the satellite. On the first revolution, three or four of the twelve exterior erosion gauges were broken, but it was uncertain whether this was

*Fig. 48.* Explorer I, the first American artificial satellite, contains a number of different kinds of instrument.

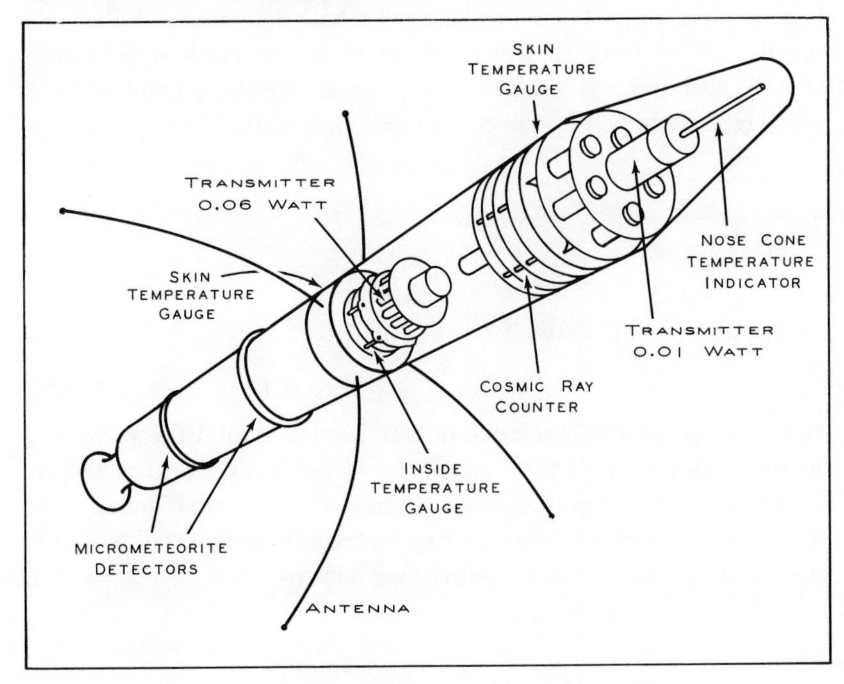

from collisions with meteoritic particles or from vibrations at take-off. The cosmic-ray counts, with a small Geiger counter, were about thirty per minute, in agreement with expectations. The interior temperature was +30° centigrade a few hours after launching.

The data gathered by these instruments are radioed to the ground by two transmitters, the stronger working at 108.03 megacycles. It has a power of 0.06 watt and an expected operating life of two to three weeks, whereas the other transmitter, at 108.00 megacycles, may operate for two or three months at 0.01 watt.

Amateur radio operators, commercial monitoring stations, and the Minitrack satellite-tracking network have all picked up the Explorer radio signals. Nearly all available orbital information has come from the Naval Research Laboratory, which has the over all responsibility for the radio tracking of artificial satellites.

For visual observers, the American moonlet is a much more difficult object to detect than either of the Russian carrier rockets. It is fainter because of its smaller size and greater height; also, its low orbital inclination is unfavorable to watchers in the northern United States.

The first definite sighting by a *Moonwatch* team was achieved by the station at Alamogordo, New Mexico, on February 1 at 7:45 P.M. Mountain standard time. There nineteen telescopes were arranged along the meridian. P. H. Grubb, watching about 10 degrees north of the zenith, was the first to see a slowly moving eighth-magnitude point of light, which was confirmed by three other members of the team. . . .

## Changes in Sputnik Orbits

(*Sky and Telescope*, March 1958)

Even though an artificial satellite may revolve around the earth at a height so great that all but a small trace of the atmosphere lies beneath it, this trace will eventually change the satellite's orbit dramatically. The effects of such air resistance were foreseen in some detail by astronomers long before the first Sputnik was launched.

The initial effect of atmospheric drag is to reduce the satellite's orbital velocity, and this loss of speed allows the satellite to fall downward into a smaller orbit. The period of revolution in this orbit is, however, shorter than the original period, in obedience to the laws of mechanics, and the net effect is a gain in the satellite's speed of revolution.

But the density of the atmosphere increases rapidly with diminishing height; hence, the moonlet will descend and its period shorten at an ever-accelerating tempo. By the time the satellite requires only about 87½ minutes to circle the earth, air drag is so great that very little lifetime remains until the satellite falls to earth or burns up like a meteor in the dense lower atmosphere. (For comparison, if a moonlet could revolve just above the earth's surface, its theoretical period of orbital revolution would be 84 minutes.)

Dr. John S. Rinehart, Smithsonian Astrophysical Observatory, proposed the diagram (Fig. 49) to show the course of period changes for the satellites launched by the Russians in 1957. The uppermost curve is for Sputnik II, the middle curve for the spherical part of Sputnik I, and the lowest curve for the third stage of the October firing. The curves are plotted from Smithsonian computations, the orbit for 1957$\alpha$1, for example, being based upon several hundred optical observations of that satellite.

To facilitate a comparison among the three bodies, their periods are plotted according to the number of days after launching, which was

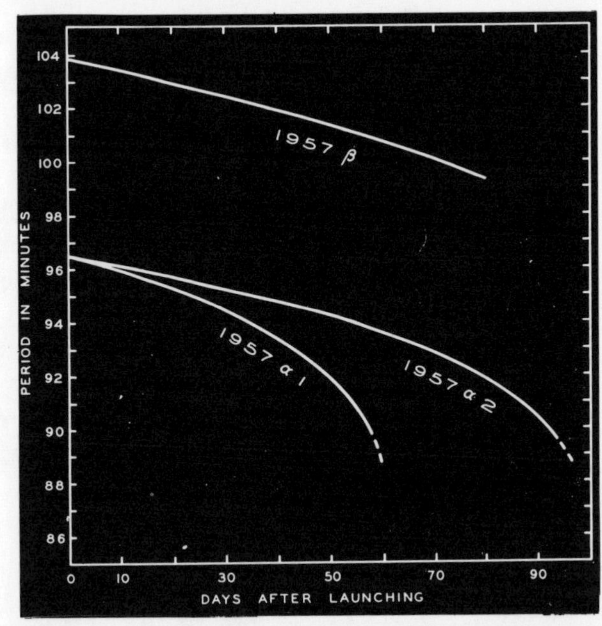


*Fig. 49.* The cumulative effect of air drag causes a progressive shortening of a satellite's period. The upper curve, for Sputnik II, showed that it would take much longer to fall to the critical period of about 87½ minutes than did the components of Sputnik I, shown in the lower curve.

October 4, 1957, for Sputnik I (1957$\alpha$), and November 3 for Sputnik II (1957$\beta$).

There is a further consequence of the steep downward increase of atmospheric density. If the satellite's orbit is elliptical, then there is more drag at perigee (the lowest point of the orbit, where the speed is greatest) than at apogee. But the effect of this is to decrease the apogee distance much more rapidly than the perigree distance, so the orbit becomes more and more nearly circular. Finally, a stage is reached in which there is appreciable drag on the object in all parts of its orbit, and from then on the fall is very rapid.

Thus, the spherical component of Sputnik I at apogee was about 1000 kilometers [620 miles] above the earth's surface on October 9, about 900 kilometers high on the fifteenth, and only 685 kilometers high on November 20. The perigee distance began at about 200 killometers above the ground, and remained nearly unchanged for weeks. . . .

## Instrumentation of Sputnik III

MARSHALL MELIN

(*Sky and Telescope*, July 1958)

The Russians describe their new satellite [launched May 15, 1958] as a space station designed for automatic, diversified observations. Data obtained by several types of apparatus are being stored in memory systems and, when the satellite passes over a recording station, are telemetered to the ground through several simultaneous radio channels.

In a cosmic-ray program more elaborate than any previously attempted in space, Sputnik III is measuring the spectrum of energy distribution of cosmic rays and their variation with altitude and latitude. It is attempting to detect gamma rays in the primary cosmic radiation, as well as nuclei of elements heavier than iron. Other equipment is measuring solar X rays and corpuscular streams from the sun. The evaluation of these observations will require knowledge of the location of the satellite and its orientation in space.

Since solar corpuscles and cosmic rays are much influenced by magnetic fields, the latter are also being studied. From an extended series of satellite observations, it is planned to determine the spatial distribution of the earth's magnetic field, and also to measure the magnetic disturbances caused by electrical current systems in the ionized layers of the atmosphere.

In Sputnik III, instruments have been installed for determining the abundance of positive ions in the ionosphere, and there is a mass spectrometer for ascertaining the atomic weights of these ions. One

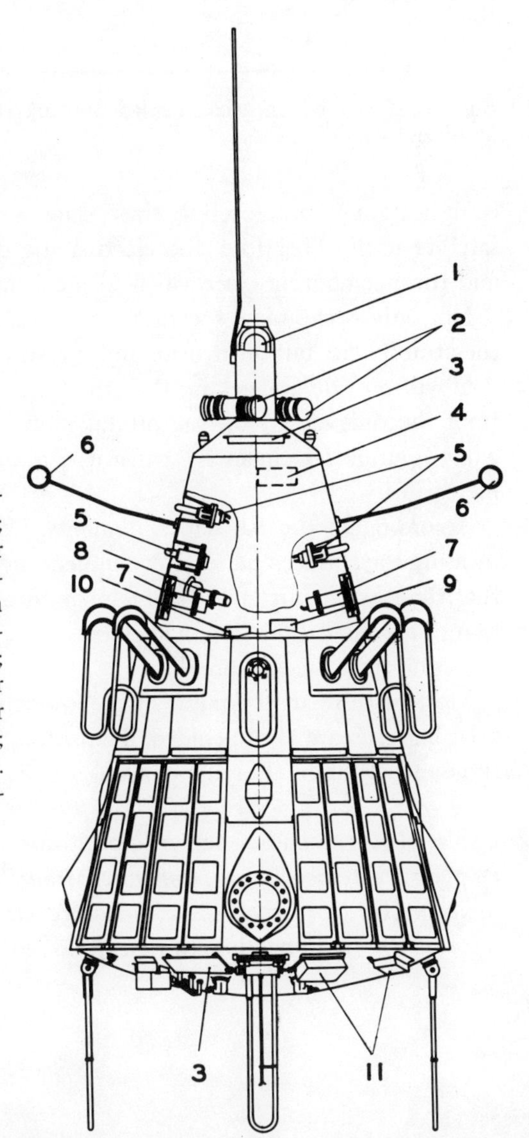


*Fig. 50.* Instruments in Sputnik III: *1.* magnetometer; *2.* photomultipliers; *3.* solar batteries; *4.* cosmic-ray detector; *5.* pressure gauges; *6.* ion catchers; *7.* electrostatic fluxmeter; *8.* mass spectrometer; *9.* cosmic-ray detector for heavy nuclei; *10.* gauge for primary cosmic-ray intensity; *11.* micrometeorite pickups. (USSR Embassy, Washington, D.C.)

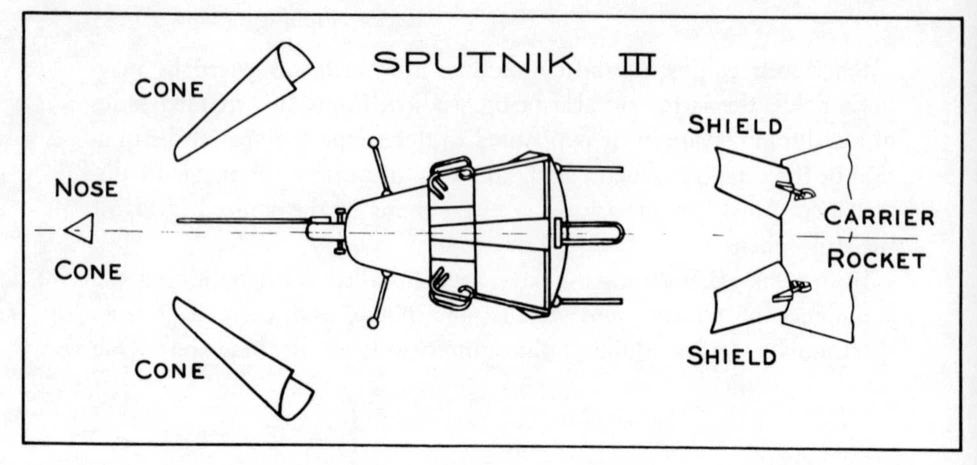


*Fig. 51.* Bodies which accompanied Sputnik III in orbit. (USSR Embassy, Washington, D.C.)

complication in interpreting these data is the electrical effect of the satellite itself. Therefore, the electrostatic charge on the satellite shell and the neighboring electrical field are being recorded.

Not only is the mass spectrometer carrying out chemical analyses of the atmosphere, but air density and pressure are being measured. These data will provide a check on the atmospheric characteristics as deduced from the drag effects on the orbital motion. As with earlier satellites, while Sputnik III circles the earth it is recording the impacts of micrometeorites.

According to the Russian statements, heat-sensing devices not only measure the surface and interior temperatures of the satellite, but insure that the instruments are at the temperature required for normal operation. This regulation is provided by devices controlling radiation and reflection from the satellite skin.

Most of this varied equipment is powered by chemical batteries, but solar batteries are also included. Transistors are extensively used, several thousand of them. (For comparison, a typical portable radio has six.)

*Table 3 lists the bodies sent into orbit during early 1958, including two empty rocket motors, one separated from Vanguard I, and one from Sputnik III. Note that these hulks are identified by the same Greek letter as the payload they carried, followed by the digit* 1. *The fainter*

TABLE 3. CHARACTERISTICS OF EARLY 1958 SATELLITES*

| SATELLITE | 1958 $\alpha$ | 1958 $\beta$ 1 | 1958 $\beta$ 2 | 1958 $\gamma$ | 1958 $\delta$ 1 | 1958 $\delta$ 2 |
|---|---|---|---|---|---|---|
| Name | Explorer I | Rocket | Vanguard I | Explorer III | Rocket | Sputnik III |
| Launching date | February 1 | March 17 | March 17 | March 26 | May 15 | May 15 |
| Launching time (UT) | 03:48 | 12:15:41 | 12:15:41 | 17:38:04 | Before $9^h$? | Before $9^h$? |
| DESCRIPTION | | | | | | |
| Shape | Cylinder | Cylinder | Sphere | Cylinder | Cylinder | Cone |
| Length (inches) | 80 | 57 | (6.4) | 80 | ? | 140 |
| Diameter (inches) | 6 | 18 | 6.4 | 6 | ? | 68 |
| Weight (pounds) | 31 | 51 | 3.2 | 31 | ? | 2925 |
| Payload weight (pounds) | 18 | None | (2.2) | 18? | None | 2135 |
| INITIAL ORBIT | | | | | | |
| Inclination (degrees) | 33.14 | 34.30 | 34.30 | 33.5 | 64.9 | 64.9 |
| Period (minutes) a = anomalistic, n = nodal | 114.95a | 134.29a | 134.29a | 115.91a | 105.82n | 105.82n |
| Perigee (miles above earth) | 229 | 405 | 405 | 117 | 123 | 123 |
| Apogee (miles above earth) | 1578 | 2463 | 2463 | 1740 | 1160 | 1160 |

* Adapted in part from G. F. Schilling's table (in *Special Report* No. 12, Smithsonian Optical Satellite Tracking Program), from other data provided by the Smithsonian, and from Russian press releases. Many of the listed values are estimated; sometimes the last two digits are uncertain.

*payload, identified with the digit 2, is in almost the same orbit. These satellite orbits are complicated not only by "atmospheric drag" (air resistance) but also by the gravitation of the moon and sun, which cause them to "precess." That is, the orbits do not remain fixed in space, but swing around, maintaining constant inclination to the earth's equator. The "anomalistic" and "nodal" periods are two slightly different definitions of the period arising from this deformation.*

*In July 1958, atmospheric drag was causing all six satellites to lose altitude. This effect was greatest on Explorer III (1958γ), with perigee at 117 miles and apogee at 1740 miles; it lost 16 miles per day in apogee height. From the observed loss of altitude it was possible to compute the density of the earth's upper atmosphere with higher precision than previously possible.*

*Another outside influence on a satellite is due to the earth's magnetic field which, for example, causes a compass needle to point toward magnetic north. Because of this influence, satellites carrying magnetic material (iron) will be twisted, or, if they are spinning, braked, as the succeeding article shows. Such a twist (torque) would interfere with accurate pointing of an orbiting telescope.*

TLP

## Magnetic-Field Effects on Artificial Satellites

**RAYMOND H. WILSON, JR.**

(*Sky and Telescope*, August 1960)

In modern times, the use of magnetic forces to influence mechanical rotation is so familiar as to go almost unnoticed. An electric motor, for instance, might more properly be called magnetic, since the electric current is merely the source of the energy for a sequence of interacting magnetic fields that actually drive the motor.

A less familiar example, in which magnetic forces retard rather than accelerate rotation, is the electromagnetic brake. A simple form of this, the Arago disk, was invented early in the nineteenth century by the director of the Paris Observatory, Dominique François Arago. He noticed that a rotating metal disk placed between the poles of a magnet was slowed down and the magnet tended to rotate with the disk, an effect caused by electric currents generated in the metal. . . .

For artificial satellites of the earth, the main spin-braking force is due to the geomagnetic field with which the compass needle had made us familiar. The magnetic field at any point above the earth can be calculated. Furthermore its braking effect can be computed for the spinning metallic shapes used in satellites—spheres and cylinders, for example.

Beginning with Sputnik I, all artificial satellites have shown a decay in their spinning. However, many of the early satellites had perigee heights of only 200 miles or less, where the relatively dense air would produce a drag on protruding antennas or a nonspherical body. In these cases the magnetic action could not be clearly separated from the atmospheric effects on the spin of each satellite.

The first two Vanguard satellites, 1958$\beta$2 and 1959$\alpha$1, are spherically symmetrical and have perigees well above 300 miles. For spheres, it is difficult to observe the spin rate optically, but there have been frequent and fairly accurate radio measures of the Vanguard rotation from its radio signals.

Ten-day averages of its observed spin rate are shown in Figure 52. Notice that the curve has, for two years, tended to follow a straight line on the logarithmic scale (an exponential decay). The spinning has been cut in half every 161 days, and the rotation of 2.7 turns per second when the satellite went into orbit is less than 1/30 of that value now.

With certain assumptions regarding the strength and direction of the earth's magnetic field as the satellite passes through it, we can compute the magnetic couple on various parts of the body: its aluminum spherical shell and ferromagnetic components. The dimensions of each element, its electrical conductivity and magnetic permeability, must be considered, as well as its position within the satellite with reference to the axis of rotation. Vanguard I data indicate within a few per cent that the slowing of the rotation is caused by the earth's magnetic field acting as a brake. . . .

Vanguard II was launched February 17, 1959, but had no solar cells, so its spin rate could be observed by radio for only a few weeks, while the batteries lasted. The slowing down was more than three times as rapid as for its predecessor, amounting to cutting the rate in half every fifty days. In ten months, Vanguard II should thus be spinning at a rate of less than 2 per cent of its initial rate, the rotation period being lengthened to over three minutes.

The much larger braking effect for this satellite is consistent with the strength of the earth's magnetic field (0.16 gauss) expected at its height.

*After a number of unmanned satellites had been successfully launched by the U.S.S.R. and U.S., interest turned to* manned *space flight.* As *Table 3 (p. 157) indicates, the Russian engineers had a clear lead in*

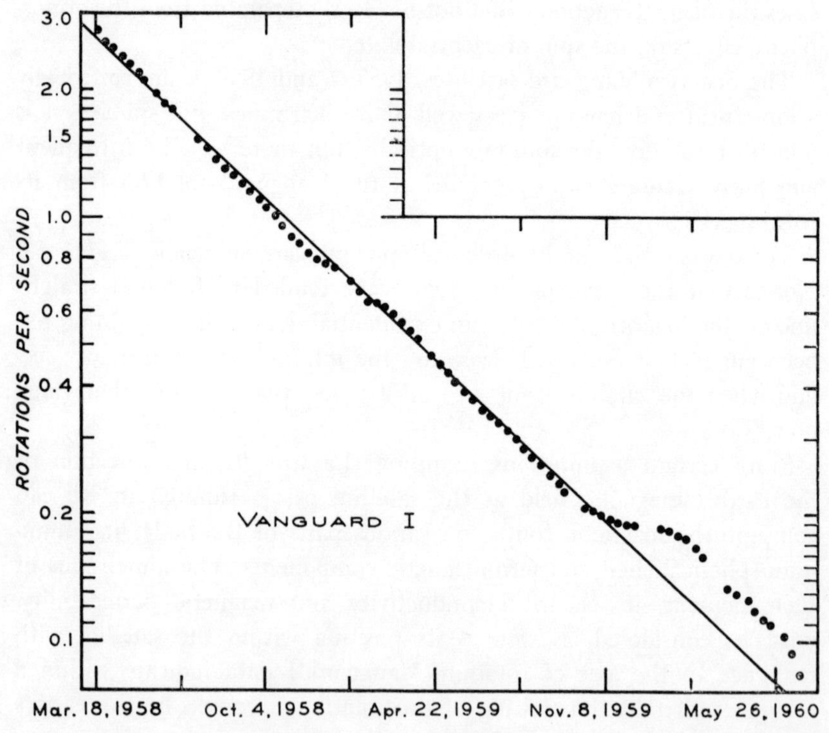


*Fig.* 52. Ten-day means of the observed rotation of Vanguard I show that in the first two years it slowed down to about 1/30 of its original spin rate.

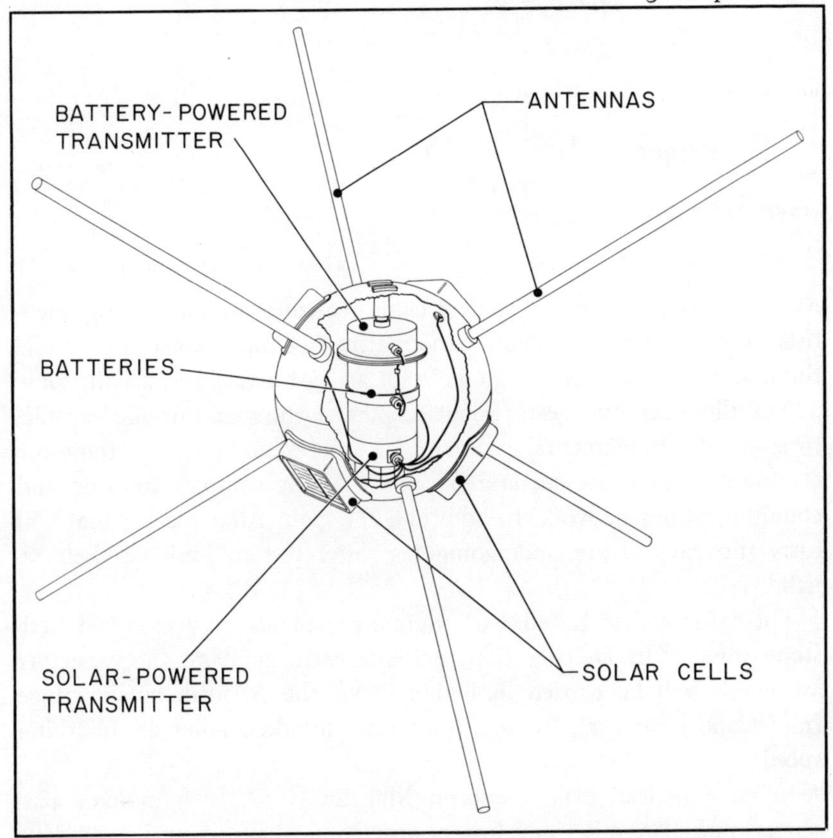


*Fig.* 53. The main sources of magnetic damping in Vanguard I were its outer shell of aluminum alloy, seven steel battery cans, three aluminum instrument packages, and six antennas. (NASA photograph)

*payload weight over U.S. engineers by mid-1958—2135 pounds against 18. This was due to their superior rocket motors of large thrust. By this time, however, American engineers were hard at work on high-thrust motors, and NASA had organized Project MERCURY to study the requirements of a manned space vehicle, then design, build, and test one. As expected, the U.S.S.R. proceeded to launch the first successful manned satellite, on April 12, 1961; the U.S. followed suit on February 20, 1962.*

TLP

## Project MERCURY

MARSHALL MELIN

(*Sky and Telescope*, July 1959)

Manned spaceflight is the goal of extensive collaboration among scientists from many fields who are participating in Project MERCURY. While the first American may not go aloft for at least a year and a half, some $200 million are now being spent to perfect the man-carrying capsule, to study the fundamental problems of survival in space, to train the astronauts, and to design and build the highly complex tracking and communications network. In addition, the giant Atlas rockets that will carry the payload are undergoing test after test to improve their reliability. . . .

The cabin will be tested, with animal passengers, on a modified Redstone missile. In another trial, perhaps early in 1960, the MERCURY astronauts will be carried in flights down the Atlantic missile range from Cape Canaveral, Florida, for several hundred miles at suborbital speeds. . . .

In an American experiment on May 28 [1959], two monkey passengers flew 1700 miles in a Jupiter nose cone which reached a 300-mile altitude. The successful recovery of the two simian passengers, Able and Baker, with a variety of other biological specimens, greatly increased our limited knowledge of how living organisms fare in a space environment. The two animals survived well their brief exposure to conditions resembling actual orbiting. . . .

Meanwhile, the training of the seven Project MERCURY astronauts is proceeding at Langley Research Center and elsewhere. Part of their time is being devoted to receiving further education in basic sciences from astrophysics to geography, to prepare them for making observations from MERCURY capsules. They must master the handling of the controls within the MERCURY cabin if command signals fail, and they must understand thoroughly the ground-support facilities.

During both launching and re-entry, the passenger is to be cushioned in a contoured frame, oriented so that the acceleration force will be

*Fig. 54.* The escape mechanism of the Project Mercury package was tested in 1959. The escape rockets lifted the capsule to 2250 feet, where the tripod (seen between the rocket exhaust flames) was ejected. First a small parachute and then a large one was released and the capsule descended to the surface of the sea for recovery by helicopter. (NASA photograph)

directed against his back. It is now believed that the peak acceleration will amount to about 9 g's during re-entry, but it may briefly reach as much as 20 g's if it is necessary to escape from a defective booster.

Project MERCURY will involve an extensive tracking and communications network. At least fourteen major stations, some aboard ocean vessels, will help maintain continuous contact with the manned vehicle. The Atlantic missile range, extending southeastward from Cape Canaveral, will be the safest area for re-entry, and the programming of the entire flight proceeds backward from this consideration. Also, the vehicle should avoid the most intense regions of the inner Van Allen belt (see p. 208), in order to minimize the weight of shielding. An orbiting altitude of 120 to 130 nautical miles has been selected, with a launching direction slightly north of east from Cape Canaveral, providing an orbital inclination of 30 degrees. . . .

During the entire time the astronaut is aloft, the position of the satellite must be known with unprecedented accuracy. At present, orbital predictions for a new satellite are commonly in error by several minutes of time and several hundred miles during the first day in orbit. In the MERCURY experiment, the life of the astronaut depends upon precise early knowledge of not only his position at every moment but his predicted point of impact, should some emergency require premature re-entry.

The new tracking facilities will be linked by direct cable or radio with the Goddard Space Research Center in Washington, D.C. Overall command of the network will be at Cape Canaveral. Secret frequencies are to be employed for all radio commands, to lessen the chance of unauthorized triggering of any equipment in the satellite.

## Manned Space Flight

MARSHALL MELIN

(*Sky and Telescope*, June 1961)

On April 12, 1961, at 6:07 Universal time, a multistage rocket was launched bearing a satellite space ship named *Vostok* (East), with the twenty-seven-year-old test pilot, Major Yuri Gagarin, aboard. Two-way

*Fig.* 55. Major Yuri Gagarin, the first astronaut to circumnavigate the earth. (Wide World Photos)

radio contact was established with him and he reported as each stage burned out in turn. Through a porthole (according to some accounts) he observed the earth and sky even before attaining orbit. The space ship's radio transmitters operated on a set of frequencies intended to permit contact over a wide range of distances. Also two television transmitters showed Gagarin in profile and full-face indicating that "he withstood the period of powered flight satisfactorily."

The pilot was closed in a space suit, for protection in case the cabin lost its pressure. He reclined in a stepped position on a contour seat, in order best to sustain the force of powered flight. The seat was ejectable from the cabin during descent, according to one version.

The cosmonaut's cabin was designed to protect him from accelerative forces, and to insulate him from the heat of passage through the atmosphere, as well as from temperature extremes on the day and night sides of the earth. It kept him pressurized, bathed in air whose oxygen, carbon-dioxide, and water-vapor content was controlled, protected him from radiation and meteorites, and provided him with a sense of orientation during orbital flight when normal gravitational stimuli were absent. Vostok's cabin was described as more spacious than that of a jet aircraft.

All the features of Gagarin's flight through space could be simulated in laboratories on earth, except for prolonged weightlessness. Reportedly, Gagarin could coordinate and control his muscles, and "work efficiently." (To illustrate one of the complications: Pressing a telegraph key would do no good unless the arm was somehow anchored; squeezing the key would operate it.) He observed through the porthole and through an "optical orientator," reporting his observations by radio and recording them in a flight book and on tape.

Gagarin told that he could see coast lines, large rivers, mountains, forests, clouds, and cloud shadows on the ground. He could discern the spherical shape of the earth, and saw its blue halo of atmosphere shading off into a deep black in which the sun and stars shone brilliantly. As he emerged from the earth's shadow (over the South Atlantic Ocean), the horizon appeared bright orange.

Vostok was approaching the southern apex of its orbit when the Soviet radio broke the news of the first manned space flight. Preliminary orbital elements announced at that time were in close agreement with refined calculations published many days afterward. The later values placed the apogee and perigee heights at 203 and 112 miles, respectively, and the inclination at 64°.95. The manned vehicle, 1961μ1, had an orbital period of about 89.33 minutes. Total weight of the spaceship in orbit was given as 4725 kilograms (10,417 pounds).

The description of Gagarin's return from orbit is the least satisfactory feature of available reports. In one version, a sun sensor was used to orient the vehicle. In another, the cosmonaut was trained to control his vehicle manually by reaction jets, in response to the position of the earth in a viewing port, or in response to sophisticated instruments, according to a third story. It is generally agreed that the ship was brought down after retro-rockets were fired, but whether the pilot played any role in this is not clear.

This is the first Soviet launching for which the time of firing was made public. From this fact, and the orbital elements for 1961μ2, it is possible to locate the launching site, though with some uncertainty since the firing program is unknown. One calculation places the launch pad in the vicinity of the Aral Sea, which supports an often repeated guess that the Soviet missile range extends northeastward from the region of Tyura Tam.

# Vostok II

MARSHALL MELIN

(*Sky and Telescope*, October 1961)

The most prolonged exposure to weightlessness ever endured to that time by a human being was experienced by twenty-six-year-old Gherman Stepanovich Titov when he made more than 17 circuits of the globe aboard Vostok II. For 24 hours and 59 minutes as he orbited the earth, both he and his space ship "fell" at the same rate so that his body felt nearly free from any external forces. Despite this strange environment, Titov pursued a full day's activities with relatively little trouble.

According to unofficial press and radio reports, Vostok II was launched at 6:00 Universal time on August 6, 1961, from Baikonur, northeast of the Aral Sea in central Asia. During the launching the rocket trajectory was monitored and controlled by radio-guidance stations. After separation of the final stage of the rocket, the manned cabin weighed 10,430 pounds. It was estimated to be about 20 feet long and 13 feet in diameter.

The launching was announced after the first orbital revolution had been completed, and thereafter detailed reports were issued. Titov ate three meals while in orbit, and slept somewhat longer than scheduled. . . .

The orbit of the space ship was chosen to be below the Van Allen radiation belts, even though the vehicle was said to carry shielding. A favorable occasion of low solar activity was selected for launching, and during the flight ground stations watched the sun in order to anticipate any dangerous increase in solar particles. If the need had arisen, the spacecraft could have been brought down from orbit at any time. . . .

Vostok II had three portholes, and through these Titov could view the earth in daylight; twice he glimpsed the waning crescent moon. He reported on the phenomena of passing into and out of the earth's shadow, and the prismatic effect at the horizon, where the atmosphere gradually shades into deep blue. As re-entry began, while one of the portholes remained uncovered, he could watch the luminescence of the atmosphere caused by the space ship's passage. Vostok II came down at Krasnykut, near Saratov.

The Vostok II experiment was the seventh orbital launching in the Soviet biomedical satellite program, which began with Sputnik II in which the laika dog lived for many days during November, 1957.

The orbit of Vostok II (1961$\tau$1) was characterized by an 88.4-minute period, an inclination of 64.8 degrees, and a height above ground varying between 106 and 159 miles. The rocket's final stage, 1961$\tau$2, with a very similar orbit, burned up in less than four days.

## First American Manned Satellite

(*Sky and Telescope*, April 1962)

John Glenn's three trips around the world on February 20, 1962, demonstrated dramatically that some important problems of manned space flight to the moon are already solved. It confirmed that the artificial environment inside a space capsule could keep a passenger safe and active during the hazards of launching, five hours in orbit, and re-entry into the earth's atmosphere.

Lieutenant Colonel Glenn is the fifth man to have traveled in a space capsule. Yuri Gagarin's pioneer single lap around the world occurred April 12, 1961, and Gherman Titov made seventeen circuits on August 6; Alan Shepard and Virgil Grissom succeeded in suborbital Mercury flights on May 5 and July 21 [1961]. In these five cases, the efforts of thousands of engineers, technicians, and ground-support personnel have been combined to put a man into space and bring him safely back. The reliability with which this highly complex task can now be done is most impressive. This, perhaps, is the most encouraging result from Glenn's flight.

At dawn on February 20, the 130-ton Atlas-D launch vehicle stood on launching pad 14 at Cape Canaveral in Florida. It was 16 feet in diameter and 93 feet tall, including the bell-shaped cabin and its escape system. At 9:47 A.M. Eastern standard time, all five engines of the Atlas were ignited, and 180 tons of thrust lifted the rocket skyward. The two boosters gave 150,000 pounds of thrust each, the sustainer provided 60,000, and there were two small vernier engines for minor course corrections during powered flight.

Everything went normally, and after about 2½ minutes the booster engines were cut off and dropped, and the now unneeded escape tower was jettisoned. The sustainer engine continued to accelerate the rocket until orbital velocity was reached. Then it too was shut down and the capsule separated.

At the moment of injection into orbit, the capsule was 500 miles east of Cape Canaveral, at an altitude of about 100 miles. As artificial satellite 1962$\gamma$, the 2900-pound capsule traveled around the earth once each 88.2 minutes, in a path inclined 32.5 degrees to the earth's equator. Its height varied between 97.6 miles at perigee and 159.5 miles at apogee. The discarded booster followed a slightly different orbit. Glenn reported

*Fig.* 56. John H. Glenn, Jr. (*left*) and M. Scott Carpenter, two of the first American astronauts. (NASA photograph)

*Fig.* 57. In the operations room of the Mercury Control Center at Cape Canaveral, Florida, Glenn's progress in orbit was followed on this large global chart. White circles indicate the locations of the stations of the tracking and communications network. (NASA photograph)

that after the capsule became free he could see the booster slowly turning around as it went under and passed ahead of him. . . .

A hundred miles above the earth's surface, the astronaut was able to see a few stars even by day against the black sky.

Sunsets were spectacular, he said. "As the sun goes down, it has a very white, brilliant light, and as it goes below the horizon and you get your light coming to you then through the atmosphere, it's a very bright orange color; down close to the surface it pales out into a blue, a darker blue, and then off into black."

Another totally unexpected phenomenon was observed at each sunrise, when through the capsule window Glenn could see against the

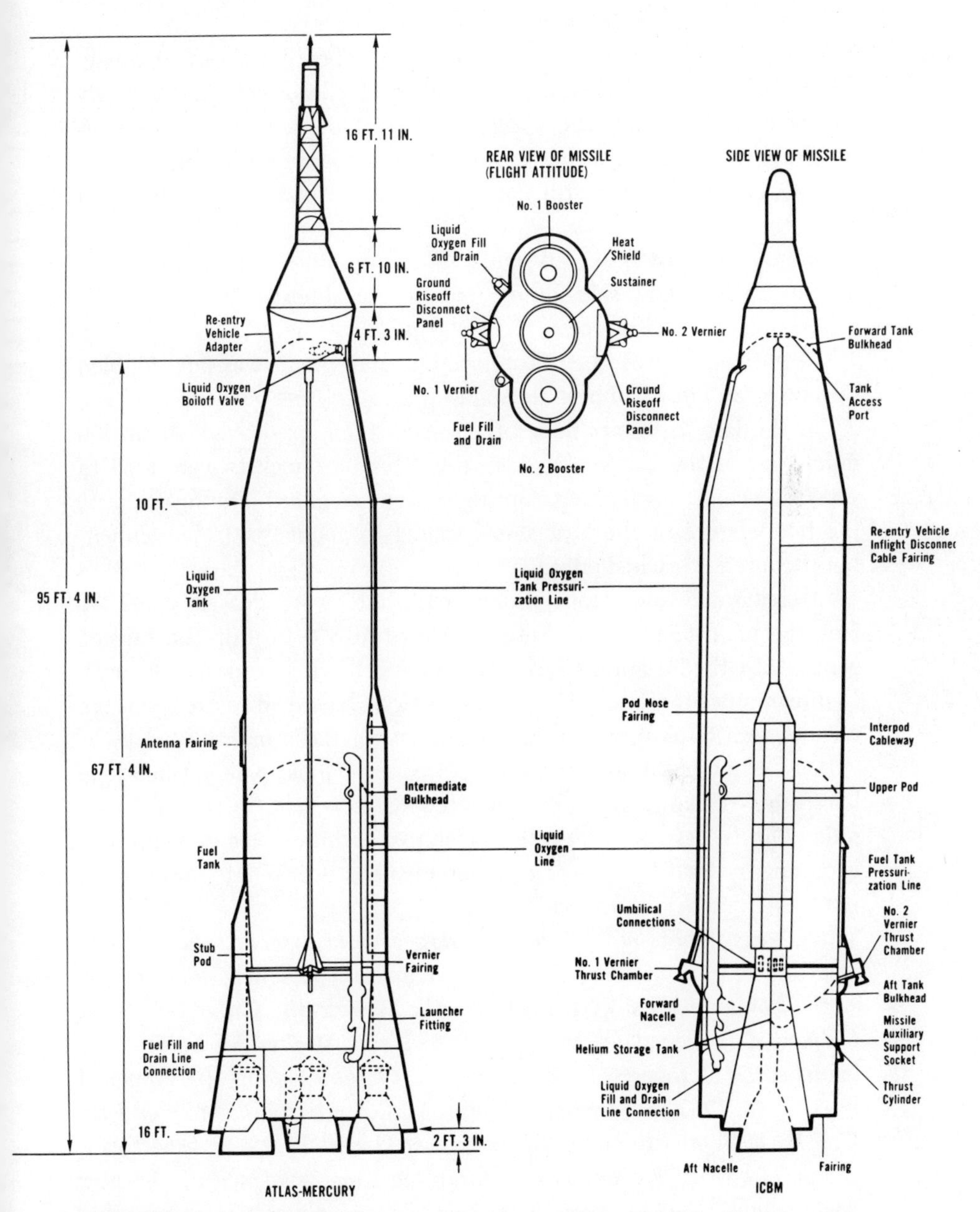


*Fig.* 58. The launching vehicle used to place Friendship 7, Glenn's space ship, in orbit—a modified Atlas-D intercontinental ballistic missile. (NASA photograph)

black sky myriads of drifting specks of light. These luminous yellowish-green particles, which made him think of fireflies, were being slowly left behind. Evidently the specks were visible by reflected sunlight, for those that went into the capsule's shadow became invisible.

The "Glenn effect" is still not satisfactorily explained, despite much conjecture. . . .

One of the most beautiful sights, Glenn reported, was to see clouds on the earth's night side illuminated by the almost full moon as he passed over the Pacific Ocean.

Weightlessness was not uncomfortable, and Glenn was not troubled by nausea, as Titov had been in August.

On the last leg of its third orbit, when the capsule was about 300 miles west of the California coast, the three retro-rockets were fired to slow the vehicle for its long slanting descent eastward. During re-entry, the temperature of the heat shield soared to about 3000° Fahrenheit, but the interior reached only 105°.

After a small and strong drogue parachute was released at 30,000 feet, the main 63-foot parachute opened at 10,800 to drop the capsule gently into the Atlantic Ocean near Grand Turk Island at 2:43 P.M. Eighteen minutes later the destroyer USS *Noa* had picked up the capsule and its pilot, who was in excellent physical condition.

It is estimated that about 30,000 persons took part in building, launching, tracking, and recovering the space vehicle in which Glenn rode. The success of this great cooperative technical achievement is a good augury for future more complex missions deeper into space.

*These space flights clearly showed that, at considerable expense, men could be orbited in space for several hours and returned safely to the earth. Longer flights were made by the Americans, Cmdr. M. Scott Carpenter, launched on May 24, 1962, Lieut. Walter M. Schirra, Jr., launched on October 3, 1962, and Maj. L. Gordon Cooper, Jr., launched on May 16, 1963, and by the Russians, Maj. Andrian Nikolayev and Lt. Col. Pavel Popovich, launched on August 11 and 12, 1962, respectively.*

*The last two were in orbit at the same time—evidence of the next goal, a rendezvous in space. There are obvious difficulties of time and maneuver in bringing two satellites together in orbit. For instance, if a second vehicle is launched to join one already in orbit (moving at more than 4 miles per second over the launch site), an error of ¼ second in the launch time produces a miss of over a mile. If the second satellite is a mile behind the first in the same orbit, and the astronaut attempts to "catch up" by forward rocket thrust, he puts his satellite into larger orbit, moves away from the earth, and falls farther behind. The formulae of Newton's mechanics can be used to find the best program of timed thrusts that avoids collision with the earth or the other vehicle, and with the least fuel expenditure.*

*Rendezvous is important—in order to resupply an orbiting observatory, for instance, or to build a larger vehicle for deeper space probing. An amusing touch was added on June 16, 1963, when the Russians launched Vostok VI carrying the first woman astronaut, Valentina Tereshkova, into an orbit close to Vostok V, launched two days earlier and carrying Lt. Col. Valery Bykovsky. No rendezvous was achieved, although the vehicles passed within three miles of each other. Both were landed safely, and Bykovsky set a new space-flight record of 81 orbits in 4 days, 23 hours.*

*Except for Glenn's "fireflies" (possibly due to something in or on the porthole window) there was little of astronomical significance reported from the manned space flights. Of course the engineering achievement is one of the outstanding "firsts" of human history, and of great practical importance in planning further astronomical research.*

*Other practical applications of space technology now come into this chronological account. A weather satellite, equipped to provide photographs of cloud patterns for meteorological studies and weather prediction, had been launched successfully by Americans in 1959. An even more practical application was the communications satellite Telstar, a federally financed project that provoked criticism because it would be exploited by industrial concerns for international TV and because of its direct value to the military forces (in Air Force or Navy communications).*

TLP

## Telstar, the Communications Satellite

(*Sky and Telescope*, August 1962)

If someday soon you watch on your home television a "live" program from Bali or some other remote land, you can thank a small pioneer satellite that this summer began circling the earth. Built by Bell Telephone Laboratories under the NASA ECHO Project, Telstar is essentially a broad-band microwave relay station whose great altitude enables it to transmit over very long distances, whereas its earthbound counterparts are limited by the curvature of the globe. A system of similar satellites could provide a world-wide communications system.

Telstar was successfully launched from Cape Canaveral on the morning of July 10, 1962. The initial orbit was inclined 44.7 degrees to the earth's equator, with a perigee 593 miles high, apogee 3502. The period was 158 minutes.

Microwave signals received from the earth on a frequency of 6390 megacycles per second are amplified about 10 billion times by 14 germanium transistors and a traveling-wave tube, then flashed back to earth at 4170 megacycles. An automatic gain control keeps the transmission essentially constant, regardless of the incoming signal strength. . . .

Specially sensitive radio receivers are located in Andover, Maine, and Holmdel, New Jersey, while overseas stations are located in England and France.

The spherical, faceted Telstar itself is 34½ inches in diameter and weighs 170 pounds. Sunlight glinting from a mirror on the satellite aids in visual tracking, but most of the 72 faces are covered by solar cells. Encircling the sphere like an equatorial belt are receiving and transmitting antennas, and one for the tracking beacon and telemetry protrudes from one "pole."

To keep the radiation pattern directed toward the ground stations, the satellite was given a definite orientation at launching by spinning the package 180 times a minute. When it departs from the desired attitude, induction coils may be energized to react with the earth's magnetic field [see p. 227] and realign the spin axis.

For electrical power, the 3600 solar cells charge nickel-cadmium batteries. . . .

Telstar acts as a probe of its environment, especially the Van Allen belt. Several experiments are to indicate just how damaging the impacts of high-energy atomic particles are to electronic components.

In all, 115 quantities are to be measured and reported, including the densities and energies of free protons and electrons in the Van Allen

*Fig. 59.* A Telstar satellite. Most of its faceted surface is covered with patches of solar-powered cells. The rings of rectangular holes at the satellite's equator are broad-band radio antennas. (Bell Telephone Laboratories)

belt, temperature and pressure within the satellite, and currents and voltages in the electronic circuitry.

*There was, of course, other space research of a practical nature bearing more specifically on astronomy. One of these projects investigated the bombardment of objects in space by atomic particles that form the Van Allen belts near the earth. Another was concerned with meteoroids, the particles of matter generally moving around the sun that cause "shooting stars" when they strike the earth's atmosphere—and cause damage when they strike a space probe. Although astronomers had studied them for decades, it was still uncertain whether these particles swarm near the earth, how large they are, what their composition is, and how much damage they will do to space vehicles or to their exposed equipment.*

TLP

## Far-Swinging Explorer XII

**MARSHALL MELIN**

(*Sky and Telescope*, October 1961)

Launched on August 13, 1961, at 3:21 Universal time from Cape Canaveral, Explorer XII 1961 repeatedly traverses the Van Allen radiation belts of the earth. It has a long-lived solar power supply, which is expected to extend measurements over many months.

The orbit is inclined about 33 degrees to the equator. The satellite reaches an apogee height of some 48,060 miles, while its perigee is only 183 miles above the earth's surface. The period is 26 hours 34 minutes, and the orbit is subject to important lunar perturbations.

For some stations on earth, this satellite is above the horizon for almost 24 hours at a time, and enormous amounts of telemetered data have been received by the three chief tracking stations: Santiago, Chile; Woomera, Australia; and Johannesburg, South Africa. For the first weeks several hundred large reels of magnetic tape were being recorded each day, but thereafter transmissions from Explorer XII were scheduled to be sampled when needed.

The instruments are designed for simultaneously detecting the elementary charged particles that move rapidly through the Van Allen region, the magnetic fields associated with them, and the earth's magnetic field. Present-day theories of the motion of charged particles from the sun—the "solar wind"—and their effects on the interplanetary magnetic field rest upon very few observations.

Three fluxgate magnetometers [small coils used to measure the magnetic field], along perpendicular axes, are carried on a boom some 32 inches away from the satellite body.

Several types of equipment detect electrons and protons with energies ranging up to 10 billion electron volts. A plasma proton analyzer will measure direction and speed of protons.

A variety of Geiger counters are provided to detect particles trapped in the Van Allen belts.

To obtain more information about the variation of cosmic rays, several kinds of cosmic-ray detectors, of different sensitivity levels, are used.

# Short-Lived Explorer XIII

MARSHALL MELIN

(*Sky and Telescope*, October 1961)

Astronomers and space engineers alike are interested in numbers, sizes, and motions of tiny particles of interplanetary matter. Recently, evidence has grown that the earth is surrounded by an extensive dust cloud.

The space engineer is concerned with the possible effects of cosmic particles (micrometeorites) that may strike earth-orbiting vehicles at relative speeds up to 45 miles per second. Do they form a significant hazard to manned spacecraft or to the orbiting space stations of the future?

Micrometeorite equipment was placed in Explorer XIII, which took off from the Virginia coast at about 18:29 Universal time on August 25, 1961.

The very short lifetime—only two days—of this satellite, 1961*x*, indicates that the perigee distance must have been well under 100 miles.

Five major types of micrometeorite detectors were carried, in order to allow a comparison of different methods, some of which had been used in earlier satellites. For example, both Vanguard III and Explorer VIII had microphones to register impacts. Two calibrated microphones were aboard the 187-pound Explorer XIII and the midsection was covered with gas-filled "beer cans." Each was a small chamber, with a bellows switch to signal when a skin puncture released its nitrogen-helium charge.

A new type of detector consisted of a sandwich of stainless-steel foil, mylar, and a printed electrically conducting circuit, designed to indicate punctures by electrical resistance changes. Yet another system consisted of rectangular plastic cards, closely wound with fine copper wire, whose breakage would cause a change in electrical resistance.

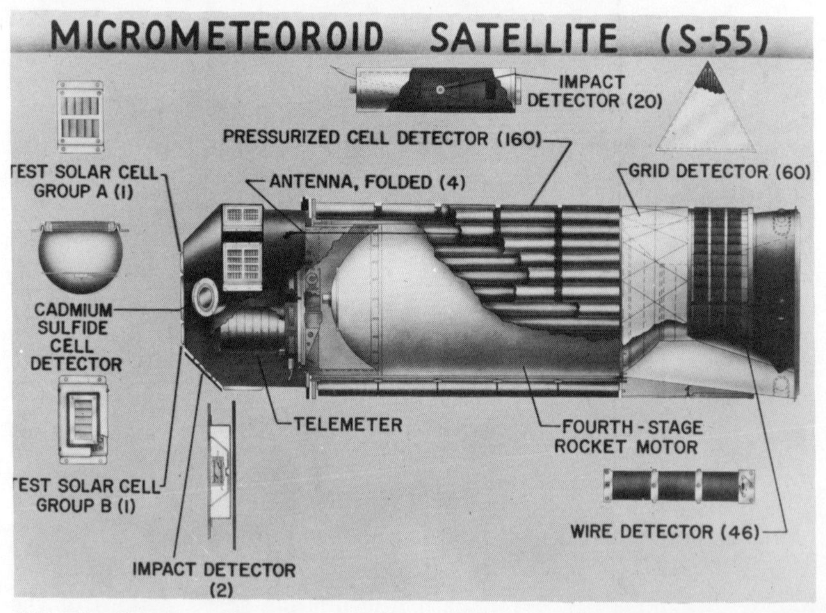


*Fig. 60.* Cutaway diagram of Explorer XIII showing the types of micrometeorite-impact detectors carried, two test groups of solar cells, and the location of the telemetry transmitter. (NASA photograph)

Finally, there were two light-sensitive detectors—photoelectric cells mounted behind aluminized mylar screens. Even very tiny punctures in a screen would admit enough light to be detected.

Together, all these detectors provided more than 28 square feet of sensitive surface, arranged compactly around a satellite only 76 inches long and 24 inches in diameter. Solar cells for power, and others for measurements of erosion, were also carried. Although the failure of Explorer XIII to attain its intended orbit prevented full use of this equipment, it indicates the nature of future payloads for investigating interplanetary dust and larger particles.

**The Moon and Beyond.** *Now that satellites orbiting the earth have become almost commonplace, it seems quite natural to extend the range of probes farther out into space. The late President Kennedy established as a national goal the manned exploration of the moon, about 240,000 miles away. The idea is not new; it has stimulated writers and provided imaginary thrills for well over a century. Jules Verne, H. G. Wells, and later science-fiction writers served a useful purpose as well as entertainment by introducing some of the practical considerations, and it is of interest to see how far such thinking had progressed by 1936.*

TLP

# To the Moon Via Rocket

G. EDWARD PENDRAY

(*The Sky*, November 1936)

Years ago before airplanes were invented, when the physics of the air was still unknown and the nature of the universe only dimly comprehended, in the seventeenth century, Bishop John Wilkins of Chester, England, wrote a little book proving that the moon is a world, like the earth, and declaring that people would some day find a way to fly there.

Some of his contemporaries agreed with him, and there was much discussion of ways and means. One man suggested that swans could be harnessed to a chariot. Another proposed the building of a huge kite, big enough to fly to the moon.

Later proposals included the construction of a hot-air balloon, the building of a mighty slingshot, and the firing of a giant cannon. Jules Verne, in his unforgettable *From the Earth to the Moon,* made use of the cannon idea, sending his space voyagers around the lunar orb in a hollow shell. H. G. Wells facetiously suggested the use of a gravity screen, which he called *Cavorite,* in his *First Men In The Moon.*

Now it happens that for one reason or another, all of these schemes are impractical except the last, and that one (which is inconsistent with both Newton's and Einstein's theories, pp. 99 and 102) has yet to be invented. The airless void between the earth and the moon precludes any attempt to fly there by any means requiring wings or buoyant gas. The cannon shell would have to start so fast and go so swiftly that its passengers would first be mashed to pulp, then burned to coke.

But all the while these ingenious men were inventing impossible ways of leaving the earth, there existed an engine capable, theoretically, of accomplishing their purpose. Its history is long but amusing.

When Greece was at the height of her culture, learned chemists mixed a fiery fuel compounded of pitch, sulphur, charcoal, and other ingredients, to which they added salt because salt made this Greek fire burn yellow, and gave the impression of greater heat. It was the custom of the Greeks to fill tubes with this fierce mixture, fasten them near the heads of their arrows, and discharge them, flaming, into the wooden sides of enemy ships.

The fame of Greek fire spread to China, where there was very little salt but large supplies of saltpeter, which they substituted in the Greek formula. This then burned so rapidly that the result was almost an explosion. The puzzled Chinese beheld their fiery arrows stopping in midair, then treacherously returning, propelled by recoil. Then some Asiatic genius, now forgotten, thought to turn the fire-case around, with its burning end toward the rear, and the rocket was born. . . .

The secret of rockets finally reached Italy, where a great fireworks industry grew and flourished. Cyrano de Bergerac, a French writer of the seventeenth century, wrote a story in which the hero traveled by rocket power, and was whisked from place to place over the earth. Others seriously proposed that rockets be used to propel flying chariots, and some even raised eyes to the moon, wondering whether rockets could go there, too.

We know now that such early rockets never could have been propelled such a distance. They were powered with dry fuel, a kind of gunpowder, and experiments have shown that such fuel is too weak. It develops too little power for its weight to fly more than a few miles. Even dynamite and TNT are too weak to propel a rocket to the moon. A rocket must leave the earth with its full fuel load. There is no stopping at filling stations along the way. Therefore it must have a fuel capable of lifting itself, plus the weight of the rocket's inert parts, away from the earth. . . .

A little calculation shows that the critical "escape" speed is about 6.664 miles a second; the enormous velocity of 26,000 miles an hour.

Now, is there any fuel that could shoot a rocket as fast as that? Sadly, we must admit that there probably is not. But there is a way out. A fuel certainly exists that can shoot a rocket a third that fast. Why not, then, make a compound rocket in three parts? Let the littlest and middle-size rockets serve as the payload of the biggest rocket. Then, launch the craft by firing the biggest rocket. By the time it is spent, the projectile will be going, say, two and a half miles a second. Then drop off the spent rocket, and fire the middle-sized one. This will give another two and a half miles a second, making a total of five. Then drop off the spent carcass, and fire the last, littlest rocket, building up the speed to the necessary velocity! . . .

There is no *theoretical* reason why this wouldn't work. Several fuel combinations have been suggested that contain enough energy to drive the rocket on its hazardous round-trip journey into space. Among them are liquid oxygen and liquid hydrogen; liquid oxygen and gasoline. This latter is actually ten times as powerful as TNT, weight for weight.

But there are enormous practical difficulties to be overcome. In the first place, nobody has succeeded yet in building a liquid-fuel rocket capable of shooting more than about a mile and a half. The present efficiency of rocket motors is so poor (development work has only just begun) that it probably would be impossible today to build a rocket capable of going more than ten miles high.

It is much too early, then, to make any kind of prediction about flight to the moon or planets. I am one of those visionaries who believes it ultimately will be done. But first we shall see rockets harnessed to many practical, terrestrial uses. In a few years we will probably be shooting them regularly into the stratosphere, carrying automatic weather instruments, and even cameras and spectrographs, to take celestial observations impossible from the surface of the earth.

We shall also see rockets whizzing at mile-a-second speed from city to city; twenty minutes from New York to Chicago.

Not until then, when the mechanics of rocket-building and navigation have been thoroughly mastered, may we look for daring shots into space. The first moon rockets probably will not carry men at all, but only large charges of magnesium flash powder, set to detonate on contact with the dark face of our satellite. Telescopes on earth will record the hits. If the target can be bull's-eyed eight times out of a dozen, perhaps a little party of scientists may be sent to explore space.

We might do some guessing as to how that rocket will be built, and what it will weigh. Let us assume that it will have four sections, or steps [now called *stages*]. We may also assume that the passengers and their scientific equipment, plus their cabin, will weigh about ten tons, our final payload, and that there will be three times as much fuel as dead weight and payload combined.

On such a basis, Hermann Oberth, a famous German experimenter, once made a calculation for the weight of a rocket capable of reaching the moon:

| *Payload* (tons) | *Construction* (tons) | *Fuel* (tons) | *Total* (tons) |
|---|---|---|---|
| | *First Step* | | |
| 10 | 10 | 60 | 80 |
| | *Second Step* | | |
| 80 | 80 | 480 | 640 |
| | *Third Step* | | |
| 640 | 640 | 3840 | 5120 |

Now a rocket weighing 5120 tons, built for the sole purpose of carrying four scientists and their equipment to the moon once, is quite a proposition. To provide for their return will take a fourth step, bringing the total to 40,960 tons.

That gives a mild idea of the problem that faces experimenters who want to get to the moon. Still, a moon rocket weighing 40,960 tons would be no bigger than a first-class battleship, would probably cost no more, and would certainly be much handsomer. And if it achieved nothing beyond giving the world an interplanetary thrill, well, what does a battleship accomplish?

*This forecast that looked so hopeless twenty-six years ago has now come into the realm of possibility. Developments in rocket engineering probably have cut the total weight requirements somewhat, and there are many who fully expect men to reach the moon during the next decade. The purpose of this enterprise is not clearly defined and, like Columbus' purpose in 1492, may have little to do with the actual gains in the final achievement. Instead of gold, scientists expect to obtain new data concerning the moon, not the least of which is the secret of the composition of its surface (see Chapter 4).*

*It now seems unlikely that any materials to be found there will be brought back to the earth in quantity, or that there is any clear military advantage in "occupying" the moon. Undoubtedly, it offers many advantages as a staging base for deeper space-probing, where materials are available for structures, shielding, fuel, and support of life. A closer artificial-satellite base would lack these, and cannot provide an unshakable foundation for telescopes and other scientific equipment. The back side of the moon offers sites shadowed from the earth and may be important for radioastronomy, and the lack of atmosphere will be a boon for optical observation.*

*However, the values of these possible benefits are still in the realm of conjecture, whereas the hazards to men are all too clear. The temperature range between day and night is extreme, the meteoroid hazard well established. The materials available generally do not include water, oxygen, or any other easily handled fluids. It is possible that much of the surface is covered with a deep layer of dust or fluffed-up material, and the lack of an atmosphere means also a lack of shielding from cosmic rays and other unpleasant radiation.*

*Nevertheless, the moon is there, within reasonable travel time, and it seems certain that men will brave hazards, known or unknown, to explore it. The first step is to learn more about it by unmanned probes.*

TLP

## Exploration of the Moon

(*Sky and Telescope*, May 1958)

A long-range program for scientific research in outer space has been presented to the National Academy of Sciences, providing a searching look into the space-exploration projects that may be undertaken as a continuation of the International Geophysical Year. . . .

A major section of the recommendations deals with the moon. The simplest lunar experiments would involve striking the moon with a rocket. The impact velocity would be about 9000 feet per second for a vehicle taking two or three days for the trip from the earth. Other observations would require circumlunar orbits, in some cases with instruments being lowered to the moon's surface. Much later, manned vehicles may be capable of landing on the moon.

The most useful experiments will be those that give information about the moon as a whole, rather than about some one place of impact. In particular, a measurement of the moon's mass is desired, for our present estimates may be in error by one part in 3000—enough to affect the calculations of moon-rocket trajectories. One method of mass determination would be to track a rocket approaching the moon.

A space vehicle could measure the moon's magnetic field, important for tracing the history of the earth-moon system.

Another project concerns whatever atmosphere the moon may have. Even heavy gases would slowly escape from the sunlit side of the moon. But perhaps gas trapped in the crust is steadily leaking out, so there would be a very tenuous but constantly replenished lunar atmosphere.

Both the density and atomic composition of such an atmosphere might be determined with a lightweight mass spectrograph.

Seismic observations would prove very valuable. For example, listening for moonquakes would be one way to establish whether or not the moon has a molten core. Also, the impacts of large meteoritic masses striking anywhere on the moon might be detectable as waves in the crust.

The methods of seismic prospecting are available if an explosion could be caused on the lunar surface at a known time and distance from the recorder. The original shock wave, after traveling a short distance in the crust, would break up into groups of waves traveling at different speeds and along different paths. The measured speed can be used to estimate properties of the rock below the surface.

To produce the shock waves, an atomic explosion might be used, or possibly simply the impact of another part of the moon rocket carrying the seismometer. If an 800-pound object struck at 9000 feet per second, the energy released would correspond to nearly its weight in TNT.

The broad program of space exploration, of which these lunar proposals are only a part, will probably first be attempted by unmanned vehicles. . . .

No timetable can be given for the achievement of the various stages in this American program for the exploration of space. But the first step was taken on March 27, 1958, with the announcement that [then] President Eisenhower had approved Department of Defense projects for the launching of small unmanned "lunar probe" rockets to the moon.

Authority to undertake one and possibly two lunar probes was given to the Army Ballistic Missile Agency at Huntsville, Alabama; modified Jupiter-C rockets will probably be used. In addition, the Air Force Ballistic Missile Division at Los Angeles, California, was assigned a program calling for three lunar probes. An initial outlay of $8 million has been made to start these two projects.

## The December 1958 Moon Shot

**MARSHALL MELIN**

(*Sky and Telescope*, January 1959)

In America's fourth attempt to establish a lunar probe, Pioneer III was launched by the U.S. Army from Cape Canaveral, Saturday, December 6, 1958, at 12:45 A.M. Eastern standard time. The 60-ton four-stage rocket was intended to carry a 12.9-pound conical instrument package to the moon's vicinity. Burn-out occurred 3.7 seconds too soon for the first stage, a modified Jupiter intermediate-range ballistic missile, and consequently when the payload was released it had a velocity of 24,000 miles per hour, about 1000 less than intended. It was also three degrees off course.

The lowered velocity caused the vehicle to follow a relatively small elliptical orbit, reaching a maximum altitude of about 65,000 miles.

Preliminary calculations announced by the National Aeronautics and Space Administration indicate that the flight lasted thirty-eight hours, the probe disintegrating in the dense lower atmosphere over French Equatorial Africa.

Despite failure to achieve its most publicized purpose, Pioneer III's two Geiger counters telemetered to earth extensive information. . . .

# Touching the Moon

MARSHALL MELIN

(*Sky and Telescope*, November 1959)

The first man-made object to reach the surface of the moon was the Soviet space probe that landed on September 13, 1959, at 21:02:23 Universal time. The 860-pound spherical instrument package and the 3331-pound final-stage rocket both struck the target, according to Soviet tracking data.

Despite the incompleteness of information about this historic operation, the great accuracy with which it was performed is evident. For a probe to strike the moon after about thirty-five hours of flight, the speed of the final stage at burn-out must be within 200 feet per second of an intended value of approximately 35,700 feet per second. Furthermore, the trajectory after burn-out may not differ by more than half a degree from the intended direction. In addition, since the earth is a rotating platform, actual launching has to occur within a fraction of a minute of the predetermined moment.

Very little has been announced concerning the multistage rocket itself. From the weights of the last stage and instrument package, it is evident that at least half a million pounds of rocket-engine thrust was employed.

Inside the probe were radio transmitters, operating at three frequencies of 19.993, 39.986, and 183.6 megacycles. When the probe was so close to the moon that it was being speeded up by lunar gravity, observers at the 250-foot Jodrell Bank radiotelescope in England noted the expected Doppler change in signal frequency. The signals ceased abruptly at 21:02:24 UT. With an allowance of 1¼ seconds for the time of transmission from the moon, the impact time was only 83 seconds later than the predicted 21:01, announced many hours earlier by Soviet scientists. This close agreement is an indication of the great accuracy of the early tracking from which the forecast was made. American and Japanese radio observers also reported successful tracking operations, but the moon was below the horizon for practically all of the United States at the moment of impact.

Like the earlier Russian lunar probe of January 2, 1959, which missed the moon and entered into orbit around the sun, the September capsule ejected a cloud of luminous sodium vapor, at 18:39 UT on September 12. Seen from the earth, at a distance of less than 100,000 miles, this produced a short-lived "artificial comet," again unobservable in America, but photographed at six or more Soviet observatories.

There appears to be no hope whatever of recognizing the impact crater on the moon caused by the fall of the probe. According to G. P. Kuiper, the craterlet would be only about 100 feet in diameter and with walls 10 feet high, thus lost among the multitudes of tiny uncharted pits that dot the lunar surface. The dust cloud thrown up by the impact might have been detectable. Press accounts of a cloud lasting fifty-eight minutes that was seen by a Hungarian watcher are probably erroneous, as any dust would have fallen back much sooner, lacking the support of an appreciable lunar atmosphere.

According to the Soviet news agency Tass, analysis of the radio-tracking data indicated that the point of fall was in the vicinity of the craters Archimedes, Aristillus, and Autolycus.

This conclusion was based in part on the readings of a "lunar altimeter," presumably a radar device whose findings were telemetered to earth on the 183.6-megacycle channel.

Some preliminary results have been announced from the data telemetered by the probe. No indication of a lunar magnetic field was found, within the limits of sensitivity of the magnetometer in the instrument capsule. Measurements of cosmic-ray flux were made along the flight path, in which nuclei of helium, carbon, nitrogen, oxygen, and heavier elements were counted.

[Several more space probes have impacted on the moon since 1958. As this volume goes to press the U. S. Ranger 7 was successful in obtaining close-up pictures of the surface, televised back to the earth before the final crash.]

*A good deal more about lunar probes is presented in Chapter 5, where the material can be related more clearly to other astronomical knowledge. Before leaving the subject of space exploration, however, it is worth noting the first efforts in deeper probing.*

TLP

## Mariners to Study Venus

(*Sky and Telescope*, September 1962)

Venus, now the evening star, is brilliant in the western sky at twilight. Despite its brightness and relative nearness to the earth, this is still a mystery planet, wrapped with an opaque atmosphere. Even its rotation period is controversial.

However, the Cytherean surface may soon be studied from nearby with space-age tools. The first attempt was made by a Soviet space probe launched in February 1961, but failure in the craft's radio transmitter ended the experiment prematurely. America's initial try was Mariner I on July 22, 1962, but during launching its booster veered off course and had to be blown up.

The possibility of such a failure had been foreseen, and another space craft was on hand at Cape Canaveral. The National Aeronautics and Space Administration plans to launch this second Mariner before September 10, the end of a fifty-day period when the positions of the earth and Venus are particularly favorable for starting the interplanetary voyage. The opportunity will not recur until early in 1964.

Mariner is not intended to hit Venus but to pass within 10,000 miles, close enough to supply much detailed information about the planet.

During the precious minutes of close passage, microwave and infrared radiometers are to scan the planet's atmosphere. The microwave radiometer is designed to detect radiation at wavelengths of 13.5 and 19 millimeters. Water vapor absorbs energy at the first of these wavelengths and not at the second. A comparison of the two readings should indicate whether water vapor exists in the Cytherean atmosphere.

The 19-millimeter sensor is also to ascertain whether the edge of Venus' disk is brighter or darker than the center. This experiment will supply a valuable clue to the explanation of the surprisingly high effective temperatures recently measured for this planet by radio astronomers. If Venus shows limb brightening at microwave frequencies, the apparent high temperature presumably is due to a dense ionosphere. A limb

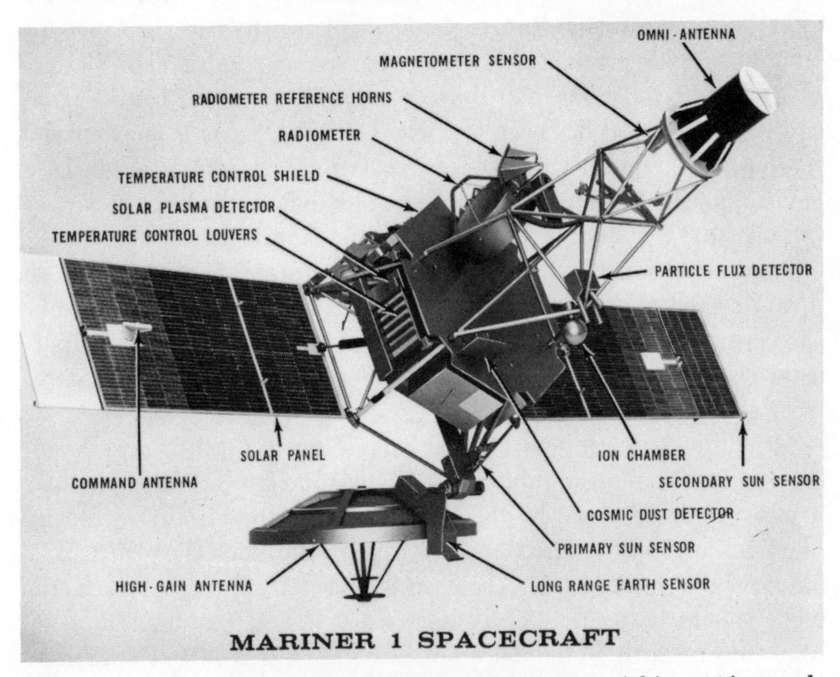


*Fig. 61.* A scale model of the 12-foot-long Mariner, weighing 446 pounds and carrying 40 pounds of observing equipment. (NASA photograph)

darkening would mean that the planet's surface is hot. . . . Terrestrial measurements of Venus in infrared rays indicate temperatures below zero, but it is not clear whether all of this radiation comes from cloud tops, or whether some originates deeper in the planet's atmosphere or at its surface.

Infrared observations from a Mariner during its close approach to Venus will clarify this problem. If the dusky markings of Venus are breaks in clouds, they should stand out in greater contrast in the infrared than in visual light. . . .

In a third experiment, magnetic fields in interplanetary space and around Venus are to be measured by a three-axis flux-gate magnetometer sensitive to fields 100,000 times weaker than the earth's.

The remaining three deep-space experiments are designed to measure the number and intensity of energetic particles in space and near the planet, the flow and density of solar plasma, and the flux and momentum of cosmic dust particles.

The long flight starts at Cape Canaveral, where an Atlas-Agena-B rocket, also used in the Ranger program, places the craft in a parking orbit. Here, at an altitude of 115 miles, the second stage and the Mariner payload coast for more than thirteen minutes, until the correct point on the circular orbit has been reached. Then the Agena B reignites and continues to fire until a velocity of 25,820 miles per hour is reached.

Planning the trajectory is a complex task. The interplanetary voyage will take 100 to 140 days, depending on the launch date.

After separation from the Agena-B second stage, a Mariner's speed should exceed escape velocity by 1215 miles per hour. Since the probe has been aimed in a direction opposite to the earth's orbital motion, it travels more than 6000 miles an hour too slowly to maintain a circular orbit around the sun.

Therefore the solar gravitational pull compels the tiny space craft to move in an elliptical orbit smaller than the earth's. Moving inward, it picks up speed, until by the time it reaches the vicinity of Venus, Mariner moves nearly 12,000 miles per hour faster than the planet, passing it on the sunward side. About an hour before closest approach, the probe should be nearly 19,000 miles from Venus, communicating information to earth 36 million miles away. . . .

If the trajectory of the instrument package needs minute velocity adjustments after it has left the influence of the earth, a small rocket motor, capable of exerting 50 pounds of thrust for a total of 43 seconds, can be fired for intervals as brief as 50 milliseconds.

## Results from Mariner 2

(*Sky and Telescope*, February 1963)

Even before it reached its December 14 rendezvous with the planet Venus, Mariner 2 had become by far the most successful of American interplanetary probes. It was launched from Cape Canaveral on August 27, 1962, at 6:53:14 Universal time. . . .

The probe, after undergoing mid-course maneuvers, approached Venus in an elliptical orbit (eccentricity 0.192) around the sun, inclined only 1.85 degrees to the ecliptic. Had the probe continued along this ellipse after encountering Venus, it would have passed through perihelion on January 7 at a minimum distance of 0.69 astronomical unit from the sun.

Actually, when Mariner 2 flew by the planet at a distance of 21,594 miles on December 14, its orbit was appreciably altered by the gravitational attraction of Venus. This gave an opportunity to redetermine the planet's mass with high precision. . . .

The change in relative velocity produced by the gravitational attraction of Venus on the probe was about 3000 miles an hour.

Preliminary reduction of these observations by the Jet Propulsion Lab scientists yielded a mass for Venus equal to 0.81485 that of the earth, with a probable error of 0.015 per cent. . . .

One purpose of the Mariner 2 flight was to search for Venus' magnetic field, if any exists. No evidence of an appreciable one was found, according to a report by P. J. Coleman, University of California at Los Angeles, to the American Association for the Advancement of Science. . . .

This does not necessarily mean that Venus has no magnetic field. The solar wind of ionized gas continuously flowing outward from the sun could confine a weak field to a small region immediately surrounding the planet. All that can be directly concluded from the observations is that the Cytherian field did not extend out to the Mariner trajectory, which at its closest was approximately 25,000 miles from Venus' center.

From that fact, however, an upper limit for the source strength of Venus' field can be estimated by a comparison with Pioneer 5's observations of the earth's magnetic environment.

Mr. Coleman and his co-workers concluded:

"If Venus has the same simple magnetic structure as the earth, the magnitude of the surface field is less than 5 to 10 per cent of the earth's field at the surface. If Venus has a complicated magnetic structure, the surface field in places could be larger than the earth's field without increasing the strength of the field along the Mariner trajectory to an observable value. . . .

"Probably the most important result is the convincing evidence that interplanetary space is rarely empty or field free. Magnetic fields of at least a few millionths the size of the earth's are nearly always present, except perhaps for occasional, transient nulls. The fields usually vary

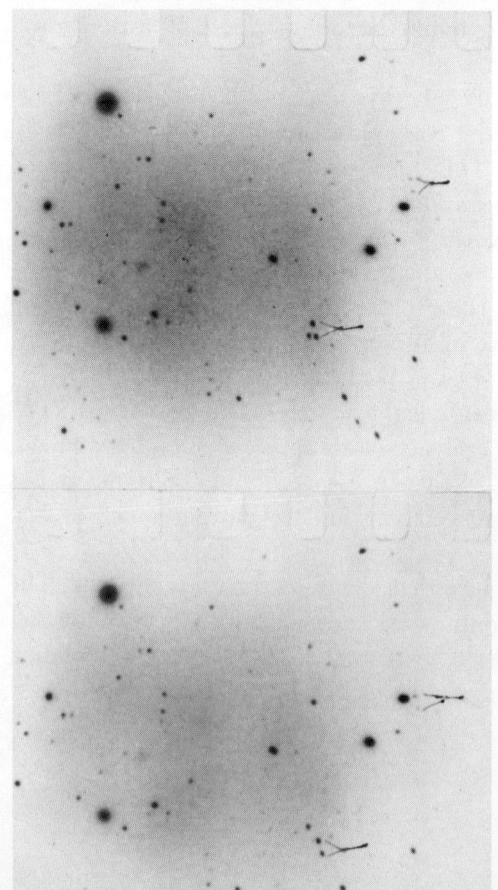

*Fig.* 62. Mars 1 and its launching rocket, marked by forked lines on two photographs taken at the Crimean Astrophysical Observatory, U.S.S.R. (United Press International)

irregularly with characteristic periods ranging from an observable lower limit of forty seconds to several hours."

Generally speaking, these Mariner-2 findings confirm and extend earlier observations by Pioneer 5.

Another Mariner-2 experiment provided valuable information about the numbers and motions of charged particles in interplanetary space. . . . On every occasion it was looked for, there was a measureable outward flow of very hot, ionized gas away from the sun. This solar wind had previously been studied close to earth by Explorer 10, but now the amount of detailed data is greatly increased. Evidently this outflow is a major feature of the solar system.

## Photographic Observations of the Mars Probe

(*Sky and Telescope*, January 1963)

When the Soviet space probe Mars I was launched in November 1962 the Crimean Astrophysical Observatory was immediately notified. According to its director, Andrei B. Severny, sufficient information was given about the spacecraft's trajectory to predict its apparent motion among the stars.

About 4:50 A.M. Moscow zone time on November 2, the 102-inch reflecting telescope took the two photographs reproduced here as negatives. Each picture contains two exposures thirty seconds apart.

Both the probe and its launching rocket are easily seen, resembling faint stars. In each picture, there is a pair of images of Mars I to the right, while below and somewhat to their left are the slightly brighter images of the rocket. The rapid motion of both objects across the star field is plain.

At the time these pictures were taken, the spacecraft was some 120,000 miles from the earth, about half the moon's distance. Latest reports indicate that the probe is performing satisfactorily, and by mid-November had traveled more than 2 million miles from earth on its eight-month voyage to the vicinity of Mars.

# 4

# The Hazards of Interplanetary Space

*The variety of space-probe developments mentioned in Chapter 3 emphasizes an obvious characteristic of research: From the small beginnings of rocket research in the '30s (p. 179), a new technology developed. Slowly at first, then with increasing tempo, the breadth of application grew—from short-range weapons to long-range missiles to defensive missiles, to unmanned satellites and space probes of many types, to manned satellites. Trips extend to the moon, Venus, Mars, and beyond. In the short space of thirty years, the problems have broadened from fuel and weight saving to accurate control, remote detection, elaborate equipment, power supply, radio communication, data storage, and measurement of cosmic rays, X rays, ultraviolet and infrared waves, charged atomic particles, dust, and larger bits of material in interplanetary space. As the advance continues, the frontier of knowledge expands.*

*The conditions in interplanetary space are of interest in themselves—and they are also of great practical importance in planning the next steps in space exploration. Far from being a "void," as imagined in 1938, the regions between the planets are cluttered with material that can have disastrous effects on space vehicles, whether manned or automated. We will start with the largest and most obvious material bodies, the minor planets, or asteroids. There are few large ones, many more smaller ones, and huge numbers of even smaller solid particles called meteoroids, some of them grouped in clouds. Continuing the sequence to micrometeoroids, molecules, atomic particles, and electrons, we find even greater numbers and discover the entirely new hazards of high-energy radiation (the Van Allen belt and solar "wind"), for men and equipment. The sun's ultraviolet light, X rays, and gamma rays are added to this, pulsating with flares on the sun's surface. The fact that these hazards are grouped or pulsing—varying in space and time—introduces further complexity, but may eventually permit avoiding-action by space probes, just as storms can be avoided by ships at sea.*

*Most of the asteroids move in orbits around the sun between those of Mars and Jupiter. They range in size from a few hundred miles diameter on down, and are probably irregular blocks of rocky material. (Where they have come from is covered in Volume 3 of this series.) As they rotate in the sunlight, their brightnesses change periodically. Plots of brightness vs. time, "light curves," show their rates of rotation.*

*A few of the larger asteroids were discovered in the early nineteenth century and were named for minor Greek gods. As the number of discoveries grew, names gave out and numbers are now used. In some astronomical research these small wanderers are a distraction, as in the search for Pluto (p. 71); a few have been of importance in establishing the scale of the solar system (Eros and Hyperion). They might serve as staging bases or sources of material for space probes to Mars and beyond—or they might be a hazard.*

T L P

## Asteroid Light Curves

(*Sky and Telescope,* March 1953)

The minor planets shine, as all the planets do, by reflecting sunlight. Therefore variations in their light must be related to their shapes, rotations, and irregularity of surface. Recently, a beginning was made at the

McDonald Observatory with systematic photometry of the brighter asteroids with a photoelectric photometer [an accurate photocell for the measurement of brightness]. The work was done by Drs. G. P. Kuiper, Daniel Harris, III, and I. I. Ahmad, of Yerkes and McDonald observatories, as part of a larger program on the asteroids and other solar system objects.

Ten asteroids have been observed so far, and light curves were presented for five of them:

4 *Vesta*. The light curve was uneven with variations in brightness of 0.10 magnitude.

7 *Iris*. The period is seven hours, seven minutes, or 0.297 day, not 0.259 day as given in the older literature. Amplitude [variation in brightness] is 0.22 magnitude.

15 *Eunomia*. The period is six hours, five minutes, exactly twice that announced before.

39 *Laetitia*. The period is five hours, thirteen minutes, or 0.217 day.

511 *Davida*. This object has the smallest range of light variation so far encountered. The period is five hours, three minutes, or 0.210 day. . . .

Although the first asteroid was found in 1801, and 1616 of them had been numbered by the end of 1957, until recently there had been no systematic photographic survey for the determination of their brightnesses on a photometric scale.

In 1950, G. P. Kuiper and his co-workers at Yerkes and McDonald observatories undertook such investigations to provide information for statistical analyses. All measures resulting from their work have now been published in *Astrophysical Journal* Supplement 32, including mean photographic magnitudes at opposition for all numbered asteroids.

Observations were made with a 10-inch telescope borrowed from the Cook Observatory in Pennsylvania. Between 1950 and 1952, the entire ecliptic was photographed (always in the direction away from the sun) nearly twice around to a width of 40 degrees, covering the zone of the sky where most asteroids would be found at their oppositions. The exposures were limited to ten minutes, enough time to show objects of magnitude 16 or 17 (see p. 66).

*Fig.* 63. Light curves of five asteroids; (*top to bottom*) Vesta, Iris, Eunomia, Laetitia, Davida. (Yerkes and McDonald Observatories)

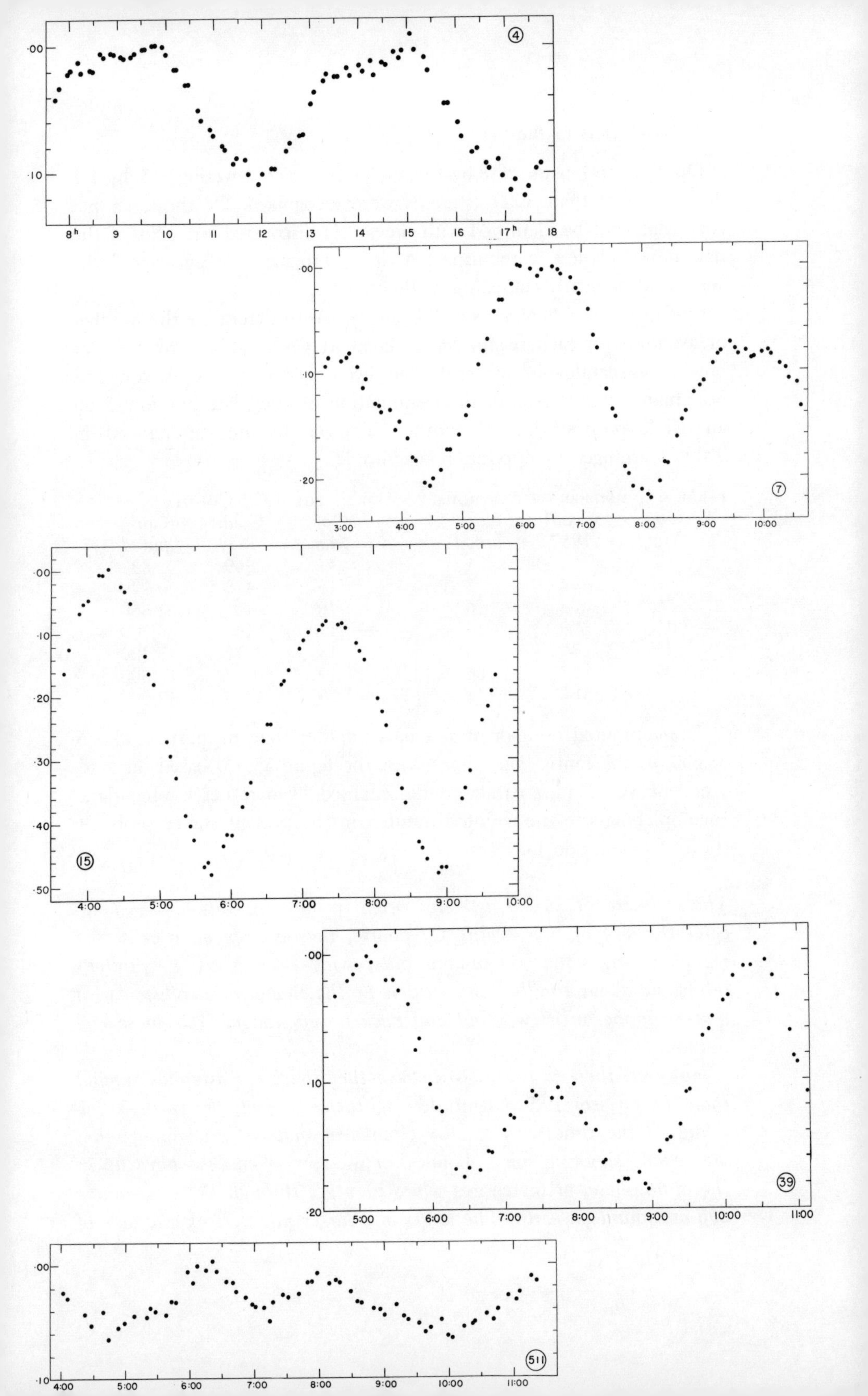
4
·00
·10
8h
9
10
11
12
13
14
15
16
17h
18
7
·00
·10
·20
3:00
4:00
5:00
6:00
7:00
8:00
9:00
10:00
15
·00
·10
·20
·30
·40
·50
4:00
5:00
6:00
7:00
8:00
9:00
10:00
39
·00
·10
·20
5:00
6:00
7:00
8:00
9:00
10:00
11:00
511
·00
·10
4:00
5:00
6:00
7:00
8:00
9:00
10:00
11:00

On the 1094 pairs of 8-by-10-inch plates, each covering 6.5 by 8.1 degrees, more than 3000 asteroids were recognized. Of these, 26 per cent could not be identified with previously discovered ones. Six of the new minor planets were suspected to be Trojans, moving around the sun in orbits nearly coinciding with Jupiter's. . . .

One of the principal aims of the survey was to determine the number of asteroids for each magnitude interval. It was necessary to find out how many catalogued asteroids had been missed in the survey, and how many were missed in the examination of one plate but found on an overlapping section of another. The results are summarized in Table 4 arranged by opposition magnitude.

TABLE 4. NUMBERS OF ASTEROIDS MISSED IN THE 1957 COUNTS

| *Opp. Mag.* | *Count 1957* | *Computed* | *Opp. Mag.* | *Count 1957* | *Computed* |
|---|---|---|---|---|---|
| 7 | 2 | 1 | 14 | 269 | 332 |
| 8 | 1 | 3 | 15 | 478 | 740 |
| 9 | 3 | 6 | 16 | 401 | 1,660 |
| 10 | 9 | 13 | 17 | 133 | 3,700 |
| 11 | 30 | 30 | 18 | 12 | 8,300 |
| 12 | 83 | 66 | 19 | 7 | 18,600 |
| 13 | 185 | 148 | 20 | 3 | 42,000 |

The computed number of asteroids brighter than magnitude 19.5 is 33,600, in substantial agreement with the figure 55,000 based on a revision of W. Baade's earlier result obtained from rather limited data. Incompleteness in the counted number in the present survey probably starts at magnitude 14.

*The estimate of 33,600 asteroids brighter than magnitude 19.5 indicates the size of this swarm. Of course, they are spread over a vast region, a ring some 300 million miles wide from Mars' to Jupiter's orbits and about a million miles thick. So the chance of a collision with a space probe on its way out and back is very roughly one in several million.*

*However, there is reason to believe that there are asteroids smaller than the ones of 19.5 magnitude brightness. In fact, the earth is colliding all the time with smaller chunks of material, meteoroids that are called* "shooting stars," bolides, or meteors *when they burn up in the atmosphere,* or meteorites *when they get through the atmosphere and are found on earth. The larger and larger numbers of asteroids of smaller and smaller sizes presumably merge with the very large numbers of meteoroids. However, there are some differences between the motions of asteroids and meteoroids: whereas the asteroids move near the plane of the ecliptic (earth's orbit, see p. 14), generally in the same direction as all the planets move around the sun, the meteoroids come at us from all directions. Of course, this motion is in accordance with Newton's laws—following elliptical orbits around the sun until diverted by near collisions with the earth or other planets. Moreover, they are related to* comets, *which also move in elliptical orbits inclined in all directions to the ecliptic.*

TLP

# Comets and Meteors

WILLIAM H. BARTON, JR.

(*The Sky*, March 1941)

Comets are queer things. It is no wonder that the early astronomers considered them in a class by themselves. Cometary orbits are varied in size and shape, and often have high inclinations so that comets do not necessarily appear along the zodiac where the more orderly members of our sun's family seem content to travel. Before Halley and Newton impressed their names on the literature of comets, all sorts of guesses were made about their behavior. Even Kepler, who discovered the laws that describe the planets' motions, hazarded the opinion that comets move in rectilinear orbits. The brightening of comets is so mysterious and stealthy that even in modern times these queer visitors have come close to the sun before being detected, and that with many observers scanning the sky for the sole purpose of trapping them. Then these celestial ghosts slip away into space, leaving such a short and hazy record that we are often uncertain when to expect their return.

As long ago as 1140 B.C., a tablet from the valley of the Euphrates River tells us that "a comet arose whose body was bright like the day, while from its luminous body a tail extended, like the sting of a scorpion."

A comet fully developed usually consists of three parts: coma, nucleus, and tail. The *coma,* or head, is apparently the only essential part, since comets sometimes fail to reveal a nucleus and when first seen often have no tail. The coma is the pale, hazy spot of light that looks like a nebula. It is very extensive and may vary in diameter from a few thousand to several hundred thousand miles. The average density of a comet's head is very low, so that stars will shine through it with undiminished brightness. However, there are no doubt many meteorlike bodies in the *nucleus,* a starlike spot within the coma. It forms most of the mass of the comet. . . .

The *tail* forms as a comet approaches the sun. The pressure of the sun's light drives gases out from the head. This pressure overcomes the slight gravity of the comet itself, and the material streams out on the side away from the sun. Since the tail is always on the side opposite the sun, the tail is not necessarily behind the comet. When the comet is coming toward the sun the tails follows it, but after perihelion, when the comet is receding, the tail precedes the head.

The planets' paths are not far from circular—ellipses of low eccentricity. Comets follow elliptic paths, too, but usually of high eccen-

*Fig. 64.* Brooks Comet, October 19, 1911, with sheetlike streamers in its tail. (Yerkes Observatory)

tricity—greatly elongated. Moreover, all the principal planets revolve nearly in one plane, but the inclination of a comet's path has no such limitation. Comets' orbits cut over and under the planets' orbits. Therefore a comet may move across the sky in any direction.

Some comets, when nearest the sun (at perihelion), are well within the earth's orbit, while one discovered in 1927 has an orbit that lies completely outside of Jupiter's path and inside Saturn's. It is more like an asteroid but has the hazy appearance of a comet. The shortest period comet known is Encke's, which goes around the sun in 3.3 years. . . .

The origin of comets is not known, but certain comets appear to have been transformed into meteor showers. Biela's comet, the Great Comet of 1882, and the fifth comet of 1889 all appeared to break up. Schiaparelli, the Italian observational astronomer, as far back as 1866, identified the Perseid shower of meteors that comes about the middle of August with Tuttle's comet, sometimes designated 1862 III. Meteors, too, have orbits around the sun, and it is the comparison of orbital elements that leads to the association of comets and showers of meteors. Some showers are annual events. Many meteors are not members of swarms, just nomads, so to speak—"sporadic."

A meteor shower seems to radiate from a point in the sky and the constellation that contains this radiant gives the shower its name. One of the most famous showers is that of November 14–15, or thereabouts —the Leonids. They appear to emanate from Leo, the Lion. This is an illusion, an effect of perspective. The meteors are all within our atmosphere when we see them, and they are coming toward us in parallel lines.

On November 12, 1799, a most remarkable shower occurred. There are several vivid accounts of it from different parts of the world. Humboldt, world traveler and writer, tells of seeing this shower in South

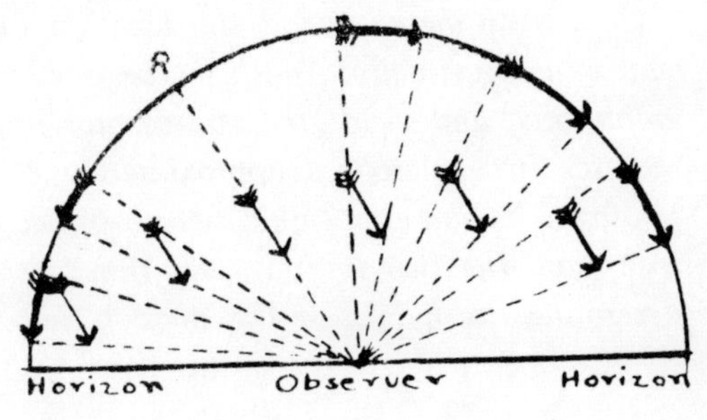


*Fig. 65.* Parallel meteors falling toward the horizon seem, as projected on the sky, to be radiating from the point R.

America. He saw thousands of meteors streaking southward across the sky, leaving luminous trains lasting seven or eight seconds. Some of the bursting fireballs left trains for fifteen or twenty minutes. For four hours this cosmic bombardment continued and a few meteors were seen even after sunup.

Again in 1833 the Leonids appeared on the night of November 12. Thousands were seen over the period of several hours during which the shower was at its best. . . .

*The connection between meteor showers and comets is confusing because pictures of comets, such as Figure 64, give the impression of rapid motion that many people associate with "shooting stars." Of course, a comet "hangs in the sky," like a planet or the moon, moving slowly relative to the stars for many weeks, whereas a meteor appears to streak a few degrees across the sky in a matter of seconds. Meteor showers recur each year at definite places in the earth's orbit, and seem to diverge from a radiant point (Fig. 65) that indicates a definite direction of approach by a cloud of meteoroids. Each stream of small particles could be the remnants of a comet whose orbit crosses the earth's path. The major Leonid showers every thirty-three years could be due to a concentration of the remnants reaching the crossing point at the same time as the earth. From the place in the earth's orbit (date of the shower) and the direction of meteor approach (radiant of the shower) it is possible to identify the comet orbit responsible for the shower. In fact, several such identifications have been made, Encke's comet with the Taurid shower (radiant in the constellation Taurus, the Bull) in November each year, for example. Not all meteors occur in showers, however. The so-called sporadic meteors come irregularly every night, most of them after midnight, when the sky we see is on the front side of the earth in its orbital motion around the sun.*

*Counts of meteors, and the location of radiant points in the sky, can be made visually. Another type of observation can be done photographically, and yields the speeds and heights of meteors. The latter requires two telescopes approximately 30 miles apart. Simultaneous photographs show any one meteor projected against different stars as seen from the two stations, and the difference allows triangulation to determine the height of the meteor trail in our atmosphere. With a little more computation, the original direction of motion can be found —that is, the radiant of each meteoroid. Thus, individual meteors can be identified as a Leonid, a Taurid, or a Perseid. These showers, or clouds of meteoroids moving through interplanetary space, were first studied by astronomers to discover their origin, and are now of practical interest to astronauts.*

TLP

# Meteor Problems and Photographs of the Perseids

FRED L. WHIPPLE

(*Sky and Telescope*, August 1947)

More than 1400 meteor trails have been recorded on Harvard photographs of the sky, with measurable trails of at least 1000 individual meteors. The current program of analysis of these meteor photographs seeks to identify as many radiants as possible with relatively high precision; to determine the positions and daily motions of these radiants; to determine the cosmic spread of individual meteors from the mean radiants; to establish frequencies and dates of maxima, and to compare these with those obtained visually; to search for correlations of such characteristics as brightnesses, velocities, spectra, and the like; and to establish the relative proportion of sporadic to shower meteors. Meteors represent our closest contact with the small particles of the universe, which are becoming increasingly important in cosmogony.

Comparison of photographic and visual determinations of shower radiants and of daily frequencies of shower meteors should provide clear evidence as to whether physical forces, such as light pressure or electric effects on charged particles, are appreciable in distributing meteoric particles about a mean orbit. As these effects may be expected to disturb smaller particles more than larger ones, the faint meteors should show systematic deviations in motion from the brighter

*Fig. 66.* A typical Harvard Observatory meteor photograph. Note that the "chopping" by a fan blade gives a pulsed trail, with a persistent afterglow between pulses.

meteors observed photographically. Observations by the writer of the Taurid and Geminid showers show no evidence of such deviations, but many more observations of this type are needed.

Measures of the daily motions of radiants (changes in the direction from which the meteors appear to come) and the cosmic spread of the radiants for individual shower meteors will provide data for studies of the orbits of meteoroid clouds around the sun. To date no theory adequately explains even the daily motion of the radiant for any shower, while no attempt has been made to utilize the information given by deviations in the directions of single meteors. Until such theories are established firmly, it will be impossible to determine the "ages" of meteor showers, or the dispersal rate of meteoric material along a comet orbit.

The analysis of Harvard meteor photographs has been completed only for the Taurid, Geminid, and Perseid showers. . . .

For the Perseid shower, forty-nine single trails and nine doubly photographed trails were accepted as Perseids. The frequency distribution with date is shown in Fig. 67 for all of the meteors observed at our northern stations from July 25 to August 22. The Delta Aquarid shower of late July shows conspicuously.

Of seventy-six (northern) meteors photographed in the interval from August 2 to 22, inclusive, fifty-six are classified as Perseids. . . .

Comparison of the daily motions and residuals of the Perseids with the Taurids and Geminids brings out the fact that the Perseids are a much more diffuse meteor shower than the other two. Unpublished results indicate that the Giacobinids and Leonids represent extremely well-defined radiants whereas the Delta Aquarids are diffuse. The "age" of a meteor shower must play a part in producing a diffuse radiant. The Geminids show the greatest daily motion of radiant, while the length of the shower is the shortest of the three. The Taurid and Perseid showers show a small and comparable daily motion, although the one represents an orbit of low inclination to the earth's orbit and the other a highly inclined orbit. . . .

*In addition to these groups of meteoroids moving around the sun, there is a general cloud of small particles giving rise to sporadic meteors.*

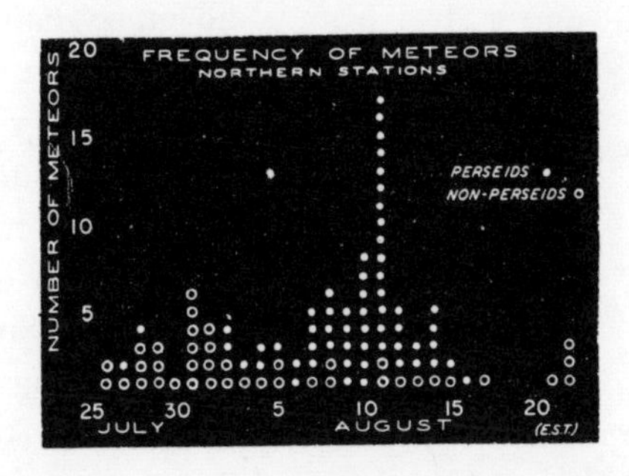


*Fig.* 67. The frequency of meteors on Harvard photographs shows the peak of the Perseid meteor shower.

*Counts of sporadic meteors by eye, by photograph, and by radar show, again, larger and larger numbers of smaller and smaller ones, all moving at speeds of several miles per second. The possible hazard to space probes was recognized many years ago.*

TLP

## Meteorites and Space Travel

(*Sky and Telescope*, November 1946)

Astronomers are being called upon to determine the hazards of travel through space in pressurized rocket ships. Dr. Fred L. Whipple, of Harvard College Observatory, has made computations of the probability that the skin of a space vessel will be punctured by a meteorite, and he proposed a "meteorite bumper" as a means of protection from meteorites.

In his study, Dr. Whipple assumed that the space ship travels in a part of the solar system where the meteoritic frequencies and velocities approximate those at the earth. He assumed that $4.5 \times 10^7$ fifth-magnitude meteors strike the earth daily and that there are twice as many that are half as bright, ten times as many one tenth as bright, and so on, as proposed by Dr. Fletcher G. Watson; following Öpik, he considered the total kinetic energy of a telescopic meteor to be 1800 times the light energy radiated as it burns up in our atmosphere.

His final postulate is that the penetrating distance of a meteorite into a steel plate is no more than the length of a right circular cone of 60-degree total apex angle, the volume of which can be heated and melted by the total kinetic energy of the meteorite.

From these premises, it follows that a spherical space probe of 12 feet diameter covered with a quarter-inch steel skin will be penetrated by a meteorite corresponding to an eighth-magnitude or brighter meteor at the rate of once in fifty years. Such a meteorite weighs approximately a milligram. For thinner coverings the probability increases rapidly.

Although the probability of meteor penetration is small, a simple protection can be provided other than by the avoidance of known meteor streams. Considerations of the conservation of momentum and energy show that when a meteorite collides with a sheet of a thickness comparable with the meteorite's diameter, the result is an explosion in which both the meteorite and the corresponding material of the sheet are vaporized and ionized at a very high temperature. Hence, a "meteorite bumper" consisting, perhaps, of a thin sheet of metal surrounding the quarter-inch skin of the space ship at a distance of an inch would dissipate the penetrating power of a meteorite several times larger than one corresponding to an eighth-magnitude meteor.

The very rare collision that may occur with a large meteorite, one the size of a pea or a walnut, would completely destroy the space vessel. Fortunately, the probability of such an encounter is exceedingly small.

*Pressing further, toward smaller and smaller particles, we finally reach the limit in atomic sizes (including electrons). The confusing term* radiation, *used to describe such particles moving at high speed, comes from the cosmic rays, first studied by physicists in the '20s and then thought to be waves shorter than X rays. Not only are cosmic rays from the sun and elsewhere striking the earth, there are intense streams of such particles just outside the atmosphere, as discovered by artificial satellites in 1958. These present a biological hazard to most living organisms, including human astronauts, and may also affect physical equipment, including plastics and electronic parts. Understanding their origin, distribution and changes in time has therefore become of practical importance to space engineers, although these articles are concerned with the more general scientific interest.*

TLP

## Van Allen Radiation Belt

(*Sky and Telescope*, June 1959)

The most significant discovery made so far with artificial satellites is the region of intense cosmic radiation girdling the earth within 20,000 miles of its center. First reported in May 1958 by James A. Van Allen, State University of Iowa, it was promptly confirmed in Soviet announcements. Great scientific interest in the phenomenon caused instruments for its study to be included in more than half of the eleven earth satellites successfully launched, and in all four of the space probes that attained great distances from the earth.

The initial announcement was based on a study of data gathered by Explorers I and III, launched last year [1958] on January 31 and March 26, respectively. Their Geiger counters met with cosmic-ray intensities over 1000 times greater than expected, and the counter circuits jammed repeatedly whenever the satellites entered the belt.

Explorer IV went into orbit July 26, carrying special instruments that provided a much more detailed map of the radiation zone. In addition, it monitored the closely similar radiation resulting from the three high-altitude nuclear explosions of Project Argus. Details have only recently been made public of these blasts on August 27, 30, and September 6, about 300 miles above latitude 45° south, longitude 10° west, over the South Atlantic Ocean.

The Argus experiment, proposed by N. C. Christofilos, of the University of California's Radiation Laboratory, has greatly aided in understanding cosmic rays. The long persistence of the extra radiation caused by the explosions, and its confinement within a thin layer bounded by surfaces of constant magnetic potential, proved the earlier conjecture that the earth's magnetic field traps charged particles from space to form the concentrations we know as the Van Allen belt. Also, the third blast produced a brilliant red aurora near the Azores, a location consistent with the entrapping theory.

Before World War I, the Norwegian physicist Carl Störmer had predicted that fast-moving charged particles from space could be captured by the earth's magnetic field. His calculations showed that under certain conditions an incoming particle would be forced to spiral around a magnetic line of force, back and forth from one hemisphere to the other (see Fig. 68). Only the points of reflection lie deep enough within the earth's atmosphere for the particles to lose appreciable energy by collision with atoms of air, thereby producing auroras.

Detailed cross sections of the radiation zone were measured by means of the space probe Pioneer III in December 1958, both on its outward flight to about 65,000 miles and on its return. Its counters indicated that there was still some remaining effect from the third Argus explosion. The measurements showed that there are actually two natural radiation regions. Peak intensity for the inner zone amounted to 40,000

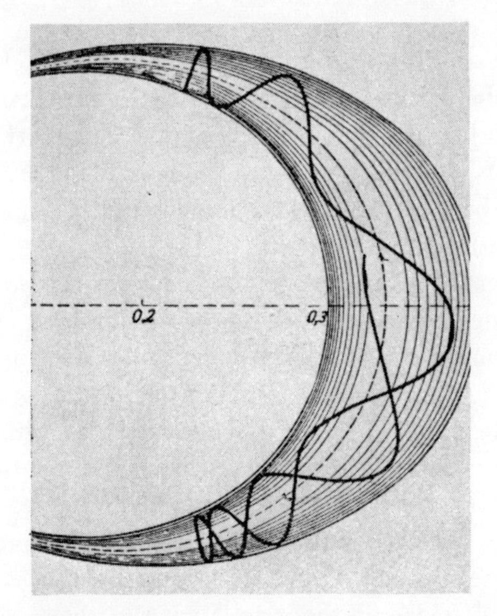


*Fig. 68*. The heavy curve is the path of a proton (or electron) trapped by the earth's magnetic field, whose lines of force, represented by the thin curves, extend from a region on the earth's surface in the Northern Hemisphere to the corresponding region in the Southern. The particle will oscillate until a collision with another particle changes its orbit. As it moves among the converging lines of force, its orbit becomes more tightly looped. (From *The Aurorae* by L. Harang, Chapman & Hall, Ltd., London, 1951)

particles per square centimeter per second, at a height of about 6000 miles from the earth's center. Higher than this, counts diminished to about 1000 per second at 10,000 miles, and then increased to a second maximum, comparable to the first, at about 14,000 miles.

Beyond 30,000 miles, the counts had dropped to less than 10 per second, and continued to decrease toward a limiting value of 2¼ a second. This limit indicates that in interplanetary space, at the earth's distance from the sun, the flux of charged particles is approximately 3.6 through each square centimeter each second.

## Van Allen Belt Produced by Neutrons

(*Sky and Telescope*, April 1961)

The source of the particles forming the inner Van Allen radiation belt has been established by Wilmot Hess of the University of California. Two experiments, described before the American Physical Society, have shown that the belt is populated by decay particles from neutrons leaking out of the earth's atmosphere.

The experiments consisted of neutron counters carried aloft by Atlas rockets, one under normal conditions, the other during an intense solar storm. They demonstrated that the number of neutrons increases during such solar activity, probably because of greater numbers of solar protons smashing into atmospheric oxygen and nitrogen nuclei.

Dr. Hess believes that neutrons are produced continually by this mechanism in amounts sufficient to cause the observed radiation belt, after they escape from the atmosphere and decay into protons and electrons. It is these charged particles, trapped by the earth's magnetic field, that actually make up the inner Van Allen belt.

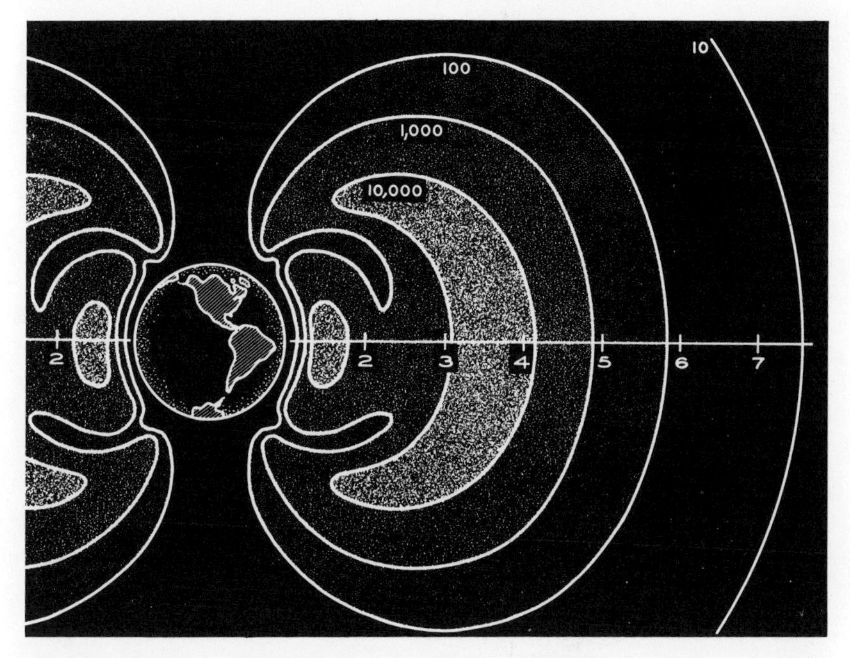


*Fig. 69.* The Van Allen radiation belts, with distances given in earth radii. Radiation intensity, represented by the contours, is in counts per second. (Adapted from *IGY Bulletin* of the National Academy of Sciences)

## Earth's Radiation Belt

(*Sky and Telescope*, June 1962)

The earth is now believed to be surrounded by one large doughnut-shaped belt of radiation instead of the two Van Allen layers discovered earlier. Measurements made by Explorer XII, launched August 15, 1961, seem to indicate one complicated, pulsating band of radiation, composed of several layers of various intensities.

Early experiments revealed only the most energetic regions, which became known as the Van Allen belts. More sensitive detectors carried by Explorer XII have measured energies ranging from a few thousand to tens of millions of electron volts at heights beyond 600 miles above the earth's surface.

The entire layer, now often called the magnetosphere, appears to have a sharp outer boundary 30,000 or 40,000 miles high. Beyond this is a turbulent region, perhaps 12,000 miles deep, with fluctuating magnetic fields and solar winds.

*The fine material between the planets is certainly influenced by the sun, and much of it may originate there—hence the term* solar wind. *In fact, as the next article shows, the interplanetary material merges with the solar corona. The solar wind consists of electrons, ions, and dust in varying proportions, and presents a serious hazard to space probes approaching the sun.*

TLP

---

# Cosmic Dust

OTTO STRUVE

(*Sky and Telescope*, October 1954)

About 150 astronomers attended the sixth international astrophysical symposium on July 15–17, 1954, organized by Professor P. Swings and the *Institut d'Astrophysique* of Liége University, Belgium. "Solid Particles in Astronomical Objects" was the theme of the sixty-three papers on the program; two thirds of these were by American, British, and German astronomers; the others came from Belgium, Czechoslovakia, France, Holland, Japan, Poland, Sweden, and the U.S.S.R.

The first of the five sections into which the program was divided was entitled "Dust in the Solar System." It started with a summary by M. Minnaert of Utrecht, who drew heavily upon the theoretical work of H. C. van de Hulst in Holland and H. Elsaesser in Germany, and upon the recent observations by the German astronomers, A. Behr and H. Siedentopf. Dr. Minnaert discussed first the connection between the zodiacal light and the F-corona of the sun. Both are caused by the scattering of sunlight: by small solid particles, and by free electrons

*Fig. 70.* The zodiacal light, drawn by E. Leopold Trouvelot, Harvard Observatory.

produced by the ionization of gaseous atoms expelled by the sun or that result from the evaporation of solid grains when they come closer to the sun's surface than four solar radii.

Although the zodiacal light appears to the eye as a narrow cone, measurements of its intensity show that it is really quite broad. Its polarization was recently found by Behr and Siedentopf to reach 20 or 30 per cent, especially at great elongations from the sun. Since solid particles cannot account for more than 4 per cent of the polarization, this result indicates that electrons are abundant at great distances from the sun. They had already been assumed to be abundant near the sun's photosphere, their motions of hundreds of kilometers per second causing the washed-out or dish-shaped appearance of the lines of the spectrum of sunlight as reflected or scattered by the F-corona.

The zodiacal light appears much brighter near the sun than at the apex of its cone at great solar distances. It had hitherto been assumed that the brightest parts had the greatest density of dust particles. But in 1947 van de Hulst showed that this earlier conclusion was erroneous because it neglected the effect of diffraction [the bending of light around the edges of dust particles], which for moderately large particles concentrates much more light in the forward direction. Therefore, relatively few particles seen in front of the sun's edge would scatter as much light as a greater number of particles devoid of diffraction.

It is therefore understandable that the new results of Behr, Siedentopf, and Elsaesser indicate a decrease in the density of zodiacal light particles at solar distances less than 0.6 astronomical unit [56 million miles]. In general, the dust seems to form a flat ringlike layer in the plane of the ecliptic, with a "hole" around the sun. The density of this layer decreases by a factor of 2.72 for every quarter of an astronomical unit above and below the ecliptic.

The distribution of the particle sizes was derived by van de Hulst in 1947 and by Elsaesser in 1954. Most particles range between about 1 and 0.001 millimeter, but their number per cubic centimeter at a distance of one astronomical unit from the sun exceeds by 10,000 the number expected from the counts of meteors. The latter are, however, mostly high-velocity particles, moving around the sun in highly eccentric, cometlike orbits. Van de Hulst concludes that the solar system contains a vast accumulation of small grains which move around the sun in approximately circular orbits, in accordance with Kepler's laws. These grains would rarely collide with the earth—it is only an exceptional cometlike interloper that we observe as the flash of a shooting star.

The electrons form a huge cloud around the sun, their surfaces of equal density comprising ellipsoids of revolution with a ratio of two to one for their axes in the ecliptic and at right angles to it.

Minnaert discussed one very strange result, derived by van de Hulst, concerning the albedo or reflecting power of the particles composing the zodiacal light. At large angles of elongation, diffraction is unimportant and ordinary Lambert-type scattering accounts for most of the surface brightness. The latter is, in turn, proportional to the albedo. Van de Hulst had derived the density distribution of the particles from the diffraction effects at small elongations from the sun, and therefore was able to compute their albedo on the basis of Lambert-type scattering at large distances. His rcsult was 0.005—almost black! Direct measurements on meteorites, which do look almost black, give about 0.1.

But Elsaesser found it is possible to reconcile the observations with the assumption that the particles are white, albedo equal to 1.0. Hence, we are still uncertain as to the reflectivity of the grains. Minnaert, following F. L. Whipple, is inclined to believe that at great solar distances these grains consist mostly of ices, with metallic impurities. Presumably, such particles would be almost white.

Where do they come from? All speakers, especially Dr. Whipple, agreed that they cannot exist for a very long time without either being drawn into the sun and evaporated or being pushed out of the solar system by radiation pressure. As Dr. Whipple has suggested, disintegrating comets may continually replenish the supply of small particles. . . .

*In the remainder of this article, not reproduced here, Struve discussed* interstellar *dust, and the effects on starlight that it introduces (matters covered in another volume of this series). The relation between studies of interplanetary and interstellar dust is of interest, but the concentration of interplanetary dust in the plane of the planetary orbits is a clear indication of a significant difference from the huge interstellar clouds. In fact, the planetary dust may be concentrated in even smaller clouds.*

TLP

# Dust Clouds Around the Earth

(*Sky and Telescope*, February 1961)

Our planet is surrounded by an enormous dust cloud over 100,000 miles in diameter, thinning out in all directions. The existence of this concentration of tiny particles, suspected in 1958 by D. B. Beard, Lockheed Aircraft Corp., has now been confirmed in detailed studies by Fred L. Whipple of the Harvard and Smithsonian Astrophysical observatories, and by Arthur Hibbs of California Institute of Technology.

Rockets, satellites, and space probes carrying micrometeorite impact counters have supplied the main evidence for this newly discovered envelope of the earth. Most such counters operate like microphones; the impact of a tiny, fast object on a piezoelectric crystal produces an electric impulse.

Last October, Dr. Whipple found that between heights of 100 and 100,000 kilometers the concentration of particles decreases roughly as the 1.4 power of distance from the earth's surface. Somewhat farther out, the cloud blends into the tenuous interplanetary dust that we observe as the zodiacal light. The innermost portion of the dust envelope may contain up to 100,000 times as many particles per unit volume as the interplanetary medium.

Most of the terrestrial envelope consists of minute dust grains, about $10^{-9}$ (one billionth) gram in mass, according to Whipple. Larger grains are scarcer by a factor of roughly 10 for every tenfold increase in mass.

The origin of the dust cloud is uncertain. Interplanetary particles are gravitationally attracted by the earth and increase the concentration near it. Beard proposed that the grains acquire large electrical charges in passing through the Van Allen radiation belts, leading to capture by the earth and electrostatic explosion of the material into finer particles.

Both mechanisms are inadequate to account for the dust envelope, Whipple believes. Instead, he now suggests a lunar origin. Meteorites striking the moon's surface should throw up dust and droplets, much of which would escape from the moon, some to pass into temporary orbits around the earth. Rough calculations show that enough material may be supplied in this manner. The higher concentration near the earth would arise from the convergence of orbits and from drag effects.

If the dust cloud is produced this way, it should be flattened toward the moon's orbit plane. This prediction could be tested with artificial satellites.

At the December meeting of the American Astronautical Society, S. F. Singer of the University of Maryland presented a theoretical model of the inner portions of the dust envelope. The earth's gravitation should produce a peak concentration of the larger dust grains at a height of about 1000 kilometers.

Smaller particles, however, will have their distribution profoundly influenced by electrical drag forces and by solar radiation pressure. Dr. Singer has calculated these effects, finding a relatively dense dust belt about 6000 kilometers above sea level. Particles below this height will be negatively charged, those above it positively. The Maryland scientist suggests this pattern may markedly affect the Van Allen belts.

*Uncertainties in the density of meteoroids and the hazards they present are becoming more clear. Dust in orbit around the earth may not be fully detected by meteor observations. The smallest particles may not puncture the skin of a space probe, but they can "frost" the windows and ruin the polished surfaces of exposed mirrors.*

TLP

# Micrometeorite Collecting with a High-Altitude Rocket

(*Sky and Telescope*, February 1962)

An Aerobee-150 rocket called the "Venus flytrap" was successfully fired from White Sands Proving Ground on June 6, 1961, at 5:31 A.M. Mountain standard time. At an altitude of 88 kilometers, its nose cone slid open to expose a number of specially prepared surfaces for collecting micrometeorites—the smallest particles of meteoric origin that enter the atmosphere.

For nearly four minutes, while the rocket attained its maximum altitude of 168 kilometers and descended to 116, the "flytrap" collectors were subject to micrometeorite bombardment. Approximately seven particles per square millimeter were collected, most of them less than a micron in size. (A micron is 0.00004 inch.) When the report was written, a total of 133 micrometeorites had been found in the 0.1-to-1-micron range, and eleven larger particles.

Details of this pioneering experiment were reported by C. L. Hemenway, of Dudley Observatory and Union College, and R. K. Soberman, Air Force Cambridge Research Laboratories. They described the elaborate precautions against contamination that were taken in preparing the surfaces and installing them in the rocket, and told of the difficulties of the electron-microscope techniques that were necessary in examining and identifying the particles collected.

On four of the flytrap leaves were placed surfaces designed to show penetration and cratering by impinging particles. The first two layers were mylar film six microns thick—preflight tests with a helium leak indicator showed no holes in these more than 10 microns in size. It was hoped that if a particle punctured more than one layer, some indication would be obtained as to the direction in space from which it came.

After the flight, only three holes were found, even though the total film area was ¼ square meter. There was no penetration of the second mylar layer, but the holes had dimensions of hundreds of microns and exhibited torn "flaps." They seem to have been produced by particles about 30, 100, and 150 microns in diameter impacting at speeds of about two kilometers per second or less.

Many attempts have been made in recent years to collect micrometeorites at sea level, on mountaintops, and by balloon or high-altitude aircraft. However, in every case there was more danger of contamination by terrestrial particles than there is at the heights rockets can reach. To make allowance for any contamination that would occur, Drs. Hemenway and Soberman applied several controls.

Boxes like those making the flight were exposed in the laboratory. A spare was uncovered at White Sands during final rocket testing, and the final cycle trial for the opening of the nose cone was carried out in a decontaminated plastic tent. Desert dust was examined to see what kind of foreign material it might introduce. The inside of the nose cone was wiped to ascertain the nature of contaminants there.

The best control was in each box itself, where one quarter of the area was blocked off by a shield. Air could flow through the half-millimeter space between the shield and the collector surface, yet at high altitudes incoming particles would be cut off from these control areas.

For trapping the smallest particles, eight sealed boxes were prepared with materials of high purity and in a manner suitable for later electron microscopy. The thin films of various materials were about 200 angstroms thick, supported with 200-mesh copper screening.

An effective way of identifying contaminants was "flagging." Just before each box was sealed, some of its slides had an aluminum coating evaporated on them grazingly. After the flight, another film was deposited obliquely, at right angles to the first. Hence, each particle on the slide had one "shadow" or two, indicating in most cases whether it had been picked up during or before the flight. In all, these eight slides comprised 0.13 square meter of collecting surface.

The boxes were opened and closed during the flight by the action of the flytrap leaves, and were sealed upon descent by the increase of atmospheric pressure. The nose cone lay in the desert an hour after landing, before being placed in a protective bag. When it was opened for examination a week later, five of the eight boxes were still under sufficient vacuum to require opening by the injection of clean air with a hypodermic syringe.

Three independent electron microscopes and observer teams were used to evaluate, count, electron micrograph, and measure the particles. With an electron microscope, the resolution is of the order of 10 to 200 angstroms, 100 or more times better than with an optical microscope. But the high magnification reduces the area that can be examined at one time, so the work proceeded slowly.

Dr. Hemenway reported the results from nitrocellulose and formvar films each about 200 angstroms thick. There are three types of particles that did not appear on the laboratory or control surfaces. They are dense spheres with sharp edges, ranging in size down to a few tenths of a micron or less; irregular submicron particles; and extremely irregular pieces of "fluff." Some smashed fluffy particles were found, and there were a number of holes in the thin collecting surfaces.

The spheres comprise about 16 per cent of the 133 micrometeorites, while 72 per cent are irregular with sharp edges and rounded texture, and 12 per cent are of the fluffy variety. Some micrometeorites were probably not included in the total count, as the examiners followed a policy of discarding even slightly doubtful cases.

In an effort to determine the particles' composition, three techniques are being applied: electron diffraction, neutron activation, and electron-beam probing. It is beginning to be suspected that micrometeorites may not have a crystalline structure, perhaps because of bombardment by cosmic rays, but much further study is needed to clarify this point.

Drs. Soberman and Hemenway summarize the project by three preliminary conclusions. The number of particles collected was unexpectedly large; most of them were falling at low velocities; and more than 90 per cent of them were less than a micron in size. Perhaps, they suggest, these particles are debris from the breakup of larger, low-density fluffy objects in interplanetary space.

*Fig. 71.* The largest sphere collected with a high-altitude rocket, 0.0001 inch in diameter. (Official USAF photograph, courtesy C. L. Hemenway)

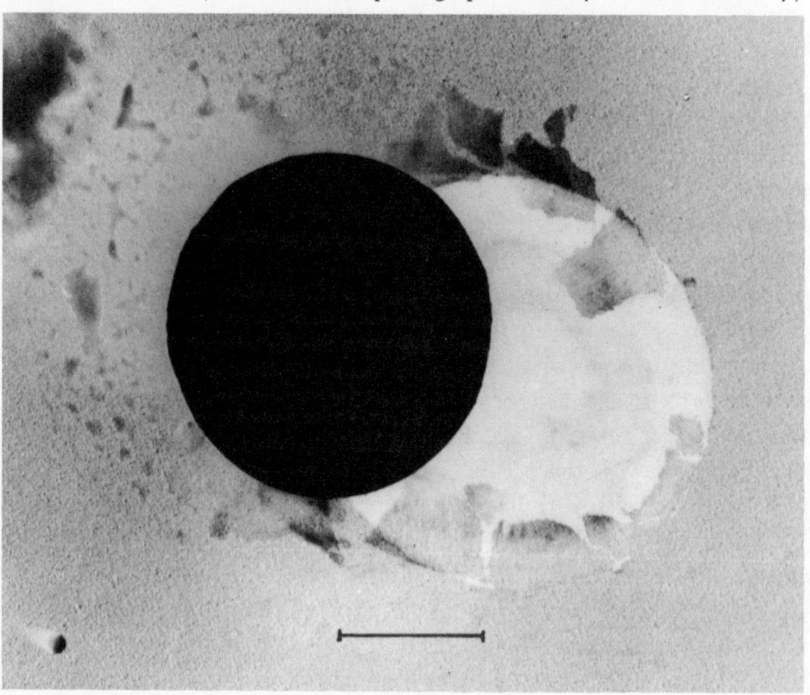

**Influence of the sun.** *The evidence presented so far shows that comets are being torn apart by the sun's action (p. 201), that the Van Allen belts are fed by the sun (p. 208), and that the zodiacal light merges with the solar corona (p. 212). A complete discussion of the sun itself is reserved for Volume 3 in this series, but it is appropriate to end this Chapter with articles on the corona and the "solar wind." This material shows, among other things, how the concept of the solar corona has been extended, and the unexpected effects of high temperature in a low-density gas.*

*In a broad sense, the sun is indirectly responsible for many of the hazards of interplanetary space due to its gravitational attraction. In addition, the solar flares are a direct hazard to space probes.*

TLP

*Fig.* 72. This irregular specimen resembles a museum meteorite, but its actual size is indicated by the one-micron line at the bottom of the picture. (Official USAF photograph, courtesy C. L. Hemenway)

# What is the Solar Corona?

DONALD H. MENZEL

(*The Telescope*, May–June 1941)

*Coronium* is no longer a mystery! The sun's corona has finally yielded the secret of its radiations. Ever since 1869, when the American astronomer Charles A. Young glimpsed the first of these colors—a brilliant green emission—in his eclipse spectrograph, astronomers and physicists have sought to discover the chemical element or elements responsible for them. And now, from Uppsala, Sweden, where Bengt Edlén, brilliant physicist, tortures atoms with hot electric sparks, comes what appears to be the conclusive answer: *Coronium* is chiefly iron.

To be sure, it is not ordinary iron. First of all, the metal is completely vaporized by the high solar temperatures. The unusual feature is that the iron atoms have had torn away almost half of their cloak of outer electrons. We find atoms that have lost nine, ten, . . . even thirteen electrons. One form of nickel, which is also present, has had fifteen electrons removed. Calcium is the third element identified thus far.

All are common elements; the chief reason we failed to prove their existence before was the difficulty of battering the atoms sufficiently hard in the laboratory to break away enough electrons. Actually, Edlén did not observe a single one of the spectral lines directly. The positions, or wavelengths, of several he accurately calculated from his hot-spark experiments. . . .

And thus vanishes a seventy-year-old mystery! But the solution brings up a host of baffling questions. How, for example, can the sun act so violently? The 6000° C., ordinarily stated as the solar temperature, could effectively pull but one electron from iron and partially dislocate a second. The removal of so many electrons demands a temperature of at least 100,000°—and probably one much higher.

Edlén has pointed out that the great breadth of the coronal lines

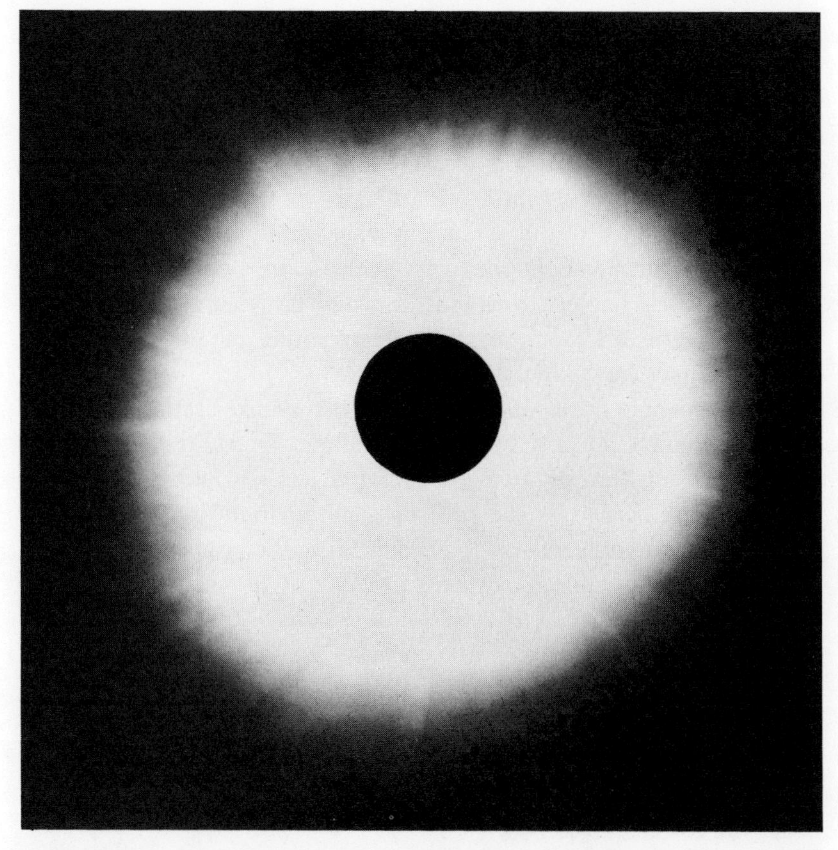

*Fig.* 73. The solar corona. Photographed by G. Van Biesbroeck in Brazil at the total eclipse of May 20, 1947. (Yerkes Observatory photograph)

(they possess a decided range of blotted colors and not a single well-defined shade) suggests that the atoms are moving very fast. This explanation would require a temperature of some 2,000,000°.

An independent study of the consequences of Edlén's discovery, by Dr. Leo Goldberg and myself, leads to similar conclusions, by entirely different arguments. We must not only account for the presence of the coronal lines; we must also explain why the ordinary radiations do not appear. For iron the question answers itself. The atoms have simply lost too many electrons to give off the familiar colors of light.

Hydrogen presents a special problem, and for two reasons. First of all, hydrogen appears to be by far the most abundant constituent of the solar atmosphere—and probably also of the corona. Secondly, hydrogen possesses but one electron. When this is removed, only the bare atomic nucleus remains. This nucleus cannot, of itself, emit radiation. But it will "snatch" at every passing electron and attempt to recombine with it, and, since such recombinations lead to the emission of ordinary hydrogen lines, we must find out what conditions will hamper the acquisitive tendency of the hydrogen nucleus. Apparently, only one answer is possible. The electrons must move so fast that the nucleus cannot take a grip on them. Again, a temperature of 1,000,000° or so is derived from the computations.

Several possible explanations exist for the source of this high temperature, though none is without difficulties. X-rays, or high-velocity particles leaking through from lower hotter levels would produce such an effect. The barriers in the path of such radiation or corpuscles are, however, truly enormous and it is doubtful if they can escape.

The more acceptable hypothesis—startling as it seems—is that the highly heated coronal matter is issuing in great jets from holes and cracks in the solar surface. These crevices, whose presence is probably associated with sunspots because the corona is most brilliant in these zones, run far down into the hot interior when the temperature is several million degrees. Coronal jets are the solar analogues of terrestrial volcanoes: gigantic eruptions that send hot material from the interior out to the cooler surface.

The gas is somewhat cooled by the expansion as it spreads out into the upper levels. The chief cooling effect, however, appears to be through the radiation of the coronal lines. . . .

There are numerous other problems which space limitation forbids my recounting in detail. The identification of the remaining coronal lines is one of the more immediate ones, along with further studies of the physical conditions in the corona. A great mystery is the tendency of the coronal material to move in well-defined arches or streamers, and not to spread out. This behavior strongly suggests that magnetic and perhaps also electric fields may exert some sort of focusing action on the coronal atoms. . . .

Edlén's discovery opens a host of interesting problems connected with the effect of the sun on the earth. The X-ray energy associated with the coronal emission may prove to be the long-sought source of electrification of the ionosphere, the layer that reflects radio waves. The new theory strengthens the view that magnetic storms and radio fade-outs are intimately connected with the corona and coronal outbursts. . . .

The coronal problem would have been solved long ago, had we been able to study the X-ray regions of the solar spectrum. Unfortunately, none of the far ultraviolet radiations seem to reach the surface of the earth—although one should search for the presence of soft X rays. Perhaps it is just as well that the earth possesses an atmosphere impervious to short-wave energy. It is doubtful if life of any sort could long survive exposure to the full blast of solar radiation.

*The motion of charged particles (ions) in the solar corona would be similar to motions in the Van Allen belts, described on page 209, governed by the well-known force acting on a charge moving through a magnetic field. At times of sunspot maximum the corona has streamers that resemble the lines of force near a bar magnet, and this magnetic force has been measured near the sun's surface. The moving electric charges produce additional magnetic force, electrons having the opposite effect from positive ions. Over a reasonably long interval, the net flow of electrons and positive ions must be equal—otherwise one region or another would become highly charged, and huge electrostatic forces would build up to correct the imbalance.*

*The sunspots, whirling storms of charged particles, have strong magnetic fields, and they, too, affect the observed structure of the corona, most generally in the eleven-year sunspot cycle. All this seems incredibly complex, but it has become better understood with the development of "plasma physics," or "magneto-hydrodynamics": the study of ionized gases moving in magnetic fields. How do clouds of ionized gas ejected from solar flares move between the sun and earth?*

T L P

# Solar Particles in Interplanetary Space

CONSTANCE WARWICK

(*Sky and Telescope*, September 1962)

On February 23, 1956, at 3:35 Universal time, a brilliant solar eruption heralded a new era in our understanding of the sun and its neighborhood. The sun was shining on Asia, and observers in Japan and India noted a flare so intense that it could be seen bright against the solar photosphere in white light—without the help of the special filters usually needed.

Simultaneously, in Japan and Okinawa a sudden fadeout of radio signals was recorded; the signals were absorbed by additional electrons produced when radiation from the flare fell on the ionosphere. Within

*Fig. 74.* Since solar short-wave radiation (*left*) is unaffected by the earth's magnetic field, it produces radio absorption on the sunlight side. Solar charged particles (*right*) follow complex paths and may end on the night

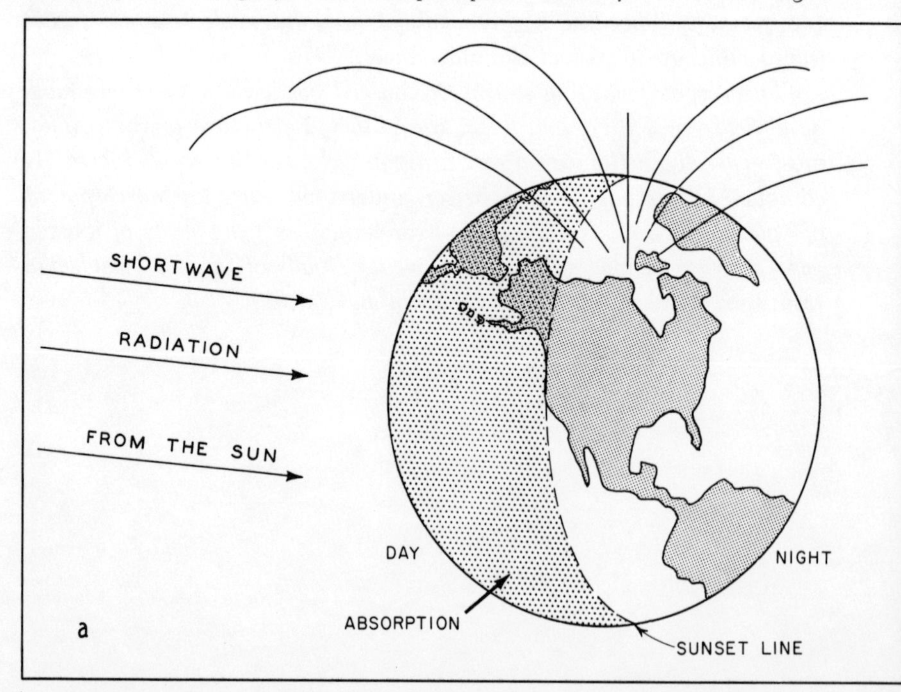

an hour, radio operators on the dark side of the earth began to suspect that something unusual was happening, for their signals were fading too.

Flare-induced fadeouts in the earth's sunlit hemisphere are not unusual, but this nighttime effect was something new. It had to be caused, not by wave radiation, which travels in straight lines, but by charged particles that curve in the terrestrial magnetic field and so can come down on the side of the earth opposite to the sun (Fig. 74). Dana K. Bailey showed that positive ions emitted at the time of the flare could penetrate to the lower ionosphere and result in absorption like that observed, and he predicted that such emission might be relatively frequent.

Systematic observations have confirmed this prophecy, for since 1956 about 50 similar events—most of them smaller than the prototype—have been detected. They are distinguished from simple fadeouts in the sunlit hemisphere by the geographic distribution of absorption (which is controlled by the earth's magnetic field), and also by the rather long delay of minutes to hours after the flare's occurrence.

Direct measurements made from balloons show that most of the

side, but only near the magnetic poles for particles of moderate energy. They cause enhanced ionization and absorption in polar regions. (National Bureau of Standards)

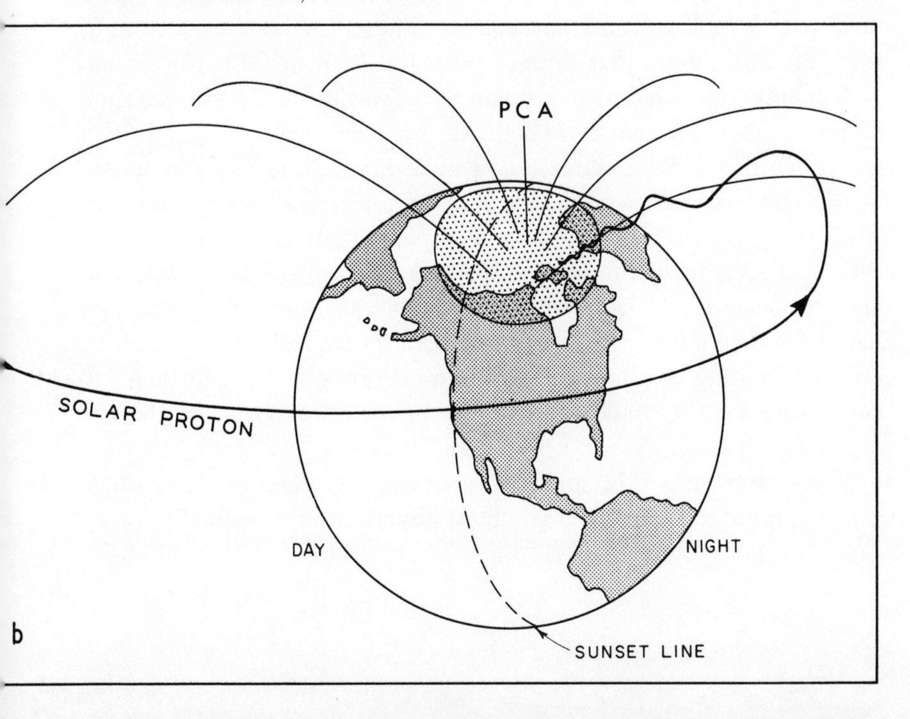

charged particles are protons (positively charged hydrogen nuclei) with low energies, in the range of only 30 million to 100 million electron volts. They cannot pass all the way through the earth's atmosphere, but are stopped as their energy goes to ionized atoms and molecules in the ionosphere. Neither can they cross the geomagnetic field that parallels the earth's surface in equatorial latitudes. They spiral in along lines of force, reaching the lower ionosphere only near the magnetic poles, to produce what is called *polar cap absorption* (PCA), as illustrated in Fig. 74.

On rare occasions, solar particles with relativistic energies—a billion electron volts or more—impinge on the earth's atmosphere. High-energy secondary particles are produced that can traverse all of the atmosphere, causing instruments that measure the flux of cosmic radiation at the surface of the earth to record a sudden increase. The high energy of such solar particles is characterized by the name *ground level event* (GLE).

The protons' observed motions furnish clues to any magnetic fields they may have encountered during their journey from the sun. If we can untangle and evaluate the evidence, we may learn about interplanetary magnetism.

Characteristically, solar emission of energetic protons is accompanied by great flares (Fig. 75) as well as intense long-lived bursts of radio noise over a wide range of wavelengths. These flare-burst events are of such unusual intensity that in most cases the PCA or GLE can be unambiguously associated with a certain flare. This permits a good measure of the position on the sun where the particles were emitted. It also tells when they left the sun and how long they took to reach the earth.

The terrestrial magnetic field acts as an analyzer to sort out the particles of different energies. As we have seen, only the most powerful can come into the earth far from the magnetic poles. The energies can also be measured by how deeply they penetrate the atmosphere, and have been determined directly, on occasion, from a balloon or a satellite. Since the energy of a proton depends on its velocity, we can then calculate how long it would take were it to come directly from the sun in a straight path.

The protons of a GLE move with nearly the speed of light, so we should expect to observe them almost simultaneously with the associated flare. For those that cause PGA, we expect a lapse of about a quarter or half an hour after the flare is seen. Observed delays range upward from these values to more than ten times longer, showing that sometimes the particles must follow long, complicated paths through magnetic fields between sun and earth. Such a large effect makes us wonder if at times they are unable to reach the earth at all.

We know that particles causing GLEs come most easily to the earth from near the west limb of the sun. Of fourteen known GLEs, nine

*Fig.* 75. This great flare burst forth May 10, 1959, in the northeast part of the sun (*upper right*) about a year after sunspot maximum. A very large polar-cap absorption event began on the earth about two hours later, and lasted for a week. No increase in high-energy particles was recorded at ground level. (Lockheed Solar Observatory)

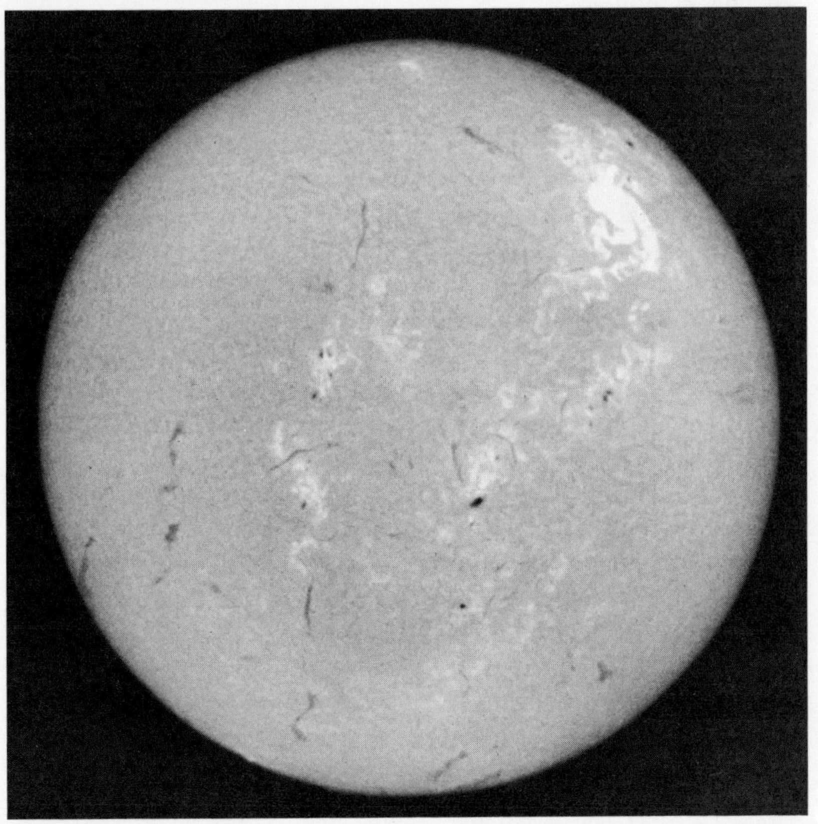

were associated with western flares, while only one was related to an eastern flare. If the high-energy protons are emitted radially outward (perpendicular to the solar surface), they must change their direction through almost 90 degrees in order to reach the earth.

For PCA events, which are caused by protons of lower energy, the preference seems to be for eruptions in the sun's central region.

In any case, we can see that the protons of lower energy are not drastically changed in direction, as are the solar particles that cause GLE. The PCA protons seem rather to travel straight ahead, spreading over a fairly wide angle.

GLE particles that start near the west limb have consistently short delay times. Thus, we can conclude that they show a clear tendency to come more frequently and rapidly from western flares, a tendency not shared by PCA protons.

Since any interplanetary magnetic field may be largely influenced by solar activity, we may expect that it will change during the eleven-year sunspot cycle. Charged-particle transit times tend to be longest near the peak of solar activity, but the change is not at all smooth and regular. The differences among the mean values come from the fact that near maximum all PCA transit times are quite long, while away from it there are occasional short delays, comparable to those expected for straight-line travel from sun to earth.

A similar effect is shown by GLEs. The travel times are consistently short in the years well away from the peak. The absence of data during greatest sunspot activity illustrates another characteristic pointed out by McCracken. These high-energy terrestrial events seldom occur then, just when the great flare-burst events of the type associated with GLEs are most common. This suggests that at sunspot maximum the particles produced by the large outbursts are unable to reach the earth.

On the other hand, the rate of occurrence of PCA events relative to that of large flares or radio bursts remains constant through the solar cycle, so these particles must almost always reach us, even near sunspot maximum, when they are delayed for hours. The interplanetary field must become either stronger or more disordered near peak solar activity, preventing some high-energy protons from reaching us at all, and delaying those that do arrive to produce PCA events.

It is puzzling that the high-energy particles appear to be affected more drastically than those of lower energy. How can the latter move with greater freedom? A uniform magnetic field tends to make a charged body travel in a spiral about a line of force. The radius of the spiral will be large for an energetic particle in a weak field, smaller if the field is stronger. If the field is weak enough, and directed perpendicular to the earth-sun line, an energetic particle can follow a path with a radius of half the distance from sun to earth, arriving with some change in direction and a short delay time (Fig. 76a).

But the field must be very weak to allow even the energetic GLE particles to reach the earth in this way, and in this weak field the radius of the orbit of a PCA proton would be almost ten times too small for it to get here at all.

*Fig. 76 (a, top, b, bottom).* Two possible paths of charged particles in different hypothetical fields.

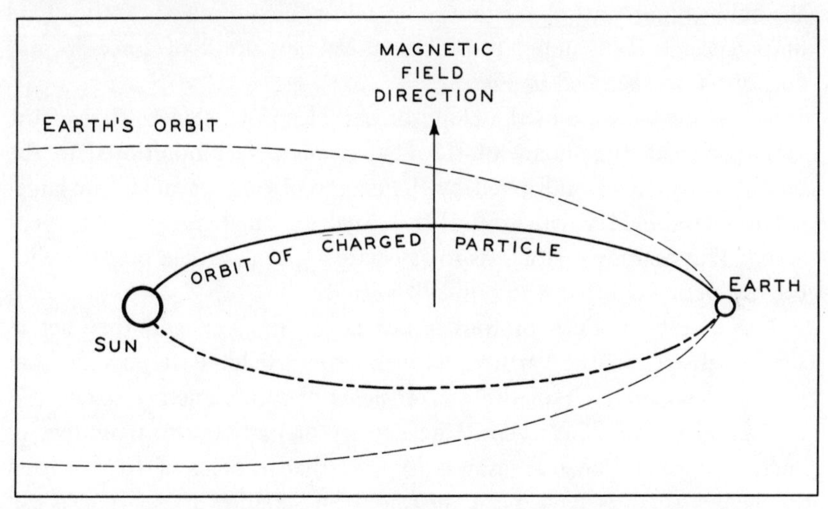


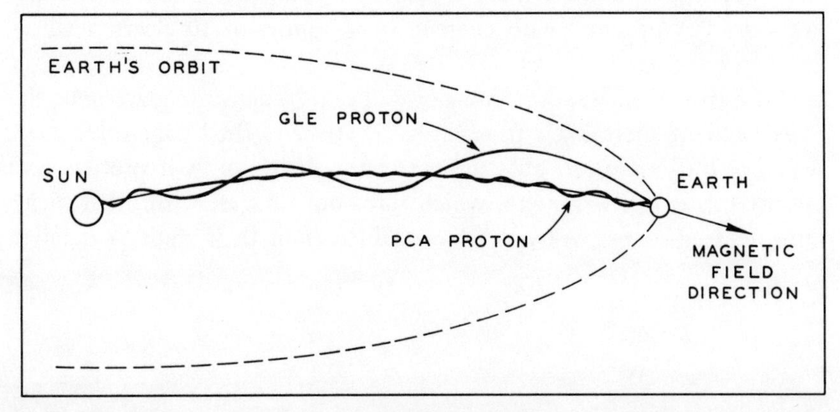

A surer path would be offered by a strong field with lines of force connecting the sun and earth. The PCA protons would have to follow the lines closely, and if the field lines were curved by solar rotation, they would show a clear change in direction, which is contrary to what we observe (Fig. 76b).

If the magnetic field were not uniform, but changed direction and strength from place to place, the particles would follow very complicated paths, tending to diffuse slowly outward from the sun. This would give long delay times, but again higher energies would give faster, more direct paths. No matter what sort of trajectory we imagine through such a field, the GLE protons would be less affected than the PCA ones.

There is, however, another way for the particles to reach us. The low-energy protons that cause geomagnetic disturbances do it by cooperative action. By sheer force of numbers, they can get through fields that are impenetrable to ions with much larger energies. Density is so great that the field cannot control the motion of all of them—indeed, as the cloud of particles rushes along, it pushes ahead any lines of force it may encounter, as sketched in Fig. 77.

When the pressure of the cloud of particles just balances that of the magnetic field, the square of the field strength is proportional to the density of particles multiplied by the energy of each particle. For larger values of the field, it will control the cloud; for smaller, it will be swept along. This relation enables us to associate a given particle pressure with the magnetic field that would just balance it.

The density of PCA protons is not large, however, and they act as single particles in the earth's relatively strong field. Is it possible that they act cooperatively in the weaker fields of interplanetary space?

During several PCA events, the density of particles in a number of energy ranges has been measured. We see that in fields of $10^{-5}$, or even $10^{-4}$ gauss, such as have been measured by satellites in space, we can expect PCA protons (with energies of the order of 10 electron volts) to move as a group.

GLE particles, however, are not sufficiently dense to overcome the field, and are more likely to reach us by virtue of their large orbits.

Since they seem just able to control the field, the PCA protons give us a measure of its strength, which turns out to agree with other measures and estimates. What we have gained from their study is detailed

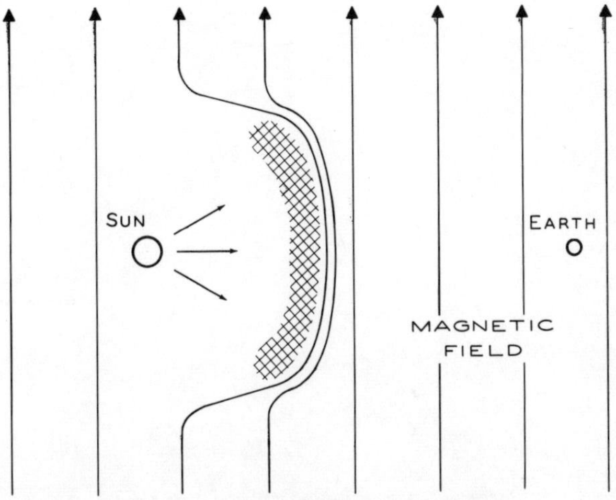

*Fig.* 77. Large clouds of particles that cause geomagnetic disturbances push aside any magnetic field in their path.

information about the variation of the interplanetary field during the solar cycle. However, because PCA protons do not in general move as single particles, they tell us less than we had hoped about the arrangement of magnetic fields within the earth's orbit. That problem will more likely be solved with the help of solar particles of higher energy, and with direct measures from space probes.

*The radio events described by Mrs. Warwick are by now the basis for a powerful new technique of exploring interplanetary space, using the earth itself as a detector and probe. The clouds of ionized gas (together with X rays) which affect our upper atmosphere undoubtedly originate from the sun. (The results of solar research, including further discussion of solar flares and the sun's magnetic field, will be treated in another volume of this series.) In any case, the plasma clouds have joined zodiacal dust, meteoroids, comets, and asteroids in the region between the planets. This interplanetary material forms a minute fraction of the mass of the solar system. Nevertheless, it presents a hazard to space probes, and it greatly increases the variety of observations that must be encompassed consistently by astrophysical theory.*

TLP

# 5

# Our Moon, A Big Satellite

*The artificial satellites launched by men, remarkable though they are, may seem to suffer by comparison with our natural satellite, so much larger and so much farther out in orbit. This is not the comparison intended by the title of this Chapter. Our moon is a* big *satellite by solar-system standards. Relative to its primary, the earth, it is the largest satellite known. Only six others are actually larger, and they accompany planets much larger than the earth—Jupiter, Saturn, and Uranus. Indeed, the earth-moon system might best be described as a unique "double planet."*

*The moon is our nearest known permanent neighbor, and for this reason is of special interest in man's exploration of space, whether by telescope or by space probe. It has been observed in great detail by astronomers since early Babylonian times. There appear to have been no changes in the side we can see, at least during the last hundred years.*

*Popular interest is now centered on space-probe exploration of the moon, particularly since the late President Kennedy announced that a national effort will be made to land a party of men there. Before discussion of these exciting developments, we must turn to the simpler, better known aspects, tracing out what man learned about the moon before he sets foot on it.*

TLP

## Phases of the Moon

HAROLD A. CHRISTIANSEN

(*The Sky*, February 1939)

The first impression we have of the moon's path across the sky is that she travels from east to west. This motion of course is only an apparent one, caused by the earth's diurnal rotation from west to east. The moon's actual movement around the earth is at the rate of about 13° per day, from west to east. This can easily be observed, by noting the changing lunar position among the stars from night to night.

The orbit of the moon is inclined to that of the earth at an angle having a mean or average value of about 5° 8′. Light from the sun will therefore always pass above or below the earth to the moon at opposition (full moon), except when this occurs at or near one of the intersecting points of the two orbits (the nodes), in which case a lunar eclipse, total or partial, will take place.

Phases of the moon can best be understood by considering the angular distance between the moon and the sun. From new to full, the illuminated surface visible from the earth increases with the angular distance from the sun; and for the waning moon, from full to the following new, it decreases as it completes its circuit of the earth (Fig. 78).

When the moon is new, it is in conjunction with the sun and the angular distance is zero.

The moon then sets in the west about the time of sunset. Since the dark hemisphere is turned toward the earth, the moon is invisible, except when conjunction occurs near one of the nodes within the ecliptic limits for a solar eclipse, when the dark lunar disc will be seen projected upon the sun's surface.

A day later the moon has moved farther along to the east, and a small section of the bright area becomes visible from the earth, in the shape of a narrow crescent on the western limb. As a certain amount of sunlight is reflected from the earth to the moon, it is usually possible to see the dark part of the lunar disk, almost resting, as it were, within the horns or cusps of the newborn moon. Hence the expression "the old moon in the new moon's arms."

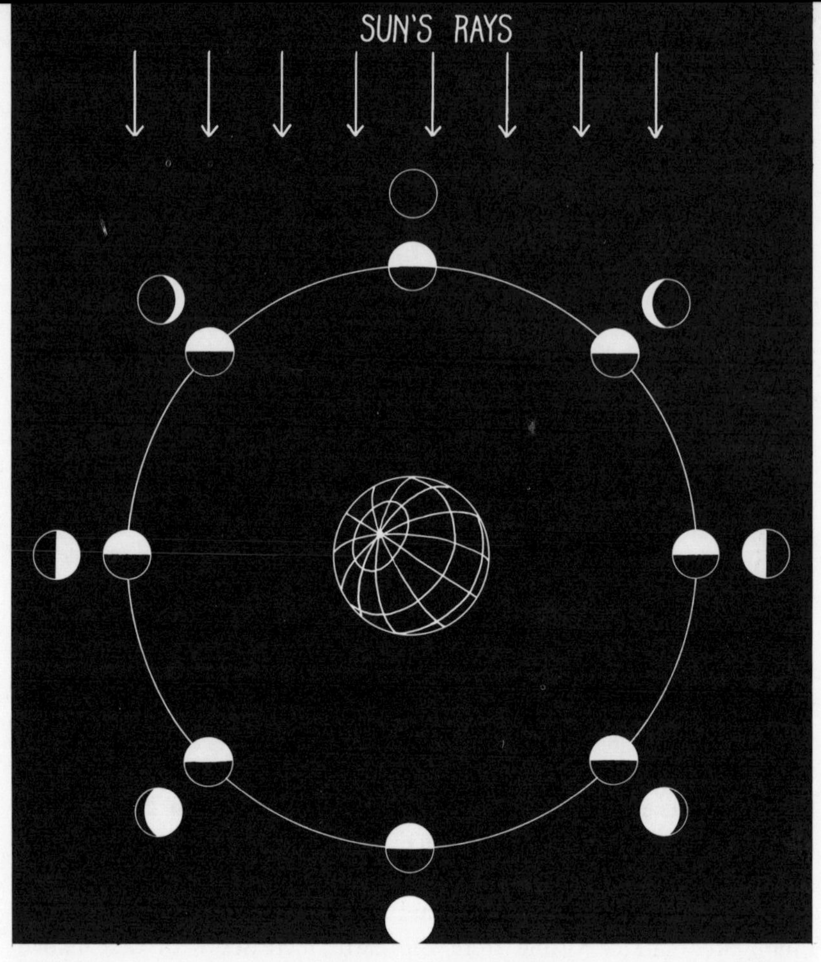


Fig. 78. Phases of the moon. (Yerkes Observatory)

*The foregoing article, and the next two, establish several basic observational facts and the terms used by astronomers in describing them. It is also interesting to note the difference in tone and style; twenty years ago astronomy was a "pure science," academic rather than of engineering importance, for schoolchildren rather than space engineers. However, this apparent gap between pure and applied science—between the academic and the practical—is bridged as we follow the sequence of thought from eclipses and occultations directly to the question of the moon's atmosphere, which certainly concerns space engineers and astronauts today.*

TLP

# The Eclipse of the Moon

PERCY W. WITHERELL

(*Sky and Telescope*, March 1942)

As the moon rises over the New England coast on March 2, 1942, it will appear a little less bright than usual because it will already be immersed in the penumbra of the earth's shadow (the cone of dashes at left of the earth in Fig. 79). A little later, as the moon moves into the principal shadow (umbra) of the earth (the shaded cone in Fig. 79), a dark segment of a circle appears on the moon's surface, which increases in area until the entire moon is covered. As we know that the earth is rotating on its axis, this round shadow of the earth is evidence that our planet is a sphere (see Fig. 2), because no rotating solid of any other shape could cast a circular shadow. The axis of this shadow is always projected to a point directly opposite to the direction of the sun.

If the path of the moon around the earth were exactly in the plane of the ecliptic and the distances of the sun and moon from the earth remained constant at about their average number of miles, there would be an eclipse of the moon every time it was full. Fortunately for the lover, poet, and astronomer, this is not true, so that a lunar eclipse

*Fig.* 79. On March 2, 1942, the full moon entered the earth's shadow and was eclipsed; on March 16 the new moon cast its shadow on the earth and caused a partial eclipse of the sun. Diagram is not to scale.

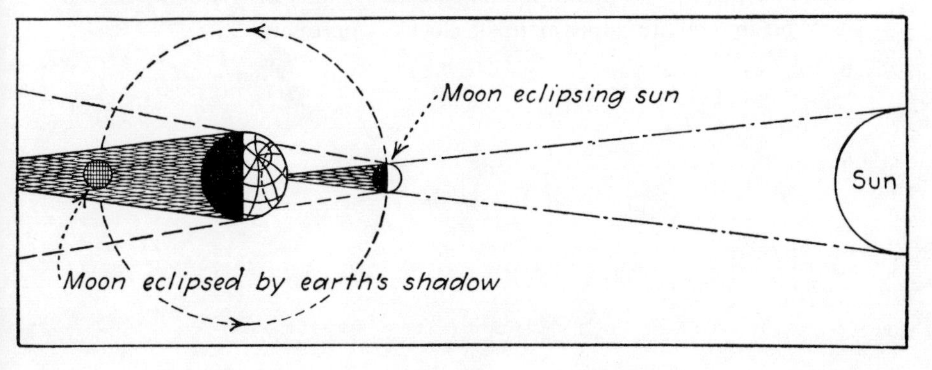

occurs usually twice a year. If one happens near the first of January, it is possible to have three. Some years there are none.

The plane of the moon's orbit around the earth is inclined about 5¼ degrees to the ecliptic, so that our satellite usually passes either north or south of the earth's shadow. When the moon crosses the ecliptic, if it is full there is an eclipse of the moon; if this happens at new moon, there is an eclipse of the sun.

The length of the cone of the earth's shadow is about 857,000 miles, but this may be as much as 14,000 miles more or less. The moon is moving 2100 miles per hour along its orbit. On the average, the cross section of the shadow where the moon is obscured is 5700 miles, or about 2⅔ times the diameter of the moon, so that it takes several hours for the moon to pass through the umbra.

Usually the moon appears copper colored during totality. This is due to the rays of the sun passing through the lower layers of the earth's atmosphere. This light travels twice as far through the air as [for us] at sunset, and the reddening effect is doubled. From the moon, the earth would be seen with a red-colored ring of bright sunshine surrounding it. . . .

Since eclipses were considered omens of fate, they were carefully recorded in relation to other important historical events. This has been of value in correlating ancient dates with our modern calendars, because if the place is known, the time can be calculated when an eclipse must have occurred at that particular site.

A comparison of the recorded times of ancient eclipses with times calculated from modern observations shows that the rotation of the earth is slowing down on account of the braking effects of the tidal friction. However, as this amounts to only 1/1000 of a second in 100 years, no immediate adjustment of clocks is necessary! . . .

## The Moon's Change in Apparent Diameter

**W. A. MAC CALLA**

(*Sky and Telescope,* September 1952)

Almost everybody has observed that the moon appears larger when on the horizon than when overhead. So much has been written about this optical illusion that we are apt to overlook the fact that the moon's apparent size actually does change appreciably, due to periodic variations in its distance from an observer on the earth.

One real change occurs which should make the moon appear smaller on the horizon than at its highest point overhead, contrary to the usual optical illusion. It should appear to be about 2 per cent smaller when on the horizon.

But a far greater change in the moon's angular diameter occurs each month as a consequence of the eccentricity of its orbit. We know that the orbit of the moon, with respect to the earth, is an ellipse, with the earth at one of its foci. The point on the orbit of the moon nearest the earth is called perigee, and the most remote point is called apogee. Because of this eccentricity, the moon may range from as near as 221,463 to as far as 252,710 miles. The change is so great that the light of the full moon may increase as much as 30 per cent from apogee to perigee. . . . [and the size by 14 per cent].

## The Moon

(*Sky and Telescope,* January 1963)

The third planet outward from the sun is remarkable for being double. Imagine it as viewed from Venus, at the minimum distance of just under 26 million miles. Our earth would appear as a brilliant bluish object of about magnitude −6, with a cloud-banded disk one minute of arc across. To the unaided eye, its most striking feature would be a yellow companion, seeming like Jupiter in brightness.

This satellite would oscillate as far as half a degree on either side of the primary, completing a revolution around it in just under a month. If the imaginary Cytherean observer used telescopes comparable to ours (and if his view could penetrate Venus' cloudy atmosphere), he would see the moon's disk about 17 seconds in diameter, dappled with dark maria, but with only a few craters discernible as minute specks.

He could establish easily from repeated observations of these surface markings that the moon rotates on its axis once for each orbital revolution around its primary. Thus he would be able to infer that the moon always turns the same face toward the earth. Our Cytherean astronomer might congratulate himself on being able to see parts of the lunar surface forever invisible to a hypothetical earthbound observer.

The main features of the moon's orbital motion could be ascertained by simple measurements made from Venus. A complete revolution, with reference to the background stars, takes 27.3 days. The plane of the orbit is inclined five degrees to the earth's orbit. The intersection of these planes—the moon's line of nodes—swings westward, a complete turn requiring 18.6 years. . . .

We on earth have the great advantage of seeing the moon a hundred times closer than is ever possible from Venus. The earth-moon distance averages 238,860 miles—about 60 terrestrial radii.

This proximity has greatly aided the determination of the moon's bulk properties. It is very nearly a sphere of 1080 miles radius, but the polar diameter is about 1.4 miles shorter than that pointing toward the earth. Lunar surface irregularities have an interesting effect. In predicting solar eclipses we must use a lunar radius 0.9 mile smaller than in predicting occultations of stars. The reason is that as total eclipse begins the last visible speck of sunlight shines between the mountains on the moon's edge; at an occultation, the point at which the star vanishes can be a mountain crest, corresponding on the average to a larger radius.

The mass of the moon is 1/81 the earth's. Its measurement depends on the fact that what is often called the earth's orbit is actually the path of the center of gravity of the earth-moon system around the sun. Earth and moon revolve about the center of gravity at distances from it that are inversely proportional to their masses. This motion of our earthly observing platform causes the apparent track of an asteroid to display a small monthly oscillation, from whose amplitude the lunar mass can be determined.

Some important facts about the moon's interior can be inferred from the surprisingly low mean lunar density, only 3.3 times that of water. This is much less than the earth's mean density (5.5), but closely matches the density of surface rocks. It may be concluded that the moon, unlike the earth, does not have a dense core. Instead, its interior seems to be nearly homogeneous.

The gravitational action of the moon upon the earth produces a wide variety of tidal phenomena in the terrestrial oceans, atmosphere, and solid crust. In addition, the sun applies a tide-raising force that is about 5/11 the moon's.

Today, the practical importance of the moon is by no means limited to tides or nocturnal illumination. Since the earth's rotation is not regular enough to serve as a fundamental standard of time for the most refined purposes, the moon's orbital motion is presently being used instead. The lunar motion is predictable with such precision that observations of the moon's position can tell whether the earth's rotation is running fast or slow. . . .

*An occultation occurs whenever the moon passes between us and a star (or planet). Such an "eclipse" is important for two reasons: first, precise timing of it provides an accurate check on the moon's location. Secondly, the suddenness of the eclipse, and the sharp edge of the moon (pictured in Fig. 80 as it cuts across the image of Jupiter) demonstrate that the moon has very little atmosphere. In contrast to the surface of the earth, which suffers erosion by the air and the rain carried by it, the surface of the moon is "preserved* in vacuo.*" Are we seeing the original landscape of the moon as it was first formed? And why is there no lunar atmosphere? Or is there some?*

TLP

# Jupiter and the Lunar Atmosphere

JESSE A. FITZPATRICK

(*Sky and Telescope*, July 1944)

. . . Walter H. Haas, of Upper Darby, Pennsylvania, writes: "The occultation of Jupiter by the moon on April 30th–May 1st [1944] was observed with the 18-inch refractor of the Flower Observatory. When the planet emerged from behind the *bright* limb of the moon, a hazy gray band concentric with the lunar limb was seen across the face of Jupiter. The angular width of the band was estimated to be three seconds of arc.

"This band was about as easy to see as either of the temperate belts on the planet. It certainly *looked* real. I saw nothing similar during immersion at the *dark* limb. Such a band was seen by at least one other observer at the recent occultation and by at least several observers at the January 13th occultation.

"I am greatly interested in this marking because of the interpretation that W. H. Pickering put upon it."

Somewhat later a letter from Cyril G. Wates, of Edmonton, Alberta, Canada, reached us:

"I am writing to you with reference to possible evidence of a lunar atmosphere, as indicated by observations of the recent occultations of Jupiter. I have received reports, either directly or indirectly, from seven other observers who saw the grey band. . . .

"I am told that Pickering observed the band more than 50 years ago. . . .

"The fact that the band was seen by eight out of 10 observers at the bright limb, but that all agree there was no trace of it at the dark limb, is easily explained on the theory that solar heat evaporates ice or $CO_2$ during the lunar day, but that the vapor condenses at once when the sun sets. There is, of course, the possibility of some optical illusion, but it seems very unlikely.

*Fig. 80.* The occultation of Jupiter, August 12, 1892, photographed by W. H. Pickering at Arequipa, Peru, using the 13-inch telescope of Harvard's Boyden Station. The last picture shows Jupiter emerging from the dark limb of the moon.

"Dr. C. S. Beals, of the staff of the Dominion Astrophysical Observatory at Victoria, and I have suggested, independently, that the existence of a tenuous lunar atmosphere might be confirmed by means of a spectrogram of a bright star just before occultation. . . ."

In 1889, Professor Pickering, then in Peru, wrote:

". . . Since this band was photographed it cannot well be due to an optical illusion, and since it was seen it can hardly be classed as a photographic defect—unless indeed we suppose that by a coincidence both conspired to produce the same result."

Other facts brought out in this article concern reported extensions of the moon's crescent tips; slight flattening of Jupiter in the direction of the moon when near its limb; combustion of meteors in the lunar atmosphere; velocity of escape of gases; and retention of the particles of gas making an atmosphere. . . .

## Search for an Atmosphere on the Moon

(*Sky and Telescope*, December 1956)

The most delicate tests yet applied show that at the moon's surface the lunar atmosphere must be less than one billionth as dense as the earth's, according to Audouin Dollfus, of Meudon Observatory in France. His observations are detailed in *Annales d'Astrophysique, 19,* 71, 1956.

Even a very tenuous gaseous envelope should produce faint extensions of the cusps of the crescent moon near first and last quarter, and this lunar twilight should be completely polarized. Using extreme care to minimize scattered light, Dr. Dollfus photographed the moon with the coronagraph of the Pic du Midi Observatory, but prolonged exposures showed no effect of this kind. [A coronagraph is a telescope specially constructed to reduce the glare of the sun while observing the corona.]

In a more sensitive test, a polarimeter attached to the coronagraph revealed no trace of the expected polarization, indicating that if a permanent lunar atmosphere exists it cannot have a density more than about one billionth of terrestrial air at sea level.

## Radio Test for a Lunar Atmosphere

(*Sky and Telescope*, November 1957)

A new demonstration, more far reaching than any before, of the extremely low density of any atmosphere the moon may have is reported in the August [1957] *Philosophical Magazine* by B. Elsmore, of the Cavendish Laboratory, Cambridge, England.

On January 24, 1956, the moon occulted the Crab nebula in Taurus, one of the most intense localized radio sources in the sky. This phenomenon was recorded with the Cambridge radio telescope on a wave length of 3.7 meters. As the diameter of the source at this wave length is about five minutes of arc, the observed radio intensity took some ten minutes to decrease to zero as the moon moved in front of the nebula, and a corresponding increase took place gradually at immersion an hour later.

The total duration of the occultation was observed to be 59.6 minutes, with an uncertainty of $\pm 0.26$ minute, as compared with the predicted duration of 59.2 minutes. While the excess of 0.4 minute may not be significant, it could be interpreted as due to a refraction of the radio waves by free electrons in a lunar atmosphere. The electron density at the moon's surface required to produce the effect would be about 1000 per cubic centimeter.

Dr. Elsmore points out that on the sunlit side of the moon whatever atmosphere there is should be completely ionized, all of its atoms broken up into ions and free electrons. Hence he could calculate the total amount of atmosphere necessary to provide an electron density of the above amount. It turns out that any permanent lunar atmosphere must have a density less than $5 \times 10^{-13}$ that of the earth's air at sea level.

## Possible Sources of a Lunar Atmosphere

(*Sky and Telescope,* May 1958)

In the February 14 issue of *Science*, W. F. Edwards, California Institute of Technology, and L. B. Borst, New York University, discuss the properties and possible origin of gases above the surface of the moon, on the assumption that such a lunar atmosphere has a density of about $10^{-13}$ the earth's. At so low a density, a molecule could travel some 600 kilometers, on the average, before colliding with another one, but most of the lunar gas would be in a layer less than 10 kilometers thick, so collisions with the lunar surface itself would predominate. The kinetic temperature of the gas would be that of the lunar surface, which reaches 135° centigrade at lunar noon.

Because the escape velocity at the moon's surface is only 2.37 kilometers per second (compared to 11.2 on the earth), gases of low molecular weight, such as oxygen and nitrogen, could not be retained. According to G. P. Kuiper, gases of molecular weight less than 60 would be lost during the heat of the lunar day. Among heavier substances, Mr. Edwards and Dr. Borst propose that the heavy, inert gases krypton and xenon might form a lunar atmosphere.

One mechanism for producing them is the spontaneous decay of uranium 238 in the surface layers of the moon.

A second process is radioactive decay of iodine 129, which would produce a gaseous envelope consisting solely of xenon 129.

If these or other possible processes for producing krypton and xenon did not operate, however, it is possible that these gases are the remnants of those trapped in the moon's mantle at the time of its formation. As inert gases, they do not enter into chemical combination with other elements. Stirring by meteorite impacts would release the gas from the moon's solid layers. The main atmospheric gas would then be krypton, with only 7 per cent xenon.

If the moon actually has an atmosphere of the amount assumed by Mr. Edwards and Dr. Borst, it may eventually be possible to distinguish among these three possibilities by analysis of gas samples. They point out, however, "Since the scale height [of the lunar atmosphere] is only a few kilometers, it is not probable that initial grazing rocket orbits would come sufficiently close to permit the collecting of a gas sample."

## A Lunar Atmosphere and Proton Bombardment

(*Sky and Telescope*, October 1959)

Although refined modern observations have not given any certain indication of an atmosphere surrounding the moon, there may be a highly tenuous envelope consisting of gases released during volcanic processes and by radioactive decay in lunar rocks.

Hitherto, it was thought that two opposing processes determined the properties of such an envelope: accumulation of gases from the surface, and escape of faster moving molecules from the weak gravitational attraction of the moon. Now, at the Goddard Space Flight Center, J. R. Herring and A. L. Licht point out another important process. They find that high-speed protons known to be ejected from the sun could be very effective in stripping the moon of a gaseous envelope.

In 1951, the German astronomer L. Biermann calculated the flux of particles from the sun. This "solar wind" can be visualized as a cloud of protons, about 1000 of them per cubic centimeter, traveling at 1000 kilometers per second. In an elastic collision with an atom, each such proton transfers an average of 1000 electron volts of kinetic energy, giving the bombarded particle a high enough velocity to escape from the moon.

The density of any lunar atmosphere would be reduced by a factor of $10^{11}$ for argon, $10^{4}$ for water vapor, $10^{15}$ for carbon dioxide, and $10^{22}$ for sulfur dioxide. The Washington, D.C., scientists note that their calculations are consistent with an estimate of $5 \times 10^{-13}$ atmosphere for the upper limit of gas density at the moon's surface, recently obtained from radio observations of an occultation of the Crab nebula.

*Well before the study of a "solar wind," it was recognized that the moon would lose most of the normal gases formed there. Heating by sunlight would cause molecules of all but the heavy gases to move so rapidly that they escaped from the moon's low gravitational attraction. Even though the* average *thermal motion of the molecules in a gas may be lower than the "velocity of escape," there will always be some fraction of the molecules in a gas moving much faster than the average, and the gas slowly "boils away."*

*Next, the surface features of the moon, and how they may have been formed, will be considered. First, and most striking in any view of the moon's surface, are the* craters, *ranging from very small size to hundreds of miles in diameter. Are the craters extinct volcanoes? or are they due to impacts (meteor splashes) or to the crystallization of molten rock? From some of the craters, straight white lines called* rays *seem to originate and run radially outward for many miles. Other straight markings appear to be walls or trenches and are called* rills. *The large dark areas that give the moon a "face" are called* maria *or* seas. *There are also many irregular mountains, and the much less obvious* domes, *or smooth hills.*

*Each of these lunar surface features is discussed below, sometimes from several points of view, and it will be apparent that there is some uncertainty in the explanations offered.*

TLP

## Lunar Crater Theories

J. FOSTER FOSTER

(*Sky and Telescope*, November 1943)

The rough and pitted character of lunar topography has long been a matter of common knowledge. Even the smallest optical instruments disclose on the moon's surface features without any exact parallel on the earth, and in the largest reflectors the face of the moon is seen to be almost covered with over 30,000 craterlike depressions. These markings range from craterlets just visible in the largest telescope to huge ring plains 150 miles in diameter. Some of the craters have central mountain peaks; others have great systems of bright rays radiating from them, stretching for hundreds of miles across craters and mountains without any apparent deviation. Even bigger than the largest craters are the maria, or "seas." Once it was thought that these were bodies of water, but the telescope reveals that they are the smooth parts of the moon, the parts which contain only a few craters. In addition to the craters and maria, there are mountains, cliffs, and huge cracks in the surface.

The origin of these markings has been a subject of controversy among astronomers, and various theories have been advanced in explanation of their source. There are a number of facts which must be explained satisfactorily, and of the theories presented only two, the volcanic and the meteoritic, seem to have explained these facts sufficiently well to be seriously considered.

The great size of some of the craters has been one of the chief stumbling blocks for the advocates of both theories. It is especially difficult to explain why volcanic craters should be so much larger on the moon than on the earth. But in the distant past, when the earth's crust was very thin, it may be that volcanoes were much larger. Such ancient volcanoes on the earth would have long since been erased by erosion and weathering. On the moon, where there is little or no such action, they would have been preserved to the present. On the other hand, a crater of the diameter of the largest of those seen on the moon could be caused by a meteor comparable in size to a small asteroid. Although the proportion of such large craters is too great when the size of present-day meteors is considered, it is quite possible that there were many more of these large meteors when the solar system was young.

The nearly circular shape of the craters has been advanced as a strong argument on the side of the supporters of the volcanic theory. They argued that the crater caused by meteoritic impact would be circular only if the fall were vertical and would be decidedly elliptical in the majority of cases. But this argument ignores one basic fact. The crater is not produced by the meteor gouging a hole in the surface of the moon; it is caused by the explosion resulting from the sudden transformation of the energy of the meteor into heat. And such an explosion will produce a crater which is very nearly circular unless the angle of fall is exceptionally low. Meteor Crater in Arizona is an example of a crater with a nearly circular rim produced by a meteor striking at an angle of about 45 degrees.

The lack of random distribution of the lunar craters is an argument frequently used in support of the volcanic theory. Meteoritic craters should be found at random, while volcanic craters should tend to follow lines of weakness in the crust of the moon. Again one fact has been overlooked. A close inspection of the maria [see Fig. 83] discloses traces of partially ruined craters on their surfaces or around their borders. This would seem to indicate that the maria were formed at a later date than were many of the craters and that the earlier craters in that area were destroyed. Then, however, distribution of the lunar craters is no longer significant; random distribution cannot be expected if craters over large areas have been destroyed.

The rays radiating from some of the lunar craters have never been adequately explained under any theory. Indeed, the various observers have not even agreed as to what they are. Some have thought that they are low mounds which were thrown out by the explosion which formed the crater from which they radiate. The velocity necessary to throw particles to the great distances observed has been calculated and found to exclude neither volcanic nor meteoritic origin. But the rays have never been observed to cast shadows, so perhaps they are not mounds at all. Other observers have come to the conclusion that the rays are cracks in the crust of the moon, but this does not seem likely, since they cross other lunar surface features, including mountains, without seeming to be even slightly deviated. Since the rays do cross these other features, the indication would seem to be that the craters from which they radiate are of comparatively recent formation. It has been shown that these ray craters have a random distribution, which suggests that they may be of meteoritic origin.

In many cases a central peak is to be found in a lunar crater, but in general there is no evidence of a crater at the top of the peak as would be expected if it were volcanic. However, it is quite possible that such a crater would be too small to be detected with existing telescopes. On the other hand, it is possible that these peaks could also be produced by the fall of meteors. Such peaks are sometimes found in the craters produced by bombs. Although none of the known meteor craters on the earth shows such central peaks, there is some indication that Meteor Crater originally possessed one which has since been obscured by erosion and deposition. . . .

Many people have tried in vain to find a newly formed lunar crater. But this lack of evidence of any new crater formation is also consistent with both the volcanic and the meteoritic theories. It is probable that volcanic activity, if it ever existed on the moon, would have ceased long ago; while if we assume the moon to be of the same age as the earth, calculation shows a meteor crater large enough to be seen from the earth would have been formed, on the average, once in 50,000 to 250,000 years. So it is not surprising that no new craters have been observed. . . .

## Laboratory Craters

S. I. GALE

(*Sky and Telescope*, May 1949)

In the course of laboratory investigation of a certain organic compound on November 16, 1948, we observed a solidification phenomenon which produced a pockmarked surface strikingly similar to that observed on the surface of the moon. Figure 81 shows a part of this sample, which is stable and has been preserved.

The phenomenon was produced by drying a small amount of this molten compound on a watch glass for three hours at 100° to 105° C. in an electrically heated oven. Then the sample was set in a desiccator where it cooled, for about one hour, down to room temperature without solidifying. Since this material has a normal solidification point of about 70° C., it is evident that extensive supercooling occurred. On removing the sample from the desiccator and setting it momentarily on a stone-table top, prior to weighing, rapid crystallization took place, forming within the space of a minute or so the peculiar surface appearance shown in the photograph.

The spectacular crystal growth, which was accompanied by sharp, crackling sounds, was so remarkable that the analyst, Miss S. Dolgin, called it to the attention of my colleague, F. Megson, and myself. Shortly afterward, while discussing this most remarkable laboratory phenomenon, we thought of the many features the sample and the lunar surface appear to have in common:

1. The craters are circular. 2. The rims are elevated slightly above the average plane. 3. The craters are surrounded by long and intimately associated radial lines. 4. There are central peaks in some craters and flat elevated plateaus in others. Each of the craters differs markedly in detail. 5. Their distribution is at random. Most of the craters are single but one pair was formed. 6. The ratio of diameter to depth, although not measured, appears to be roughly proportional to such ratios on the moon.

These miniature craters seem to have been formed by a chance com-

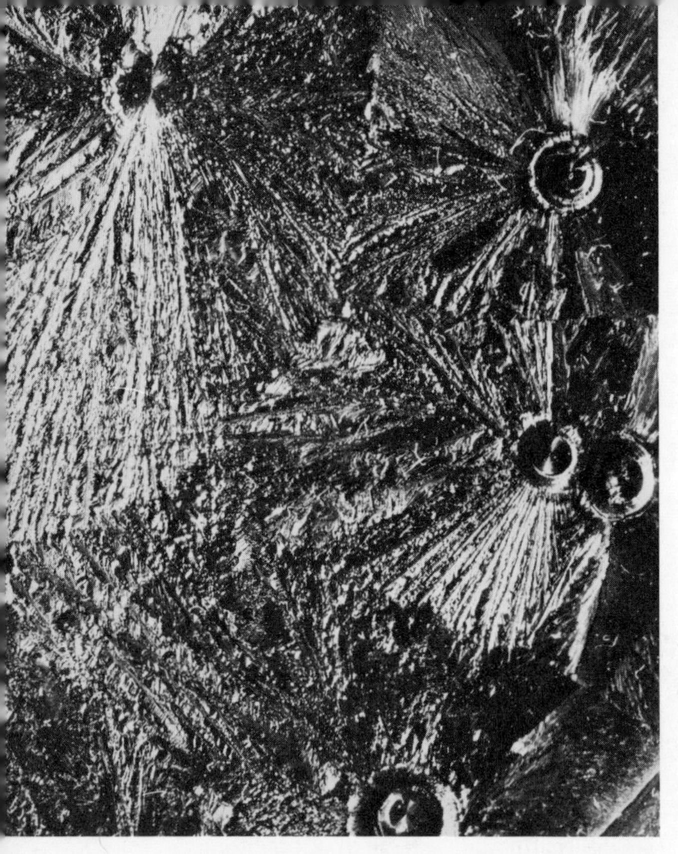

*Fig. 81.* Craters formed in the laboratory. (Courtesy S. I. Gale)

bination of crystallization and contraction effects as the result of extensive supercooling initiated quite possibly by minute dust particles. We have not before seen or heard of a similar phenomenon.

Perhaps some of the craters on the moon were formed by meteoritic impact on a critically supercooled surface. It is significant, we think, that in the laboratory minute dust particles could act to produce such enormous craters. It suggests that the impact of a rather small meteoritic particle might, in like manner, initiate the release of latent but powerful solidification forces on the moon and result in a crater the size of which would be out of proportion to that of the meteoritic particle or the force of its impact. Meteoritic impacts prior to this critical period would not have formed craters because they would be absorbed by the semiplastic mass of cooling rock; subsequent impacts would be quite ineffective on a solidified surface. . . .

## Lunar Craters in the Laboratory

**S. I. GALE AND F. H. MEGSON**

(*Sky and Telescope*, November 1949)

So much interest was aroused in the laboratory craters that we have been encouraged to investigate the oddity further. . . .

Attempts to reproduce the original phenomenon have been unsuccessful. Evidently the unusual formation of craters was the result of a fortuitous combination of conditions which was not reproduced in subsequent experiments. There is no doubt that the conditions necessary for the desired result could be reproduced, but to do so at will would require systematic investigation of all the factors involved, such as rate of cooling, degree of supercooling, quality, seeding, and so on.

Most conspicuous in the photograph are the coarse radial lines. These are sometimes much finer, giving a smooth surface corresponding in appearance to the lunar maria. The crater clusters are strikingly similar to those on the moon. Here can be seen a great variety of forms. Some have raised plateaus in their centers, others have tiny craters on their rims. These forms are so divergent that if they had not been observed in the process of formation, they would be believed to have been produced by a variety of causes; yet they appear here as manifestation of one agency, namely, solidification. This suggests that a wide variety of forms could also be possible on the moon. It does not exclude the probability that many lunar craters were formed by meteoric impact or by volcanic action. However, here are craters formed without violent meteoric impact.

This mechanism of crater formation on a sheet of material by surface and subsurface cooling is especially applicable to the moon if one assumes, as has been claimed, that large areas of lunar surfaces were once flooded by seas of molten lava which subsequently solidified by cooling from above and below. Contraction on cooling might be expected to produce cavities of some sort, also cracks in the material and cleavage at the interface just as it did in the laboratory. . . .

# The Origin of the Moon's Surface Features

HAROLD C. UREY

(*Sky and Telescope*, January and February 1956)

Since the publication of R. B. Baldwin's book, *The Face of the Moon*, in 1949,[1] there has been little reason to argue the old question of collisions versus plutonic (volcanic) action as the cause of the large craters. Most of the collision arguments were advanced by the American geologist G. K. Gilbert in 1893[2] and have been ignored or discarded for much too superficial reasons by subsequent students. The plutonic theory of crater origin was advanced before the modern scientific world knew that meteorites fell on the earth, and it has required nearly a century of discussion for astronomers substantially to agree that the moon's surface was fashioned mostly by collisions.

Gilbert showed that most lunar structures are not similar to terrestrial ones, that the pattern of overlap of the craters is that expected for chance collisions, and he discussed many other points. Baldwin marshaled the evidence most effectively and conclusively. We assume that most of the lunar features are due to collisions of objects with its surface, though some small formations were caused by volcanic processes, and explanations must be given for what appear to be lava flows. . . .

## The moon was accumulated at low temperatures

The moon's radius toward and away from our earth is greater than the radius along the poles, by about one kilometer; whereas the equilibrium value resulting from the forces acting on the moon should be only 60 meters. This irregular shape results in a difference of stresses at the moon's center of about 20 atmospheres, and this requires the

[1] *The Face of the Moon*, R. B. Baldwin, University of Chicago Press, 1949.

[2] "The Moon's Face," G. K. Gilbert, *Bulletin*, Philosophical Society of Washington, *12*, 241, 1893.

## MOUNTAINS AND VALLEYS

a. Alpine Valley
b. Alps Mts.
c. Altai Mts.
d. Apennine Mts.
e. Carpathian Mts.
f. Caucasus Mts.
g. D'Alembert Mts.
h. Doerfel Mts.
i. Haemus Mts.
j. Harbinger Mts.
k. Heraclides Prom.
l. Hyginus Cleft
m. Jura Mts.
n. Laplace Prom.
o. Leibnitz Mts.
p. Pico
q. Piton
r. Pyrenees Mts.
s. Rheita Valley
t. Riphaeus Mts.
u. Rook Mts.
v. Spitzbergen
w. Straight Range
x. Straight Wall
y. Taurus Mts.
z. Teneriffe Mts.

## LUNAR CRATERS

1. Abenezra
2. Abulfeda
3. Agatharchides
4. Agrippa
5. Albategnius
6. Alexander
7. Aliacensis
8. Almanon
9. Alpetragius
10. Alphonsus
11. Apianus
12. Apollonius
13. Arago
14. Archimedes
15. Archytas
16. Aristarchus
17. Aristillus
18. Aristoteles
19. Arzachel
20. Asclepi
21. Atlas
22. Autolycus
23. Azophi
24. Baco
25. Bailly
26. Barocius
27. Bayer
28. Beaumont
29. Bernouilli
30. Berzelius
31. Bessel
32. Bettinus
33. Bianchini
34. Biela
35. Billy
36. Birmingham
37. Birt
38. Blancanus
39. Blanchinus
40. Boguslawsky
41. Bohnenberger
42. Bond, W. C.
43. Bonpland
44. Borda
45. Boscovich
46. Bouguer
47. Boussingault
48. Bullialdus
49. Burckhardt
50. Bürg
51. Calippus
52. Campanus
53. Capella
54. Capuanus
55. Cardanus
56. Casatus
57. Cassini
58. Catharina
59. Cavalerius
60. Cavendish
61. Celsius
62. Cepheus
63. Chacornac
64. Cichus
65. Clairaut
66. Clausius
67. Clavius
68. Cleomedes
69. Colombo
70. Condamine
71. Condorcet
72. Conon
73. Cook
74. Copernicus
75. Crüger
76. Curtius
77. Cuvier
78. Cyrillus
79. Damoiseau
80. Daniell
81. Davy
82. Dawes
83. De Gasparis
84. Delambre
85. De la Rue
86. Delaunay
87. Delisle
88. Deluc
89. Descartes
90. Diophantus
91. Dollond
92. Doppelmayer
93. Eichstädt
94. Encke
95. Endymion
96. Epigenes
97. Eratosthenes
98. Euclides
99. Eudoxus
100. Euler
101. Fabricius
102. Faraday
103. Fermat
104. Fernelius
105. Firmicus
106. Flamsteed
107. Fontenelle
108. Fracastorius
109. Fra Mauro
110. Franklin
111. Furnerius
112. Gambart
113. Gassendi
114. Gauricus
115. Gauss
116. Gay-Lussac
117. Geber
118. Geminus
119. Gemma Frisius
120. Goclenius
121. Godin
122. Goodacre
123. Grimaldi
124. Gruithuisen
125. Guericke
126. Gutenberg
127. Hahn
128. Hainzel
129. Halley
130. Hansteen
131. Harpalus
132. Hase
133. Heinsius
134. Helicon
135. Hell
136. Heraclitus
137. Hercules
138. Herigonius
139. Herodotus
140. Herschel
141. Herschel, J.
142. Hesiodus
143. Hevelius
144. Hippalus
145. Hipparchus
146. Horrebow
147. Horrocks
148. Hortensius
149. Humboldt, W.
150. Hypatia
151. Isidorus
152. Jansen
153. Janssen
154. Julius Caesar
155. Kepler
156. Kies
157. Kirch
158. Klaproth
159. Klein
160. Krafft
161. Landsberg C
162. Lagrange
163. Lalande
164. Lambert
165. Landsberg
166. Langrenus
167. Lassell
168. Lee
169. Lehmann
170. Letronne
171. Leverrier
172. Lexell
173. Licetus
174. Lilius
175. Lindenau
176. Linné
177. Littrow
178. Lohrmann
179. Longomontanus
180. Lubiniezky
181. Maclear
182. Macrobius
183. Mädler
184. Magelhaens
185. Maginus
186. Mairan
187. Manilius
188. Manzinus
189. Maraldi
190. Marinus
191. Maskelyne
192. Maupertuis
193. Maurolycus
194. Mayer, Tobias
195. Menelaus
196. Mercator
197. Mersenius
198. Messala
199. Messier
200. Metius
201. Meton
202. Milichius
203. Miller
204. Monge
205. Moretus
206. Mösting
207. Mutus
208. Nasireddin
209. Neander
210. Nearchus
211. Nicolai
212. Oken
213. Orontius
214. Palisa
215. Pallas
216. Parrot
217. Parry
218. Peirce
219. Petavius
220. Philolaus
221. Phocylides
222. Piazzi
223. Picard
224. Piccolomini
225. Pickering, W. H.
226. Pictet
227. Pitatus
228. Pitiscus
229. Plana
230. Plato
231. Playfair
232. Plinius
233. Pontanus
234. Pontécoulant
235. Posidonius
236. Prinz
237. Proclus
238. Protagoras
239. Ptolemaeus
240. Purbach
241. Pythagoras
242. Pytheas
243. Rabbi Levi
244. Ramsden
245. Regiomontanus
246. Reichenbach
247. Reiner
248. Reinhold
249. Repsold
250. Rhaeticus
251. Rheita
252. Riccioli
253. Römer
254. Ross
255. Rothmann
256. Sacrobosco
257. Santbech
258. Sasserides
259. Saussure
260. Scheiner
261. Schickard
262. Schiller
263. Schröter
264. Seleucus
265. Sharp
266. Simpelius
267. Snellius
268. Sosigenes
269. Stadius
270. Stevinus
271. Stöfler
272. Strabo
273. Struve
274. Struve, Otto
275. Tacitus
276. Taruntius
277. Theaetetus
278. Thebit
279. Theophilus
280. Timaeus
281. Timocharis
282. Torricelli
283. Triesnecker
284. Tycho
285. Ukert
286. Vendelinus
287. Vieta
288. Vitello
289. Vitruvius
290. Vlacq
291. Walter
292. Weiss
293. Werner
294. Wilhelm I
295. Wilkins
296. Wurzelbauer
297. Zach
298. Zagut
299. Zuchius
300. Zupus

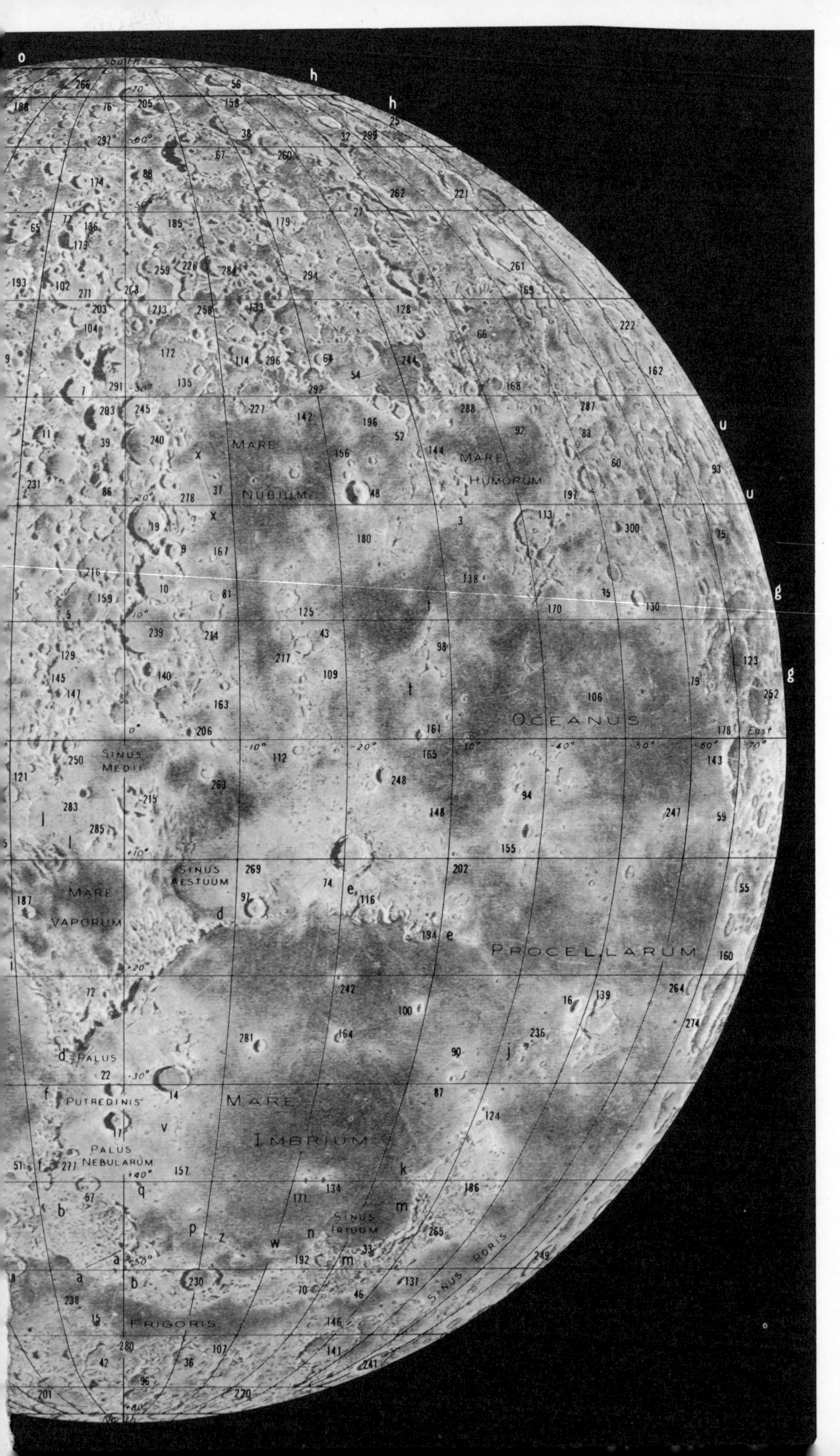

South
o
h
h
70°
60°
50°
30°
20°
10°
0°
-10°
-20°
-30°
-40°
-50°
-60°
-70°
East
40°
North
MARE NUBIUM
MARE HUMORUM
OCEANUS PROCELLARUM
SINUS MEDII
SINUS AESTUUM
MARE VAPORUM
PALUS PUTREDINIS
PALUS NEBULARUM
MARE IMBRIUM
SINUS IRIDUM
SINUS RORIS
FRIGORIS
266 56 188 76 205 158 25 38 32 299 297 67 260 88 174 262 221 27 77 65 136 185 179 173 261 259 226 284 294 169 193 102 271 268 213 258 133 128 203 222 104 66 9 172 114 296 64 244 162 54 7 291 135 292 168 283 245 227 142 288 287 11 196 52 92 83 39 240 x 156 144 60 93 u 231 86 37 278 48 197 u x 19 9 167 3 113 300 75 180 216 138 g 10 81 35 159 125 170 130 5 43 239 214 98 129 217 123 g 145 109 140 79 252 147 t 106 163 206 161 178 250 112 165 143 121 263 248 215 94 283 247 59 148 285 155 269 202 187 74 e 116 55 97 d 194 e 160 72 242 264 16 139 100 274 281 164 236 d 22 90 j f 14 87 124 v 17 51 f 277 157 k q 134 186 67 171 m b p z n 265 w 33 a 192 m 249 a b 230 137 70 46 238 15 146 280 141 107 42 36 241 96 201 220

# ‿unar Map

ig. 82. Lunar Map. This
ap of the moon is based on
e original drawing by Karel
ndel. A grid of selenogra-
ic coordinates has been su-
erimposed. The listing of
ountains, valleys and lunar
aters, as well as the posi-
ons of the numbered craters
the nearest 10 degrees of
ngitude are given in the
cating table on the reverse
de of the map.

Vanderers in the Sky
he Motions of Planets and
pace Probes
olume 1, *Sky and Telescope*
ibrary of Astronomy

## LUNAR MAP LOCATING TABLE

For each crater in the alphabetical list that accompanies the lunar map are given here the selenographic longitude and latitude, respectively, of the co-ordinate grid intersection that is nearest to the crater. This permits quick location of features that are known by name only.

| No. | Long. | Lat. | No. | Long. | Lat. | No. | Long. | Lat. | No. | Long. | Lat. |
|---|---|---|---|---|---|---|---|---|---|---|---|
| 1 | +10 | −20 | 76 | 0 | −70 | 151 | +30 | −10 | 226 | −10 | −40 |
| 2 | +10 | −10 | 77 | +10 | −50 | 152 | +30 | +10 | 227 | −10 | −30 |
| 3 | −30 | −20 | 78 | +30 | −10 | 153 | +40 | −40 | 228 | +30 | −50 |
| 4 | +10 | 0 | 79 | −60 | 0 | 154 | +10 | +10 | 229 | +30 | +40 |
| 5 | 0 | −10 | 80 | +30 | +30 | 155 | −40 | +10 | 230 | −10 | +50 |
| 6 | +10 | +40 | 81 | −10 | −10 | 156 | −20 | −30 | 231 | +10 | −20 |
| 7 | 0 | −30 | 82 | +30 | +20 | 157 | −10 | +40 | 232 | +20 | +20 |
| 8 | +20 | −20 | 83 | −50 | −30 | 158 | −30 | −70 | 233 | +10 | −30 |
| 9 | 0 | −20 | 84 | +20 | 0 | 159 | 0 | −10 | 234 | +70 | −60 |
| 10 | 0 | −10 | 85 | +50 | +60 | 160 | −70 | +20 | 235 | +30 | +30 |
| 11 | +10 | −30 | 86 | 0 | −20 | 161 | −30 | 0 | 236 | −50 | +30 |
| 12 | +60 | 0 | 87 | −30 | +30 | 162 | −70 | −30 | 237 | +50 | +20 |
| 13 | +20 | +10 | 88 | 0 | −50 | 163 | −10 | 0 | 238 | +10 | +50 |
| 14 | 0 | +30 | 89 | +20 | −10 | 164 | −20 | +30 | 239 | 0 | −10 |
| 15 | 0 | +60 | 90 | −30 | +30 | 165 | −30 | 0 | 240 | 0 | −30 |
| 16 | −50 | +20 | 91 | +10 | −10 | 166 | +60 | −10 | 241 | −60 | +60 |
| 17 | 0 | +30 | 92 | −40 | −30 | 167 | −10 | −20 | 242 | −20 | +20 |
| 18 | +20 | +50 | 93 | −70 | −20 | 168 | −40 | −30 | 243 | +20 | −30 |
| 19 | 0 | −20 | 94 | −40 | 0 | 169 | −60 | −40 | 244 | −30 | −30 |
| 20 | +20 | −50 | 95 | +60 | +50 | 170 | −40 | −10 | 245 | 0 | −30 |
| 21 | +50 | +50 | 96 | 0 | +70 | 171 | −20 | +40 | 246 | +50 | −30 |
| 22 | 0 | +30 | 97 | −10 | +10 | 172 | 0 | −40 | 247 | −60 | +10 |
| 23 | +10 | −20 | 98 | −30 | −10 | 173 | +10 | −50 | 248 | −20 | 0 |
| 24 | +20 | −50 | 99 | +20 | +40 | 174 | +10 | −50 | 249 | −70 | +50 |
| 25 | −70 | −70 | 100 | −30 | +20 | 175 | +30 | −30 | 250 | 0 | 0 |
| 26 | +20 | −40 | 101 | +40 | −40 | 176 | +10 | +30 | 251 | +50 | −40 |
| 27 | −30 | −50 | 102 | +10 | −40 | 177 | +30 | +20 | 252 | −70 | 0 |
| 28 | +30 | −20 | 103 | +20 | −20 | 178 | −70 | 0 | 253 | +40 | +30 |
| 29 | +60 | +30 | 104 | 0 | −40 | 179 | −20 | −50 | 254 | +20 | +10 |
| 30 | +50 | +40 | 105 | +60 | +10 | 180 | −20 | −20 | 255 | +30 | −30 |
| 31 | +20 | +20 | 106 | −40 | 0 | 181 | +20 | +10 | 256 | +20 | −20 |
| 32 | −40 | −60 | 107 | −20 | +60 | 182 | +50 | +20 | 257 | +50 | −20 |
| 33 | −30 | +50 | 108 | +30 | −20 | 183 | +30 | −10 | 258 | −10 | −40 |
| 34 | +50 | −50 | 109 | −20 | −10 | 184 | +40 | −10 | 259 | 0 | −40 |
| 35 | −50 | −10 | 110 | +50 | +40 | 185 | −10 | −50 | 260 | −30 | −60 |
| 36 | −10 | +60 | 111 | +60 | −40 | 186 | −40 | +40 | 261 | −50 | −40 |
| 37 | −10 | −20 | 112 | −10 | 0 | 187 | +10 | +10 | 262 | −40 | −50 |
| 38 | −20 | −60 | 113 | −40 | −20 | 188 | +30 | −70 | 263 | −10 | 0 |
| 39 | 0 | −30 | 114 | −10 | −30 | 189 | +30 | +20 | 264 | −70 | +20 |
| 40 | +50 | −70 | 115 | +70 | +40 | 190 | +70 | −40 | 265 | −40 | +50 |
| 41 | +40 | −20 | 116 | −20 | +10 | 191 | +30 | 0 | 266 | +20 | −70 |
| 42 | 0 | +60 | 117 | +10 | −20 | 192 | −30 | +50 | 267 | +60 | −30 |
| 43 | −20 | −10 | 118 | +60 | +30 | 193 | +10 | −40 | 268 | +20 | +10 |
| 44 | +50 | −20 | 119 | +10 | −30 | 194 | −30 | +20 | 269 | −10 | +10 |
| 45 | +10 | +10 | 120 | +50 | −10 | 195 | +20 | +20 | 270 | +60 | −30 |
| 46 | −40 | +50 | 121 | +10 | 0 | 196 | −30 | −30 | 271 | +10 | −40 |
| 47 | +70 | −70 | 122 | +10 | −30 | 197 | −50 | −20 | 272 | +50 | +60 |
| 48 | −20 | −20 | 123 | −70 | −10 | 198 | +60 | +40 | 273 | +60 | +40 |
| 49 | +60 | +30 | 124 | −40 | +30 | 199 | +50 | 0 | 274 | −70 | +20 |
| 50 | +30 | +40 | 125 | −10 | −10 | 200 | +40 | −40 | 275 | +20 | −20 |
| 51 | +10 | +40 | 126 | +40 | −10 | 201 | +20 | +70 | 276 | +50 | +10 |
| 52 | −30 | −30 | 127 | +70 | +30 | 202 | −30 | +10 | 277 | +10 | +40 |
| 53 | +30 | −10 | 128 | −30 | −40 | 203 | 0 | −40 | 278 | 0 | −20 |
| 54 | −30 | −30 | 129 | +10 | −10 | 204 | +50 | −20 | 279 | +30 | −10 |
| 55 | −70 | +10 | 130 | −50 | −10 | 205 | 0 | −70 | 280 | 0 | +60 |
| 56 | −30 | −70 | 131 | −40 | +50 | 206 | −10 | 0 | 281 | −10 | +30 |
| 57 | 0 | +40 | 132 | +60 | −30 | 207 | +30 | −60 | 282 | +30 | 0 |
| 58 | +20 | −20 | 133 | −20 | −40 | 208 | 0 | −40 | 283 | 0 | 0 |
| 59 | −70 | +10 | 134 | −20 | +40 | 209 | +40 | −30 | 284 | −10 | −40 |
| 60 | −50 | −20 | 135 | −10 | −30 | 210 | +40 | −60 | 285 | 0 | +10 |
| 61 | +20 | −30 | 136 | +10 | −50 | 211 | +30 | −40 | 286 | +60 | −20 |
| 62 | +50 | +40 | 137 | +40 | +50 | 212 | +70 | −50 | 287 | −60 | −30 |
| 63 | +30 | +30 | 138 | −30 | −10 | 213 | 0 | −40 | 288 | −40 | −30 |
| 64 | −20 | −30 | 139 | −50 | +20 | 214 | −10 | −10 | 289 | +30 | +20 |
| 65 | +10 | −50 | 140 | 0 | −10 | 215 | 0 | 0 | 290 | +40 | −50 |
| 66 | −40 | −40 | 141 | −40 | +60 | 216 | 0 | −10 | 291 | 0 | −30 |
| 67 | −10 | −60 | 142 | −20 | −30 | 217 | −20 | −10 | 292 | −20 | −30 |
| 68 | +60 | +30 | 143 | −70 | 0 | 218 | +50 | +20 | 293 | 0 | −30 |
| 69 | +50 | −10 | 144 | −30 | −20 | 219 | +60 | −20 | 294 | −20 | −40 |
| 70 | −30 | +50 | 145 | 0 | 0 | 220 | −30 | +70 | 295 | +20 | −30 |
| 71 | +70 | +10 | 146 | −40 | +60 | 221 | −60 | −50 | 296 | −20 | −30 |
| 72 | 0 | +20 | 147 | 0 | 0 | 222 | −70 | −40 | 297 | 0 | −60 |
| 73 | +50 | −20 | 148 | −30 | +10 | 223 | +60 | +10 | 298 | +20 | −30 |
| 74 | −20 | +10 | 149 | +70 | −30 | 224 | +30 | −30 | 299 | −50 | −60 |
| 75 | −70 | −20 | 150 | +20 | 0 | 225 | +50 | 0 | 300 | −50 | −20 |

strength of the moon's substance at its center to be about that of brick. Therefore, the center of the moon cannot be a liquid at the present time.

The next important point is that an object as large as the moon can cool only very slowly, even in a time as long as the moon has existed, which we believe to be 4½ billion years. This now seems a well-established age of meteorites, from three methods of dating by radioactive elements. The cooling of a sphere is a readily solved problem in terms of its thermal conductivity, which is also a known quantity for igneous rocks. Such a calculation shows that the center of the moon will lose very little of its heat in $4.5 \times 10^9$ years. If the moon were ever molten, then the center must be close to the melting point now, and hence it would not have the required strength to support the irregular shape.

The presence of the radioactive elements, potassium, uranium, and thorium, would increase the temperatures throughout the moon. The extent to which the temperatures are raised by this source of heat depends upon the amounts and distribution of these elements in the moon. We have no direct evidence in regard to these data for the moon and, in fact, have great difficulty in estimating them for the earth. However, if the rate of heat loss from the interior of the earth is now entirely due to heat generated from radioactive substances, we can estimate the amounts of these elements in the earth as a whole. Then, from analytical data on the rocks and our knowledge of the thickness of the crust from seismic data, we can conclude that perhaps one third to one half of this radioactive material is now in the earth's crust and the remainder is probably distributed throughout the earth's mantle. Similar amounts of radioactivity, distributed in the same way, would require the interior of the moon to be melted or near its melting point out to about 0.8 of its radius, if its initial temperature were at the melting point.

Such a conclusion is inconsistent with our satellite's irregular shape. Hence, the moon must have been formed at low temperatures and never heated by radioactive sources to its melting point.

**The Imbrian collision**

The great collision in Mare Imbrium was discovered by Gilbert in 1893. In the composite picture (Fig. 84), the region of this collision is shown. It is not possible to see much detail in a picture of the full

*Fig.* 83. A composite picture of the moon made by matching photographs taken at first and last quarter. (Lick Observatory, Courtesy H. C. Urey)

moon, yet unless both halves of the moon are shown, the relationships between the two are not observed. Figure 84 exhibits the Imbrian region as it would appear to an observer above Mare Imbrium looking toward Sinus Iridum. This picture was obtained by projecting photographs of the moon upon a sphere, and then photographing the sphere from the proper angle. We see that, with foreshortening thus eliminated, the crater Plato is circular in outline in this picture and not elliptical as ordinarily observed. Superimposed on Figure 84 is a drawing outlining the relative positions of Sinus Iridum, a circular area before it, and the entire Mare Imbrium. Radiating from the circular area are many grooves and ridges, particularly near the center of the moon's disk. Gilbert noted all these features, except that this pattern originated in one event, and that this event was the collision of a large object with the moon. The pattern of ridges and grooves and of the deep area before Sinus Iridum is unsymmetrical. Hence, this object arrived from the northeast at a substantial angle from the vertical, bored out a deep hole in the moon, and spread some of its substance and some of the moon's substance in a wide pattern for great distances over the moon's surface. . . .

The velocity of an object in a surface-grazing orbit about the moon is 1.7 kilometers per second, and since these objects fell some 1000 or

*Fig. 84.* Composite of three photographs of the moon projected on a sphere (with south at the top), showing the structures produced by the proposed Imbrian collision. Mare Imbrium, outlined by solid line, is seen as if the viewer were directly above it. Copernicus is the large bright crater south of Mare Imbrium; Sinus Iridum is the semicircular bay on the lower right, within the solid curve; left of it is the great dark-colored ring plain, Plato. No large craters or mountains lie inside the dashed circle that marks the collision area. Arrows indicate mountains just outside this circle; three of the arrows point to ones not seen in this picture, but detectable on good originals. (Courtesy H. C. Urey)

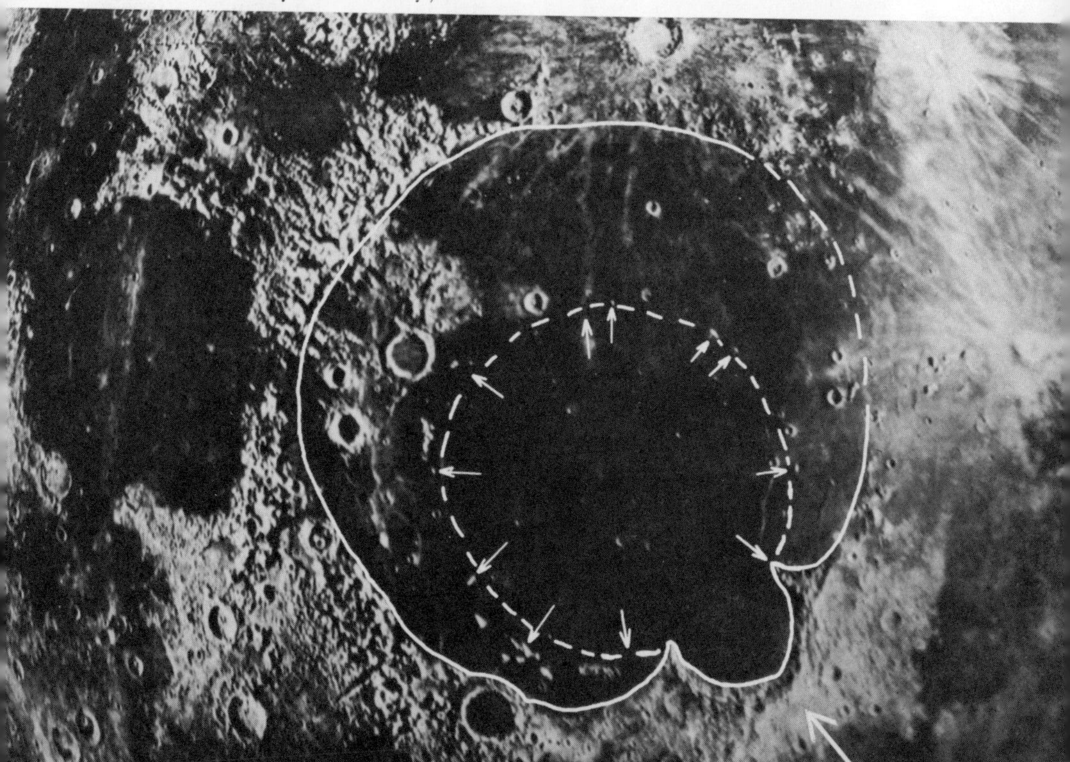

1500 kilometers from the point of the collision, they must have been moving with about this speed. I can find no evidence for objects with much higher velocities. The distribution of these grooves and ridges indicates that the colliding body or planetesimal arrived with moderate speed. If the velocity had been 30 kilometers per second, for example, the object would have behaved like an explosive, making a symmetrical crater. But with a low arrival speed, say 2.4 kilometers per second, the escape velocity of the moon, the pattern can be understood.

How large was the object? This planetesimal either produced Sinus Iridum as it plowed into the moon, or fell on a previous walled plain in exactly this location, destroying one half of the structure cleanly and exactly, so that the remnant faces precisely the circular area in Mare Imbrium. I think it is most probable that it produced Sinus Iridum and that the distance of 230 kilometers between the two promontories of Laplace and Heraclides is approximately, but somewhat greater than, the diameter of the planetesimal.

We take a diameter of 200 kilometers as most likely. With a density of 3.5, the mass of the body would have been $1.47 \times 10^{22}$ grams. Using 2.38 kilometers per second as its velocity, the kinetic energy at collision was $4.15 \times 10^{32}$ ergs. This is equivalent to $4.6 \times 10^{11}$ atomic bombs.

Evidently the object plowed into the solid surface, flattened out in the collision area, produced an elevated bulge in the moon's surface all around this area but more in the direction toward which the object moved, namely toward the center of the moon's apparent disk. This bulged area was badly broken up, perhaps even to fine sand, and after the collision, part of the loose material subsided again, producing the shelf area between the inner and outer rings of Figure 84.

Part of the surface of the moon was lifted and dropped as big chunks, forming the Straight Range, Piton, Pico, Spitzbergen, and so on, within Mare Imbrium; and the Alps, Apennines, Caucasus, and Carpathian mountains. The Alps and Caucasus look particularly like this sort of material. On the other hand, the Carpathians and the Apennines may consist of part of the planetesimal. Great masses of the planetesimal formed the Haemus Mountains and produced the grooves. But it requires high-density material to cut these long grooves and this material must be nickel-iron alloy; it is most probable that it was part of the planetesimal because of the great distance of the grooves from the point of origin. Such nickel-iron objects remind us of iron meteorites. Presumably, this planetesimal was made by the same processes as those which produced the parent of the meteorites. . . .

**When did these collisions occur?**

Some of the ordinary large craters, which we are assuming were formed by collisions, antedate the Imbrian collision and others post-date this event. Thus Ptolemaeus has walls which are scarred by the missiles from the Imbrian collision. Over one side of its crater, Julius Caesar has a mountainous mass which is part of the debris.

If the moon had been near the earth while this happened, the earth would have been bombarded more intensely than the moon because of the greater energy of the objects arriving at the earth. Furthermore, the earth with its greater gravitational field would have a larger effective collision radius than the moon and hence more objects would fall per unit time. Such a bombardment would have destroyed all the geological record in sediments that later formed rocks on earth. The oldest sedimentary rocks which have been reliably dated are about three billion years old. Perhaps this bombardment occurred between 4½ and three billion years ago. This is long enough in the past so that one wonders whether what we see on the moon is not a record of the last phases of the formation of the earth and moon.

**Of what are the maria composed?**

It is a common assumption that the maria consist of solidified lava. We have previously concluded that the moon was formed at a low temperature. Also, the high mountain ranges would sink into the moon if it were now or ever had been as plastic as the earth. There is no evidence that this occurred. The conclusion is that the lavas did not come from the moon's interior.

It is proposed that the melting was caused by the collision energy of the objects falling on the moon. The energy of collision of objects with a 2.4-kilometer velocity arounts to 2800 joules per gram, and about 2000 joules of heat energy are required to heat silicates to their melting points and melt them. Of course, the energy of collision would be expended in sound waves also, but it does seem possible that some melting would occur.

T. Gold [now at Cornell University] has suggested that the maria consist of deep layers of dust which have moved over the surface of the moon in various ways, even from the great land areas to the maria. He believes that heating and cooling of the surface and the effects of ultraviolet light from the sun are producing such dust, and that it is moving over the surface now. He points out that many small lunar craters and the hollows between ridges are filled with this gray material, also that neither lava from the interior nor from collisions seems to be a reasonable explanation for these grayish markings. I propose for the dust a somewhat modified origin.

The Imbrian planetesimal, if spread uniformly over the moon's surface, would make a layer 110 meters deep and, if it contained 1 per cent of water by weight, would hold sufficient water to cover the moon to a depth of 3.9 meters. The other large planetesimals could have supplied similar amounts of material. Moreover, with reasonable amounts of volatiles, they would explode if they fell with as little as the escape velocity of the moon. Here is a plausible mechanism for the distribution of dust over the moon's surface. After each large planetesimal collision, perhaps a great cloud of dust and water vapor rose above the moon. The dust settled out and the water fell as rain, washed the dust off the mountain peaks into the low places, and sank into the dust and crevices, hydrating the silicates and disappearing.

What evidence can we find to decide such a question as lava flow versus the fall of dust? Lava is a dense, heavy liquid and should push over crater walls in its path and distort the shapes of buried craters. I can find no evidence for this in Oceanus Procellarum and Mare Nubium. The nearly buried crater near Flamsteed is circular in outline, after foreshortening is allowed for. I see no indication of distortion of other craters in this region. But lava must flow downhill, while dust can fall anywhere from an atmosphere. . . .

Perhaps both lava and dust were produced by the collision energy, sometimes one and sometimes the other. Let us try a specific course of events. A large planetesimal fell nearly from the vertical in Mare Serenitatis. It contained little volatile matter and its material was not distributed widely over the moon. It melted and a black lava flowed over the adjoining region of Mare Tranquillitatis. Then the Imbrian planetesimal fell with an appreciable content of volatiles. Dust was spread far over the moon. The hot lava of Mare Tranquillitatis supplied water and hydrogen sulfide which blackened the surface.

**Duration of the bombardment**

One of the most remarkable features of the moon is the absence of large post-mare craters in the collision maria. (In the case of Mare Imbrium this statement applies only to the collision area within the smaller dashed circle of Fig. 84.) Near Mare Nectaris we find Theophilus and Piccolomini, which certainly are post-Mare Nectaris, and others also seem to be the same. These circular collision maria must have been fluid, that is, either dust or liquid, at the time this bombardment stopped. A similar argument applies to the absence of mountainous masses in Mare Serenitatis. If it were formed after Mare Imbrium, the immense collision left remarkably intact the radiating structures of the Imbrian collision in the Haemus Mountains and in the region between the two maria. For this reason, I believe that Mare Serenitatis antedates Mare Imbrium. But then the absence of mountainous masses on Mare Serenitatis similar to the Haemus Mountains means that it was fluid at the time of the Imbrian collision. Liquid would solidify in a short time, say a hundred thousand years or less.

These arguments lead to the conclusion that the surface of the moon was formed remarkably quickly for the most part. The ray craters and many small craters may be the result of the fall of meteorites over geologic time, but the maria and most of the craters were formed probably within a million years or less. Two explanations occur to me. Either the bombardment was due to a flock of objects passing through the solar system and out again, or this bombardment was part of the terminal stage of the formation of the earth and moon. I subscribe to the latter view. . . .

Only minor modifications, due to the fall of high-velocity meteorites and the expulsion of some gases from the interior, have changed its surface since.

This requires an explanation of the sudden termination of the bombardment. If the objects falling on the moon were satellites of the earth-moon system and they were gathered by the earth in a short time, or if only a few of them had orbits extending into the region of the moon's orbit, then a bombardment of the moon for a short interval could be understood. It is difficult to explain this sudden termination of the bombardment if the objects moved in orbits around the sun. This argument agrees with the previous assumption that the objects arrived with about the escape velocity of the moon, 2.4 kilometers per second.

### Some other features of the moon's surface

The big valleys have not been considered in this article. The Rheita and Borda valleys are hundreds of kilometers long and the Alpine Valley extends nearly as far. I have subscribed to the view that these were caused by high-velocity nickel-iron objects originating within the planetesimals that formed the collision maria. Others, G. P. Kuiper most recently, believe they are cracks caused by the great collisions. Perhaps this is the correct explanation. They are remarkably straight if they are cracks, and the Rheita Valley has a sharp and prominent bend in it which is difficult to explain if it is due to a missile. But regardless of which explanation is correct, the over all story of the moon's surface is not changed in an important way. (The writer does not subscribe to Kuiper's completely molten moon theory.)

One could continue to discuss the moon's surface in much detail. It is a fascinating object. It would be wonderful to see the other hemisphere and to have a few samples of lunar surface material.

## Dust on the Moon

(*Sky and Telescope*, March 1957)

The lunar maria are probably low-lying regions covered with dust slowly being eroded from the moon's highlands, according to Thomas Gold, Royal Greenwich Observatory in England. While the proposal of erosion on the moon is not novel, many new ideas are developed by him on the physical processes involved.

If the maria are dust plains, it is no longer necessary to suppose that there have been lava flows on the moon. No large-scale melting of our satellite during its history need then be postulated, and the moon may have been a relatively cold body throughout its evolution. . . .

Observational evidence for lunar erosion is afforded by overlapping craters, the one with an unbroken rim presumably being the younger. According to Professor Gold, its rim is sharper and less weathered than the walls of the older crater. In the absence of an appreciable atmosphere on the moon, the weathering would be due mainly to meteoritic bombardment over long periods. This would produce dust, which would be augmented by the destruction of surface crystalline material by the sun's ultraviolet light and X rays. Micrometeorites would also add to the dust accumulation.

Several physical processes should enable the dust from the lunar highlands to flow slowly over the moon's surface and to accumulate in low areas. Among these agencies are agitation by micrometeorite impacts, effects of electric charge, evaporation, and recondensation. The darker color of the maria may be produced by chemical action or X rays; recently eroded parts of the crater wall and mountainous regions would show the light shade of the moon's underlying material.

## Texture of the Moon's Surface

(*Sky and Telescope*, July 1958)

A conference on lunar problems was part of the astronautics symposium held in April [1958] at Boulder, Colorado, under U.S. Air Force auspices. At this conference F. L. Whipple discussed the question of roughness of the lunar surface.

The Smithsonian astonomer first summarized the strong evidence that the moon's surface is largely covered by a very thin layer of dust or fine-grained porous material. The fact that the edge of the lunar disk appears practically as bright as its center shows that the surface must be highly irregular on a microscopic scale. Furthermore, measurements of lunar radiation at centimeter wavelengths indicate a very thin covering layer of material, perhaps a millimeter thick, that is an excellent insulator of heat.

The moon's surface is also irregular on a scale of a few meters, as shown by radar-echo studies made in Australia and England. However, it is much smoother over somewhat shorter distances, for with 10-centimeter radar our satellite gives a nearly specular reflection—practically all the echo comes from the central portion of the hemisphere that faces us.

Dr. Whipple proposed that the surface layer may not be loose dust, as T. Gold has suggested (p. 262), but that the particles are weakly cemented together. Unprotected by any appreciable atmosphere, the moon is continually bombarded by small, high-velocity meteoritic and atomic particles. Thus the dust grains are subjected to a sputtering process, analogous to the action in a high-vacuum aluminizing tank where evaporation takes place from a hot filament. The chemically mixed spray may produce a coating on the grains that acts as a weak cement. Because of this, Dr. Whipple believes, a low-density semiporous matrix will be formed, fragile compared to normal sedimentary rocks on earth, but strong compared to a layer of dust alone.

Except in the vicinity of craters (including some too small to be observed directly), the lunar surface may therefore be comparatively smooth, although microscopically rough. This is not discordant with the rugged appearance of the moon viewed telescopically, which results mainly from very much larger irregularities having low surface inclinations.

## Lunar Domes

**PATRICK MOORE**

(*Sky and Telescope*, December 1958)

Because the surface of the moon is virtually changeless, and because it has been studied by many in great detail, there is a widespread but incorrect impression that its various features are already known with complete accuracy. It is true that there are many large-scale maps and excellent photographs, but there is always something new to discover, and every now and then attention is drawn to some overlooked kind of formation.

The dark radial bands inside certain craters are a good example of this. Up to a decade ago, only a few cases were known, the most prominent being the system inside Aristarchus. Then a few papers on the subject appeared, and new radial band systems were soon being reported in great numbers. Of course, they had been there all the time, but nobody had looked closely for them.

Much the same thing happened in the case of summit craterlets. In 1949, R. B. Baldwin listed only twelve of these in his book, *The Face of the Moon*. This led me to search especially for them, and with a telescope of fair size I rapidly found another twenty or thirty.

The lunar domes provide another excellent instance. Basically, a dome is a low, gentle swelling of the moon's surface. Older works say little about them, but in 1932 the veteran British observer, Robert Barker, drew general attention to one example. The object seen by Barker with his 12½-inch reflector lay inside the crater Darwin.

The Darwin dome is quite unlike a normal mountain. Its slopes are gentle, and there is no well-defined crest. Even a 3-inch refractor will show it clearly under suitable conditions.

Although a fine specimen, the Darwin dome was not unique; smaller domes were already known near the crater Arago and inside Capuanus, for example. Still it was generally thought that domes were rarities, until after 1945. Then many other domes were described, largely through the skillful work of S. R. B. Cooke.

In the last few years, P. J. Cattermole and I have been searching systematically for domes, both visually and photographically, in order to compile a complete catalogue.

The first two parts of this catalogue, containing forty-five domes, have already been published in the *Journal* of the International Lunar Society. Although it will take years to complete the project, some tentative conclusions are possible.

First, the domes are unexpectedly common. As a rough estimate, at least 200 may be within the range of my 12½-inch reflector. Some visual work in 1953, 1954, and 1956 with the 33-inch Meudon refractor indicates that larger aperture increases this number considerably.

Second, the distribution of domes is decidedly not random. The fact that they are more easily detected on the smooth maria than on the rougher continents may make the distribution charts incomplete. However, certain limited areas are crowded with these formations, such as the Arago region, the Prinz area in the Harbinger Mountains, and parts of Oceanus Procellarum. Inside the crater Capuanus, on the border of Palus Epidemiarum, there are eight domes visible in my telescope. On the other hand, wide areas of the moon seem completely devoid of them.

There is some evidence that domes, like the large walled formations, tend to occur in well-defined belts, one of which stretches from southern Mare Nubium across Oceanus Procellarum toward Sinus Roris. Also, domes seem to be numerous in areas where clefts are common, though there are exceptions to this general rule. These distribution relationships may have important bearing on the problem of the origin of the domes.

A fundamental question is whether or not domes are features of

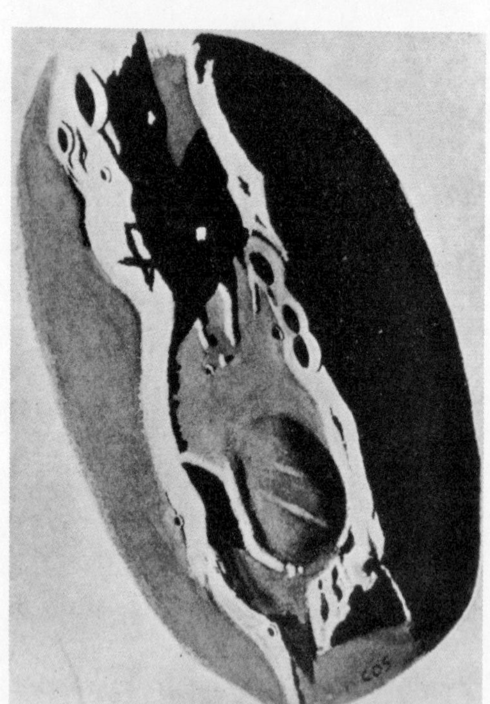


*Fig.* 85. A drawing of the lunar crater Darwin, showing the characteristic appearance of a lunar dome. About 25 miles in diameter, the Darwin dome is a low swelling traversed by two clefts. (From *Memoirs* of the British Astronomical Association)

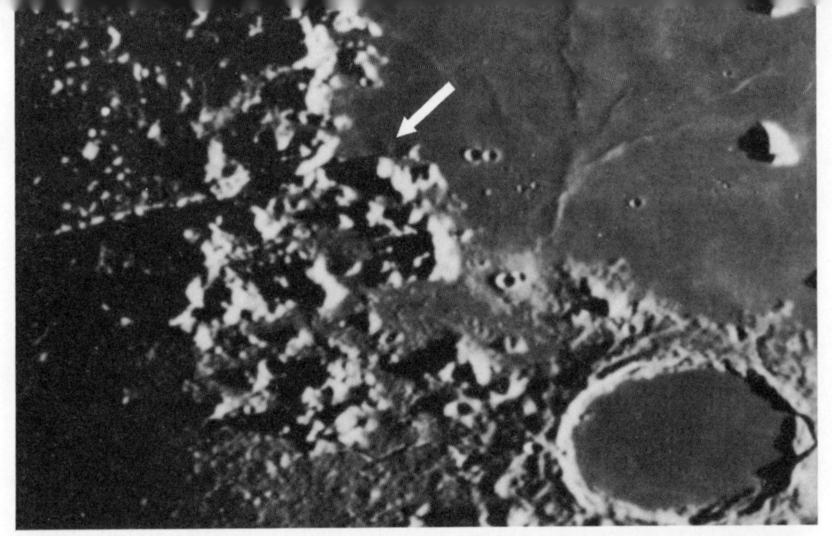

*Fig. 86.* A small but distinct lunar dome (one inch from the top of the photograph and 2⅛ inches from its left margin), situated where the great Alpine Valley opens into Mare Imbrium. Plato is the large, walled plain at the lower right. (Photograph from the Mt. Wilson and Palomar Observatories)

entirely different type from rounded hills. Unfortunately, exact measurements of their slope angles are very difficult, and the available data are inconclusive. My own studies have led me to believe that there is a real difference between a dome and an ordinary hill. On the other hand, some craters like Alpetragius, Capella, and Römer have large, rounded central summits which might well be called domes if they lay in open regions. These central elevations usually have summit craterlets, always either in the middle or, as in the case of Alpetragius, two of them symmetrically placed. Many domes have similar summit pits, equally symmetrical; better telescopes show more cases. In my opinion, summit pits are the rule rather than the exception.

Dr. Cooke has noted that the domes are invisible when the solar altitude is more than 10 or 15 degrees, and that under a low sun they appear darker than their surroundings, as if seamed with minute shadow-filled fissures. My observations confirm this for some domes, in particular that in Darwin. But this darkness does not seem to be a general rule, and therefore does not contradict the suggested relationship with the rounded central elevations in craters like Römer.

Domes do not seem to be the youngest of lunar formations; some of them are cut by clefts. One example is in Mare Serenitatis near Menelaus, where a small dome is completely divided by a branched cleft—a delicate object. . . .

## Lunar Ray Formation

(*Sky and Telescope*, January 1960)

Among the full moon's most conspicuous surface features are the long, narrow, bright streaks diverging from the crater Tycho. Other rays are associated with such craters as Copernicus and Aristarchus. Many of the rays if extended backward, however, do not pass through the center of the crater involved, and some of them appear to be double. It has been suggested that material ejected explosively from a crater would be projected to great distances and that the displacement of the nonradial rays was caused by rotation of the moon during the flight of the debris.

A further proposal has been made by Louis A. Giamboni, of the Rand Corporation, in the July 1959 *Astrophysical Journal*. He points out that large terrestrial explosions indicate that ejection, whether from meteoritic impact or volcanic craters, could occur in vertical fans with restricted extent in azimuth. Material projected vertically upward would have fallen east of Tycho, for example, because the moon was rotating during the relatively long time of flight. Debris that moved in low trajectories would fall sooner and suffer less deviation. Some fans might produce double rays, the high-trajectory nonradial branch lying to the east of the low-trajectory one in each case.

Dr. Giamboni compared the pattern of sixty-eight Tycho rays or segments of rays with the predictions of his model. He finds that the Tycho ray system could have its actual form only if it were laid down when the moon was rotating much more rapidly than it does now, with a period between 0.5 and 6.8 days. It is known that the moon's rotation has been gradually slowing down as a consequence of tidal friction. While this process has a highly uncertain time scale, Dr. Giamboni has used it to deduce that the ray system was produced less than 80 million years after creation of the moon itself. This would be roughly contemporary with the formation of the lunar tidal bulge.

## Lunar Rays

(*Sky and Telescope*, February 1962)

The bright streaks or rays, so prominent at full moon, that spread out from many lunar craters, such as Tycho and Copernicus, are currently the subject of much scientific discussion.

Usually astronomers regard a lunar ray system as having formed from material ejected from its central crater. Gilbert Fielder's study of the dynamics of this ejection is published in the September 1961 *Astrophysical Journal*. The Tycho rays, he deduces, are material that traveled outward from that crater at a speed of approximately one kilometer per second, along low trajectories.

A radically different interpretation of rays is proposed by Dinsmore Alter in the December 1961 *Griffith Observer*. From his study of photographs, he believes that the ejection hypothesis is incorrect. To him, the rays of the Tycho system are related to faults in the moon's crust that were formed radial to the crater when the crater was born. It is difficult to explain on any ejection theory why the rays from two distinct craters sometimes form a unified pattern.

The very fact that lunar rays are observable poses a paradox, to which I. M. Levitt of the Franklin Institute has called attention. He points out that the vertical thickness of the Tycho ray material can be only a few meters, if it once filled the crater. During the several billion years that have elapsed since the moon's surface is believed to have formed, the fall of meteoritic dust should have buried the rays many times over.

From this Dr. Levitt concludes that the age of Tycho and its ray system may be less than a million years. An alternative explanation of why we can still see the rays could be that accumulation of meteoritic dust on the moon is much slower than assumed.

*From the various interpretations of these many different features there seemed to emerge some agreement, in the late 50s, that craters are due to impacts with meteoroids of various sizes—possibly even with comets in the cases of large, circular maria. Evidence of volcanoes was limited to what looked like "lava flows," alternatively explained as meteoric dust, and some astronomers thought that the domes and hills were extinct volcanoes.*

*One trouble with the old "volcano idea" was the lack of any substantiated report of a live volcano on the moon during the million man-hours of observing in the past century or more. There are active volcanoes on the earth; why not on the moon, also?*

*It is true that there have been reports of "lights" on the dark side of the moon—at least one (reprinted below) by a truly distinguished astronomer—but these have been generally explained as sunlight on the peak of a high mountain, or earth light reflected by a whitish area. A real volcano gushing hot lava would be expected to last for several days and should be confirmed by other observers. Then, in November 1958, photographic evidence was obtained.*

TLP

# An Account of Three Volcanoes on the Moon

**SIR WILLIAM HERSCHEL**

(*Sky and Telescope,* May 1956)

*One of the curiosities of lunar literature is the report read by William Herschel before the Royal Society on April 26, 1787, which is here reprinted from his* Collected Works *(1912), at the suggestion of Frank H. Boothby, of Portland, Oregon.*

It will be necessary to say a few words by way of introduction to the account I have to give of some appearances upon the moon, which I perceived the 19th and 20th of this month [April 1787]. The phenomena of nature, especially those that fall under the inspection of the astronomer, are to be viewed, not only with the usual attention to facts as they occur, but with the eye of reason and experience. In this we are however not allowed to depart from plain appearances; though their origin and signification should be indicated by the most characterising features. Thus, when we see, on the surface of the moon, a great number of elevations, from half a mile to a mile and an half in height, we are strictly entitled to call them mountains; but, when we attend to their particular shape, in which many of them resemble the craters of our volcanos, and thence argue, that they owe their origin to the same cause which has modelled many of these, we may be said to see by analogy, or with the eye of reason. Now, in this latter case, though it may be convenient, in speaking of phenomena, to use expressions that can only be justified by reasoning upon the facts themselves, it will certainly be the safest way not to neglect a full description of them, that it may appear to others how far we have been authorized to use the mental eye. This being premised, I may safely proceed to give my observations.

*April 19, 1787,* $10^{h}$ $36^{m}$ sidereal time. I perceive three volcanoes in different places of the dark part of the new moon. Two of them are either already nearly extinct, or otherwise in a state of going to break out; which perhaps may be decided next lunation. The third shews an actual eruption of fire, or luminous matter. I measured the distance of the crater from the northern limb of the moon, and found it 3′57″.3. Its light is much brighter than the nucleus of the comet which M. Méchain discovered at Paris the 10th of this month.

*April 20, 1787,* $10^{h}$ $02^{m}$ sidereal time. The volcano burns with greater violence than last night. I believe its diameter cannot be less than 3″, by comparing it with that of the Georgian planet [Uranus]; as Jupiter was near at hand, I turned the telescope to his third satellite, and estimated the diameter of the burning part of the volcano to be equal to at least twice that of the satellite. Hence we may compute that the shining or burning matter must be above three miles in diameter. It is of an irregular round figure, and very sharply defined on the edges. The other two volcanos are much farther towards the center of the moon, and resemble large, pretty faint nebulae, that are gradually much brighter in the middle; but no well defined luminous spot can be discerned in them. These three spots are plainly to be distinguished from the rest of the marks upon the moon; for the reflection of the sun's rays from the earth is, in its present situation, sufficiently bright, with a ten-feet [focal length] reflector, to shew the moon's spots, even the darkest of them: nor did I perceive any similar phenomena last lunation, though I then viewed the same places with the same instrument.

The appearance of what I have called the actual fire or eruption of a volcano, exactly resembled a small piece of burning charcoal, when it is covered by a very thin coat of white ashes, which frequently adhere to it when it has been some time ignited; and it had a degree of brightness, about as strong as that with which such a coal would be seen to glow in faint daylight.

All the adjacent parts of the volcanic mountain seemed to be fairly illuminated by the eruption, and were gradually more obscure as they lay at a greater distance from the crater.

This eruption resembled much that which I saw on the 4th of May, in the year 1783; an account of which, with many remarkable particulars relating to volcanic mountains in the moon, I shall take an early opportunity of communicating to this Society. It differed, however, considerably in magnitude and brightness; for the volcano of the year 1783, though much brighter than that which is now burning, was not nearly so large in the dimensions of its eruption: The former seen in the telescope resembled a star of the fourth magnitude as it appears to the natural eye; this, on the contrary, shews a visible disk of luminous matter, very different from the sparkling brightness of star-light.

ED. NOTE (1956): In this case, the great observer was mistaken, for it is clear that his "burning volcano" was the interior of the crater Aristarchus, which can readily be seen as a luminous spot on the faintly visible earthlit portion of the moon, when it appears in the western sky shortly after new moon. Aristarchus is often so seen in amateur telescopes. Herschel's 1787 observations were made when the moon was two and three days old, and it was three days old on May 4, 1783.

But it is noteworthy that Herschel, in his preliminary remarks, clearly distinguishes between observation "of the facts as they occur" and inferences from observation. The term *volcano* he uses for convenience. The promised further report to the Royal Society was never published, as if Sir William soon realized his mistake. Perhaps it was this misadventure, early in his astronomical career, that tended to turn Herschel from lunar studies. He never again wrote concerning the moon. Instead, his attention was concentrated on planets, double stars, clusters and nebulae, and the construction of the visible stellar universe—in these studies he established his place as one of the founders of modern astronomy.

# Observation of a Volcanic Process on the Moon

**NIKOLAI A. KOZYREV**

Translated from the Russian by Luigi G. Jacchia

(*Sky and Telescope*, February 1959)

For many years in the past, observers have reported possible changes on the moon's surface. Especially interesting among such reports are those of the appearance of haze that veiled details of the lunar craters. These visual observations, however, remained unconfirmed, since the visibility of such details depends strongly on the angle of illumination by the sun and possibly on the quality of the atmospheric seeing.

More objective evidence for such haze was obtained in October 1956, by Dinsmore Alter, on a series of photographs of the craters Ptolemaeus, Alphonsus, and Arzachel, in blue and infrared light (*Publications* of the Astronomical Society of the Pacific, April 1957, p. 158). He used the 60-inch reflector of Mount Wilson Observatory.

This part of the lunar surface, located near the center of the disk, is very interesting because it contains a number of parallel fissures, which presumably came into existence after the formation of the craters. Due to the diffusion of light by the earth's atmosphere, all photographs in blue light are considerably less contrasty than are infrared ones. But the details on the floor of the crater Alphonsus appeared particularly washed out in Dr. Alter's photographs in blue light. I became convinced that this effect deserved serious attention and that on the floor of that crater there might occur an effusion of gases.

It should be understood at the outset that the washing-out effect cannot be caused by the diffusion of light in such gases on the moon.

For this to occur, the layer would require a total density like that of the earth's atmosphere, that is, of the order of $10^{25}$ molecules per square centimeter of surface. But if the gases can be made fluorescent under the action of strong solar radiation, then for veiling to occur the gas need only absorb all such radiation of the sun.

Therefore, we might suppose that a layer of gas of the order of $10^{15}$ molecules per square centimeter—about $10^{-10}$ atmosphere—would have considerable fluorescence. The existence of such a localized "atmosphere" due to the effusion of gases from lunar craters seems entirely possible.

The question remains of whether the sun's short-wave energy is intense enough to produce fluorescent radiation in the visible part of the spectrum that could be seen against the background of the ordinary solar spectrum reflected by the moon.

In October and November 1958, with V. I. Ezerski of the Kharkov Observatory, I was conducting spectral investigations of Mars, using the 50-inch reflector of the Crimean Observatory of the Academy of Sciences of the Soviet Union. At that same time, I decided to obtain systematically some photometrically standardized spectrograms of lunar details, in particular of the crater Alphonsus.

During these observations, the slit of the spectrograph was always oriented east-west on the sky. The linear dispersion [separation of colors in the spectrum] was 23 angstroms per millimeter in the vicinity of the hydrogen-gamma line, and the scale of lunar details about 10 seconds of arc per millimeter. The normal exposure on Kodak 103a-F emulsion was 10 to 30 minutes.

Nothing special was noticed on the spectrograms of Alphonsus up to the night of November 2-3, when three spectrograms were taken with the slit running through its central peak, as shown in Figure 87. While I was taking the first spectrogram, at $1^h$ Universal time, and guiding on the image of the central peak, the latter became strongly washed out and of an unusual reddish hue.

After taking this spectrogram, however, and in accordance with our program, we changed over to observe Mars, and the next spectrogram of Alphonsus was made from 3:00 to 3:30 UT, a 30-minute exposure. Only the central peak of this crater showed on the slit, and I was struck by its unusual brightness and whiteness at the time.

During the exposure I did not take my eye away from the guiding eyepiece, but suddenly I noticed that the brightness of the peak had fallen to its normal value. The spectrogram exposure was then immediately stopped and the following one was taken, from 3:30 to 3:40, with the same position of the slit.

I did not give serious thought to my visual impressions, believing that all the peculiarities I had noticed were caused by a change in the quality of the observing conditions. Therefore, it came somewhat as a surprise when development of the spectrograms showed that all the changes noted visually had in reality occurred on the central peak of Alphonsus.

On the first spectrogram (not reproduced), the central peak is considerably weakened in violet light compared with the neighboring details of the crater, a fact that was not observed on earlier spectra. Measurement of this photograph showed that the absorption varied inversely with the wave length, and the calculated general absorption turned out to be equal to 15 or 20 per cent in the visual region.

On the second spectrogram (Fig. 88) this absorption is not noticeable, and an emission spectrum stands out, composed of a series of broad bands, superimposed on the usual spectrum of the central peak. Below this second spectrogram is reproduced the 10-minute spectrum that was

*Fig.* 87. The position of the spectrograph slit during Kozyrev's observation of the lunar crater Alphonsus is marked by the white line. Arzachel is the crater on the right, and Ptolemaeus is on the left.

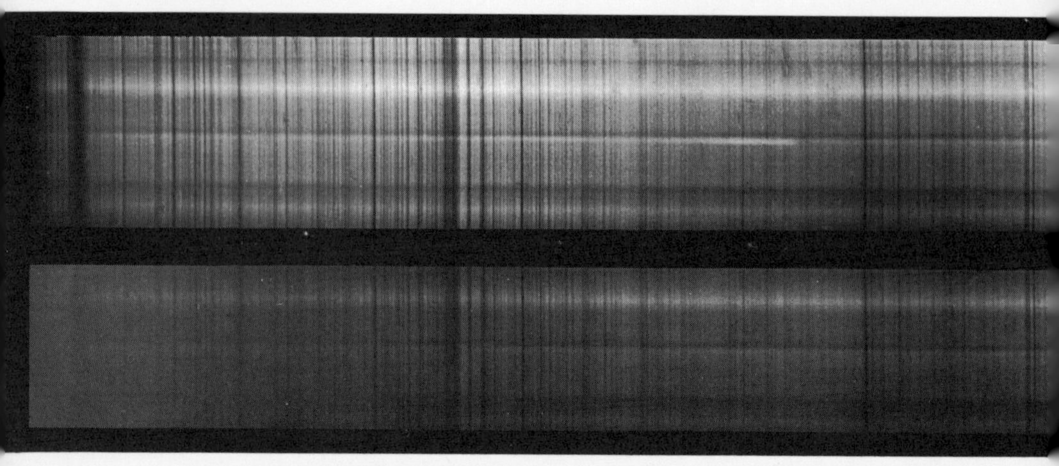

*Figs. 88, 89.* These two spectrograms are the evidence for an eruption on the moon on November 3, 1958. Strong emission bands (light-colored), extending from 4737A toward shorter wavelengths, are conspicuous on the upper spectrogram, an exposure from 3:00 to 3:30 Universal time, and absent from the lower one, taken from 3:30 to 3:40. The spectrograms were obtained with the 50-inch reflector of the Crimean Astrophysical Observatory. On the chart below, the absorption lines (black) are identified and the position of the strong emission originating close to the central peak of Alphonsus is indicated. (Pulkovo Observatory; chart by Z. Kopal)

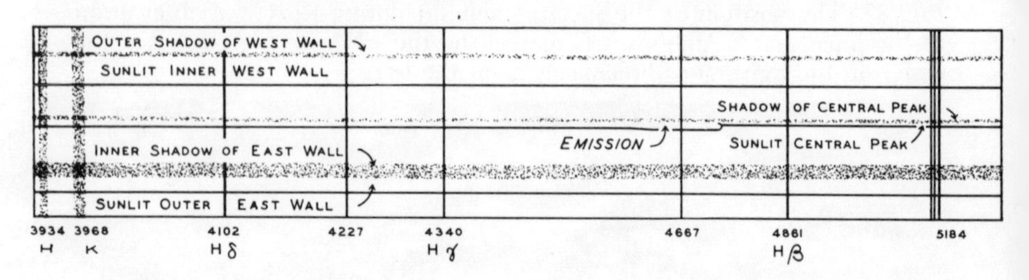


taken immediately afterward, showing the normal appearance of the crater. Therefore, the phenomenon of gas effusion lasted not longer than 2½ hours and not less than half an hour.

On the following night, November 3-4, I obtained two more spectra of Alphonsus, but its condition continued to be normal. Then the moon entered the last quarter phase and this region of its surface was in shadow and unobservable.

These observations are interpreted as showing that on the morning of November 3, 1958, there occurred a volcanic phenomenon. First there was an ejection of dust—volcanic ash (appearing reddish in the guiding eyepiece)—and afterward an efflux of gas (causing the emission spectrum). The effusion of gas could come from magma rising to the lunar surface.

The most noticeable peculiarity of the emission spectrum of the central peak is the group of bands starting at 4737 angstroms, sharply delimited on the long-wave side. These bands have 40 per cent of the normal luminosity of the peak in these wave lengths. But the emission is not superimposed directly on the peak, being slightly shifted away from the shadow, that is, toward the sun. This shift amounts to approximately 0.7 second of arc, or about 1½ kilometers on the moon's surface. It can probably be explained by the sun's short-wave radiation penetrating only those parts of the gaseous layer that were nearest the sun.

One must presume that the shining of these gases was produced similarly to the luminescence of a comet, the solar radiation causing dissociation of the molecules issuing from beneath the surface. . . .

To obtain a full interpretation of the emission spectrum, it is necessary to analyze its intensity carefully, subtracting step by step from its observed intensity at each wave length the intensity of the neighboring part of the crater bottom. Such measurements require great precision and are not yet finished. But some information has already been obtained.

In the strong group of bands that start at 4737 angstroms, progressively weakening toward the violet, there appears as a very strong component the Swan band[1] of the carbon molecule $C_2$. The distinct maximum at 4737 is the beginning of the vibrational band of this molecule. The presence of $C_2$ is confirmed by other considerably weaker groups of Swan bands, with maxima at 5165 and 5636 angstroms. The existence of the $C_2$ molecule in the effusing gases can therefore be considered as established. . . .

It is possible that the observations just described will be unique for some time to come. But the existence today of internal energy and the possibility of orogenic processes (mountain formation) on the moon

[1] Molecules absorb and emit light in a complex sequence of colors that show up as groups of lines, or a "band" in a spectrum. Each band is characteristic of one kind of molecule, and the green Swan band, named after its discoverer, can only be caused by $C_2$.

seem to have been established. The coincidence of the observed phenomenon with the position of the central peak can hardly have been accidental, and may indicate that the basic relief of the moon originated from within rather than from the impact of giant meteorites. The low thermal conductivity of the lunar surface layers may result from the porous character of volcanic material rather than from a dust layer.

## Exchange of Letters on Kozyrev's Observation

(*Sky and Telescope*, April and August 1959)

Sir:

The remarkable report by N. A. Kozyrev on visual and spectrographic observations of volcanic activity in the lunar crater Alphonsus, merits close examination. Obviously, the conclusions have a direct bearing on the processes invoked to account for the lunar craters and their central mountains.

One aspect of the report must be questioned, the nature of the emission bands mentioned in the text. Inspection of photographic copies of the spectrum fails to show any band structure superposed on the Fraunhofer [solar] spectrum of sunlight reflected from the central peak; only a continuous emission patch appears to overlay the Fraunhofer spectrum near 4700 angstroms. The rest of the peak spectrum has, in relation to the walls and floor, very nearly the intensity to be expected for a well-guided spectrum, as was found by comparison with a number of spectra taken at the McDonald Observatory, and as follows also from the intensity of the peak on direct photographs, which for all phases is considerably greater than that of the crater floor. An appreciable difference exists between the two published spectra regarding their intensity distribution with wave length; but this difference does not seem to be present in other copies that have been in circulation among astronomers.

The article attributes the 4700-angstrom emission to the Swan band of the diatomic carbon molecule $C_2$, which has its bandhead at 4737, a value in close agreement with the spectrum reproduced. It should be pointed out, however, that against the sunlit moon the 4737 Swan band of $C_2$ would have been observed not in emission, but in absorption; while the associated band at 5129 angstroms should have been present weakly in emission. This follows from the classification of the relevant vibrational states and the known transition probabilities. It seems evident that $C_2$ has not been observed (nor would it be expected on the basis of terrestrial experience) and that the nature of the 4700 feature is not explained.

*Gerard P. Kuiper*
Yerkes Observatory
Williams Bay, Wis.

Sir:

In a letter published in the April issue of SKY AND TELESCOPE, Gerard P. Kuiper discusses my spectroscopic observations of the lunar crater Alphonsus on November 2–3, 1958. He states that my identification of a bright band in the spectrum of the central peak as the Swan band at 4737 angstroms of molecular carbon ($C_2$) is incorrect. I cannot agree with this.

Dr. Kuiper refers to the absence of structure in the observed emission band. However, this structure, while inconspicuous in the photograph (Fig. 88) stands out quite clearly in the microphotometric measurements of the original. These show a very complex structure of the band, with well-pronounced maxima of intensity which agree within one angstrom with those of the Swan band. The most pronounced of the maxima are 4737 and 4715. At the same time, undoubtedly, other bands of unknown origin are superimposed on the Swan band.

The other objection of Kuiper's is of a fundamental character; he states that the Swan band must be observed in absorption, not in emission, on the sunlit surface of the moon. But we must take into account the extreme rarefaction of the effusing gases. At such very low densities, molecular collisions cannot play any role. Therefore, all processes of radiation transfer will be of the pure scattering type, without true absorption.

In this case, if the optical depth is large the reflection coefficient must be close to unity for the wave lengths in question. The background on which this radiation was projected has the reflection coefficient of the

Alphonsus central peak, equal to only 0.013 when the sun's altitude is 18 degrees, as at the time of my observation. Actually the Swan band was only 40 per cent brighter than this background, and consequently the optical depth was about 0.005. From these considerations it follows that a very rarefied lunar or planetary atmosphere must give emission and not absorption bands. The bands in the spectra of Jupiter, Saturn, and other planets are formed by true absorption in their atmospheres, which arises from collisions between molecules under conditions of considerable density.

From this value of the optical depth of the gases above the Alphonsus central peak, we can estimate the amount of gas. Assuming the oscillator strength as $2 \times 10^{-2}$ and the effective width of the band as 100 angstroms, we deduce that over each square centimeter of the lunar surface there were $10^{14}$ molecules of $C_2$. The spectrogram shows that the Swan radiation was observed over an area of about 100 square kilometers. Hence the total number of carbon molecules was $10^{26}$.

The velocity of the $C_2$ molecules, formed as sunlight dissociated the primary molecules, must have been of the order of one kilometer per second. Hence, a halt in the outflow of gas would stop all radiation phenomena within about 10 seconds. For the maintenance of a constant density, an outflow of $10^{25}$ $C_2$ molecules per second was necessary—approximately one cubic meter of this gas at terrestrial atmospheric pressure. Since the gas flow continued for not less than half an hour the total amount of carbon gas that emerged from the central peak of Alphonsus was approximately a few thousand cubic meters. As probably not more than one per cent of the primary molecules formed $C_2$, the total amount of gas released from the central peak was of the order of a few hundred thousand cubic meters.

The probable density of the gas was approximately one-billionth that of the earth's atmosphere at sea level. As said above, at such a density collisions cannot play any role and we can expect to observe only emission bands in the spectrum.

*N. A. Kozyrev*
Poulkovo Observatory
Poulkovo, U.S.S.R.

The photographs of spectra published by Kozyrev are substantial evidence of gases escaping from the central peak in the crater Alphonsus. His two spectra (Fig. 88) show the various colors of light between ultraviolet (on the left) through blue to green (on the right) from a strip across the crater, the dark Fraunhofer lines being characteristic of sunlight reflected from the crater surface. The thin, bright stripe of blue light in the upper spectrum does not appear in the lower one, nor in other spectra taken of the same strip across the crater at other times.

Kozyrev's explanation of this brief bluish glint as due to carbon vapor is acceptable. It was, of course, examined critically at first, partly because of the many earlier discredited reports of volcanic action on the moon. The significance of this blue light should by now be clear: it supports the idea of lava flows forming parts of the moon's surface, and it may have practical bearing on later manned exploration of the moon. For instance, it implies the possibility of useful sources of heat and gaseous material on the moon.

From this development, we also see that a more complete understanding of the lunar surface may be possible by using geological concepts and reasoning. Of course, selenology (the study of the moon's structure) differs from geology (structure of the earth) in that the surface material is probably different, there is no erosion or shifting of material by water or air, and the force of lunar gravity is only one fifth as great as that on the surface of the earth.

Nevertheless, there may be several similarities, as noted in the next article. Faults, which are shifts along cracks in the crust of the earth, are ascribed to stresses extending over wide areas. In many cases the crust behaves like a thin layer of ice floating on water and cracked by forces tending to twist, bend, squeeze, or stretch it. A thrust fault is a crack in the surface, along which the crust on one side is squeezed up and over the crust on the other side.

Magma is the geologists' term for the underlying liquid that has often been forced up in cracks between solid rocks of the earth's crust, and appears as lava plus gas in a volcanic eruption. Urey has summarized arguments on page 260 against widespread layers of magma in the moon, but localized pools may have played a role in forming the rills, as suggested below.

TLP

# A Theory of the Origin of Lunar Rills

GILBERT FIELDER

(*Sky and Telescope*, April 1960)

Distributed over the visible face of the moon are many hundreds of major rills. Two of the most prominent and best known are the Hyginus and Ariadaeus rills [Fig. 90]. These two are readily observed even in small telescopes.

In general, rills are like trenches, sometimes 200 to 300 kilometers long, a few kilometers wide, and in depth frequently about a third of their widths. In many cases, ridges run along their bottoms. As observations of the Ariadaeus rill demonstrate, they are not simply cracks in the lunar surface.

*Fig. 90.* The Ariadaeus rill, named after the larger of the twin craters at its left (western) end, is a long trough stretching across the central part of the moon's surface. (Pic du Midi Observatory photograph)

When the directions of lunar rills, faults, and ridges are charted, they tend to form a pattern of overlapping parallel arrays, known as the lunar grid system. Although R. Baldwin has criticized grouping these three classes of objects in the same analysis, I believe there is a fundamental connection between the directions of rills, faults, and mountain striae.

A fault in the moon's surface may be classed as a *thrust, wrench,* or *normal fracture.* The stress at any point in the lunar crust may be resolved into three components, two horizontal and at right angles to each other, the other vertical. If the greatest component is horizontal, it may cause one portion of the surface to ride up over another, producing a thrust fault. Or it may cause one portion to slide past an adjacent area, this shearing action forming a wrench fault. Finally, where the strongest component is vertical, the raising or lowering of one part of the surface will produce a normal fault between it and adjoining regions. When the weakest stress component is vertical, thrust faulting may occur at small depths.

When thrust faults occur, the plane of throw or fracture is always inclined at angles considerably less than 45 degrees to the direction of the strongest stress component. For normal faulting, the plane of throw is between 45 and 90 degrees to the horizontal, in a direction perpendicular to the least principal stress.

These phenomena are familiar to geologists in terrestrial applications, and it is my belief that they may be used to explain the principal features of the Ariadaeus and Hyginus rills. Neither object is associated with high mountains, such as may be expected to lead to normal faulting, and I therefore have looked for indications that thrust and wrench faults are involved, as a result of horizontal forces.

Look first at the sketch of the region, noting how Ariadaeus and Hyginus are linked by another rill, which is a key feature in the interpretation I propose. Then observe how the rills have directions related to those of nearby ridges, which seem to form three families. The members of each family run roughly parallel, though the families themselves have three different directions.

Often, the ridges form parts of the walls of craters, many of which have been deformed almost beyond recognition. The broken curves in the sketch map indicate their probable original outlines. These ruined

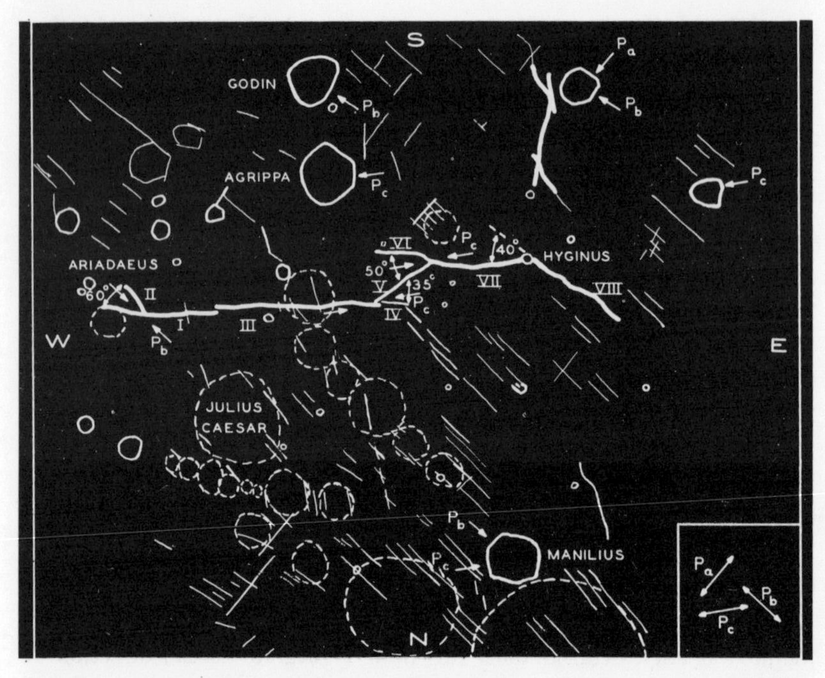


*Fig. 91.* Sketch of the Ariadaeus-Hyginus region on the moon.

craters clearly antedate the distortions and must therefore be very ancient.

It seems plausible that these ridges or striae represent overthrusts or folds caused by unequal horizontal pressures. Heretofore several writers, including myself, have suggested that the prominent striae of the best-developed family (running roughly northeast to southwest) originated as part of a collisional explosion centered in Mare Imbrium. That hypothesis cannot account for all the parallel linear formations simply by the grooving action of projectiles and by the splashing silicates, since it is evident that many of the ridges have a less superficial origin.

A second, less well-developed family runs perpendicular to the first, while the third and possibly weakest set goes from north-northeast to south-southwest. We shall assume that these three families originated from transverse horizontal pressures, $P_a$, $P_b$, and $P_c$, respectively, each acting independently of the other and at different periods of lunar history. Their directions, indicated on the sketch, have been determined from the trends observed for the ridges and striae in the Ariadaeus-Hyginus region, but independently of the directions of the rills.

In the sketch, parts of the two main rills have been labeled with Roman numerals, starting at the western end of Ariadaeus, where *I* and *II* join at an angle of about 60 degrees. Farther east *IV* and V meet at about 35 degrees, while V and *VI* (Hyginus rill) make an angle of about 50 degrees. The direction of the transverse pressure $P_b$ approximately bisects the first angle (*I-II*), and $P_c$ bisects each of the other two. If we consider a shifting of the lunar surface within these angles with respect to the surface outside of them, it is evident that the associated rills could follow wrench faults.

Such fractures are usually more nearly perpendicular to the surface than normal faults; thus, they may tap a deeper layer of the moon than other faults do. Presumably the moon contains, or used to contain, at least isolated chambers of magma. Can we consider rills to be dikes, where molten material has risen along these already existing fractures?

If so, the rills would appear to be of two kinds: those associated with normal fractures and the mountain masses, and the wide, prominent rills of the Ariadaeus-Hyginus system that originated deeper in the moon. In the two cases, the intruding magmas may have differed in chemical composition and physical conditions, yielding rills of different dimensions. On earth, dikes are rarely intruded along wrench fractures, because the latter are held closed by compression, but such a fracture could be opened by subsequent tension of the surface layers.

After the fractures formed, relief of pressure would lower the melting point of any trapped magma. If its specific gravity were greater than that of the surrounding rocks, the melt would not, subject to equal horizontal pressures, reach the surface of the moon. The sides of the fractures would be displaced outward, yet no such movement of the *surface* has been detected. Whatever movement of this kind that may have occurred is probably not more than one tenth of the widest rill's width.

Rock debris may be seen on the slopes and bottoms of the broader rills, and the longitudinal ridges within the rills often appear to be blocky and of irregular contour. It would seem that the rising magma had undermined the essentially fragmentary surface layer of the moon,

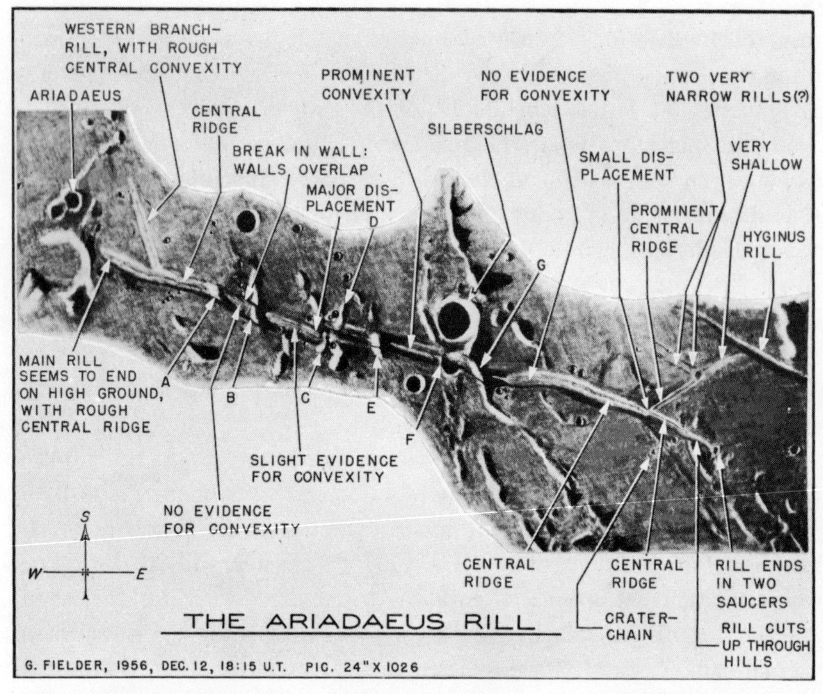


*Fig.* 92. Drawing of details in the Ariadaeus rill as seen through the 24-inch refracting telescope at Pic du Midi.

and then subsided. Rocks were engulfed and detached, and there was further subsidence, so the rill became considerably wider than the original dike.

The ridges across the Ariadaeus rill slumped into it as a result of this subsidence. Meanwhile, the magma tended to a level consistent with hydrostatic equilibrium, thereby forcing up the central longitudinal ridges. The same mechanism probably arched the cross ridges to some extent. Fig. 91 shows the proposed sequence of events.

Inspection of the photographs indicates that the walls of the well-formed craters Godin, Agrippa, and Manilius tend to be polygonal rather than circular. These three craters have been apparently modified by $P_b$ and $P_c$, but not by $P_a$. On the other hand, the ancient craters (dashed outlines) have been affected more by $P_a$ than the other two pressures, indicating that $P_a$ acted before the others. Another piece of evidence agrees with this: Rills *I*, *III*, and *IV* are crossed by ridges older than themselves, those ridges being overthrusts evidently formed by $P_a$ or $P_c$.

Rill *VIII*, the eastern part of the Hyginus system, runs parallel to the best developed overthrusts. But it was not formed simultaneously with them unless it was associated with a thrust fracture, which seems unlikely. Since it is probably of about the same age as the other rills nearby, it would have been more recent than the overthrusts that made the ridges. But this rill does not have quite the direction that would be expected if it lay along a wrench fault, unless it was deflected at shallow depths along previously existing folds of weakness.

Working on this problem, I made the detailed drawing of the Hyginus cleft [Fig. 92], using the 24-inch refractor of Pic du Midi Observatory. As was previously known, rill *VIII* contains a line of craterlets. These objects are not well formed. Their centers lie along the axis of the rill, and they must be associated in some way with the formation of this part of the rill itself.

By contrast, the western portion of the Hyginus rill, *VII*, contains a longitudinal ridge like that in Ariadaeus. There is no such convexity of the floor in *VIII*. Suppose in the latter case the magma was of low viscosity and actually became exposed to the surface. It would radiate heat rapidly into space, with the more volatile constituents concentrated in the top of the dike. The pressure of gases occluded in the magma might cause local explosions along the top of the seam, as soon as the gas pressure exceeded a critical value. It is suggested that the pseudocraters in rill *VIII* were formed in this way, which differs only in detail from the formation of the other parts of the Hyginus-Ariadaeus system.

*A great deal more can be said in speculation about the moon's interior, most of it based on what geologists have pieced together about the earth's interior. Much of what is known about the structure of the earth comes from seismograph readings—records of the tremors transmitted through the earth from earthquakes and man-made explosions. Because these seismic waves are of two kinds (compressional and transverse, or "push-waves" and "shake-waves") that travel at different speeds, it is possible to use the times of arrival at two or more seismograph stations to plot the location of an earthquake or explosion. (This is one widely discussed method of detecting atomic bomb tests on the earth.) Since the speeds at which the waves travel also depend on the kind of rock, and since "shake-waves" cannot pass through liquid magma, the seismologists also plot the layers of various composition within the earth and may have evidence of a liquid core.*

*The same kind of information might be obtained on the moon if a few seismometers can be emplaced on solid rock and their readings transmitted to the earth. If "moonquakes" are detected, there will be many inferences relating selenology to geology. Moonquakes would be evidence of internal mountain-building movements called* diastrophism *by the geologists. Of course, it will be uncertain whether the shock originated in a moonquake or a meteor impact (just as small earthquakes and atomic-bomb bursts can be confused). Nevertheless, plans have been underway for lunar seismology since 1959, even before the first recorded impact of a space probe on the moon.*

TLP

## Lunar Seismology

MARSHALL MELIN

(*Sky and Telescope*, September 1959)

Before the first astronaut lands on the moon, it is expected that much information concerning the nature of the lunar environment he will encounter will have been telemetered to earth from unmanned lunar probes, now under development.

At Columbia University's Lamont Observatory and the Seismological Laboratory of California Institute of Technology, seismometers for detecting moonquakes are being devised. Several years will be required for the development of a relatively light, reliable, and rugged instrument capable of detecting seismic activity on the moon.

When seismographs and other instruments can be planted on the moon's surface, we may be able to answer such questions as whether the moon has a core as the earth does; what lunar rocks are like; and how much, if any, radioactive heat is being generated in the moon's interior. In addition, the fall of large meteorites will produce seismic vibrations that may lead to conclusions about the size and velocity of the impacting masses.

Not only is this project dependent on the development of seismometers and telemetering systems but adequate rockets are needed. Probably the Vega will be the first United States vehicle capable of this mission. This rocket will employ, in its two-stage version, a modified Atlas and an altered Vanguard power plant designed to burn during two different portions of the flight. At present, it is planned to use retro-rockets to "soft-land" the seismometer on the moon.

Experiments that can be performed from orbiting lunar probes or that can withstand the full force of an unbraked lunar landing will doubtless be tried earlier. Contracts have been awarded to Massachusetts Institute of Technology for measuring the density of electrified gases in the moon's vicinity and to the Naval Research Laboratory for measures of the moon's radioactivity.

## Lunik II's Landing on the Moon

(*Sky and Telescope*, November 1960)

On the afternoon of September 13, 1959, as the Soviet rocket Lunik II was nearing the moon, the news agency Tass distributed a prediction that the object would strike the lunar surface at 21:01 Universal time, in the region between Mare Tranquillitatis, Mare Serenitatis, and Mare Vaporum. The forecast led many European observers to watch this area for visible signs of impact, such as a short-lived dust cloud. (At the time in question, the moon was still below the horizon for the United States.)

In the next few days a number of press notices reported optical observations of impact, but the evidence appeared unsatisfactory. There was disagreement on the location of the point of fall, and in most cases the details were lacking. Only the sudden cessation of the space probe's transmissions at the predicted time, and the analyses of radio tracking observations in the United States, Great Britain, Japan, and the U.S.S.R. demonstrated that Lunik had in fact reached the moon.

This situation has now been placed in an entirely new light by L. Detre, an internationally known astronomer who is director of the Budapest-Szabadsaghegy Observatory in Hungary. In No. 45 of the *Contributions* of that institution, he gives a full account of certain decisive observations in Hungary and Sweden.

At the Budapest Observatory, staff member M. Lovas was viewing the moon at the crucial time with the 7-inch refractor. The seeing was good, and he could use a magnification of 500. With him in the dome were two other staff astronomers, Julia Balazs and B. Balazs. Very shortly after 21:02:30 UT, Lovas said, "There is a dark point I did not see before." A few seconds later, he called out that the spot was expanding. Both his colleagues took a turn at the eyepiece, and were able

*Fig.* 93. X on the sketch map marks the spot where M. Ill, at the Public Observatory, Baja, saw a temporary dark spot on the moon on the night that Lunik II landed. Most of the area of his map is shown on the accompanying Mount Wilson 100-inch-telescope photograph. (Yerkes Observatory)

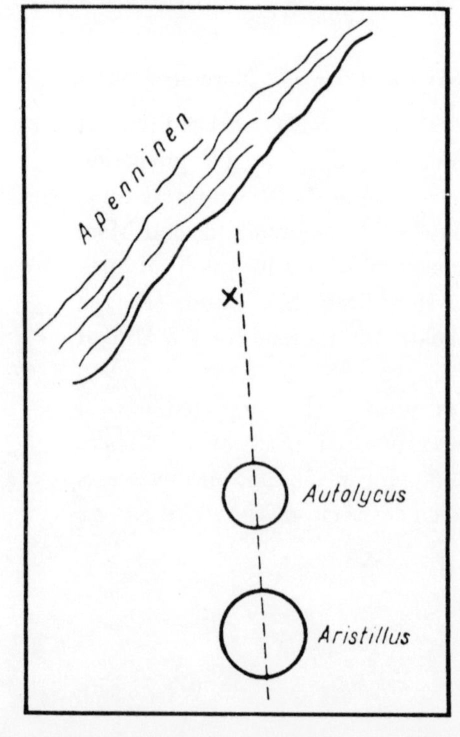

to verify the expansion. As the spot grew, it faded, and was about 40 kilometers in diameter when it was last definitely seen, at 21:07.

Lovas estimated the position of the marking as close to a small crater plotted in the International Astronomical Union's lunar atlas at selenographic coordinates $\xi = +.024$, $\eta = +.434$. This is in Mare Imbrium, south of the crater Autolycus and not far from the Apennines, but somewhat outside of the predicted impact area of Lunik II.

The same dark marking was independently seen in a 10-inch reflector by Mr. Ill at the public observatory and satellite-tracking station of Baja, in southern Hungary. He devoted particular attention to fixing the location of the spot, whose coordinates he estimated as $\xi = +.03$, $\eta = +.45$, a position 25 kilometers northwest of Lovas'. Mr. Ill could keep the marking in view until 21:08. Because his observations were reported in Hungarian provincial newspapers the next day, before he could know of the details of the Budapest sighting, this appears to be an independent confirmation.

Also on the night of September 13, a good series of lunar photographs was taken at Uppsala, Sweden, by E. Tengström, with the Markowitz moon camera of the university's geodetic institute. Professor Detre wrote to Uppsala to ask if these photographs showed any unusual feature at the coordinates +.024, +.434.

Tengström replied that he found nothing definite in that position, but 25 *kilometers northwest* there seemed to be a very small, sharp, dark spot on his photograph of 21:03.6 UT, and a trace of it on the next exposure, taken 1.9 minutes later.

Professor Detre summarizes his conclusions in the following words:

"1. Shortly after the radio signals from Lunik II ended, an expanding spot on the moon could be observed in the position +.03, +.45, which was at first black and pointlike, a few minutes later gray and diffuse, with a diameter of about 40 kilometers. The reality of the phenomenon is beyond doubt. It was most probably a cloud of dust.

"2. There is a faint photographic trace, still awaiting confirmation, of this phenomenon on the plates taken by Tengström in Uppsala, which should furnish a precise positional determination.

"3. The phenomenon observed by the Hungarian astronomers is the only one compatible with the impact point subsequently deduced by Soviet radio tracking of the instrument section of Lunik II."

# Ranger Reaches Lunar Far Side

(*Sky and Telescope*, June 1962)

The moon now carries the remains of two rocket ships, Ranger 4 having joined Lunik II at 12:49:53 Universal time April 26, 1962. After a flight of seven seconds less than 64 hours, the American vehicle struck the far side of the moon diametrically opposite the well-known crater Proclus.

Although similar to the earlier craft that flew past the moon in January 1962, Ranger 4 had been modified in some respects to improve performance. It carried the same scientific instruments—a television camera, gamma-ray spectrometer, radar altimeter, and seismometer.

The Cape Canaveral launching was at 3:50 P.M. Eastern standard time on April 23. Flawless performance by the Atlas-Agena-B rocket raised hopes for a successful mission; after burning once and coasting in a parking orbit, the second-stage Agena B restarted and sent the spacecraft on the correct trajectory at the right speed.

Shortly thereafter, however, signals from the high-powered transmitter became garbled and then stopped altogether. The low-powered radio that was intended to send seismic information from the moon for a month or more continued to operate, but its signal intensity varied rhythmically, indicating that the Ranger was tumbling end over end.

Fortunately, the small transmitter, although rated at only 50 milliwatts, enabled tracking stations to follow the vehicle as it neared the moon. Speeding up under the pull of the lunar gravitational field, Ranger passed about 900 miles east of our satellite, looped around behind it, and crashed at nearly 6000 miles per hour.

Had the failure (blamed on a faulty timer in the computer) not occurred, Ranger 4 would have changed course slightly in mid-flight and fired its retro-rocket as it approached the moon. Thus it would have accomplished a soft landing on the near side.

*As the time approaches when manned exploration of the moon will be undertaken, more precise mapping is under way. The next three articles give only a hint of the extended efforts to map the moon accurately and to recognize broad patterns in its features.*

**TLP**

## The Moon

(*Sky and Telescope,* March 1963)

Sixty terrestrial radii distant from us swings an alien world, airless and arid, subjected to alternations of intense heat and cold. Its surface is overspread with features that for the most part are quite unlike those familiar to us on earth.

In recent years a remarkable variety of tools have helped in the exploration of the moon. Giant California reflectors have photographed it, small amateur telescopes have made detailed topographical surveys, a space probe has televised to earth views of the far side, radars have tested the roughness of the lunar surface, and radio telescopes and infrared detectors have revealed an overlying dust layer.

The state of selenography today is much like that of geography in, say, 1700. We have fairly detailed and reasonably correct maps, and know a good deal about the general configuration of land masses.

The lunar "seas" or maria are enormous level expanses, of which the largest, Oceanus Procellarum, has an area of about two million square miles. Their surfaces are seamed with long, low ridges, often arranged roughly parallel to the mare boundaries. Everywhere the relief is gentle, but modern measurements demonstrate that the floor of a mare is depressed below the general surface of the moon, with a slight downward gradient toward the mare center.

Actually there is little difference between some of the smaller seas, such as Mare Serenitatis, and some of the larger craters with flat floors, such as Plato. The craters are the most characteristic of lunar surface features. While many varieties occur, their general pattern is a more or less circular depression, surrounded by a rim that slopes gradually inward and very gradually outward.

A telescopic view of sunrise on a large crater like Ptolemaeus, seen half-filled with shadow, can convey a very misleading impression of rugged relief. When we appreciate how, with grazing illumination, a wall or hill can cast a shadow 50 or 100 times as long as it is high, we have a more correct notion of the extreme shallowness of Ptolemaeus.

The classification of crater forms is difficult. Traditionally, a distinction has been drawn between "true craters" with concave floors (often with a central hill) and "ring plains" with flat bottoms. One complication is suggested by the large number of damaged craters, with low or broken walls. Seemingly we are dealing with objects at different evolutionary stages. Perhaps a two-dimensional system of crater classification is needed, in which one characteristic may be crater diameter, the other its age.

There is a general dependence of crater properties upon diameter. As we turn to smaller and smaller objects, their interiors become steeper and relatively deeper. For one crater five kilometers in diameter, the rim reaches about 180 meters above the surrounding plain, and about 950 meters above the floor. The slope angle of the inner wall is of the order of 35 degrees, while the outer slope is only a few degrees, but steepening to 10 or 20 at the crestline.

The number of small craterlets is very large. One approximate formula states that on the visible hemisphere the number of those at least $d$ kilometers in diameter is $300{,}000/d^2$.

Until fairly recent years, the moon's mountains had received much less observing attention than its craters. One reason is that mountain systems like the lunar Apennines and Alps are much too complex for adequate visual charting. Before modern, high-quality photographs became available, little had been done except some height measurements of the more prominent peaks.

The highest ranges in the limb regions of the moon are the Liebnitz and Doerfel mountains, both visible in profile near the south pole when the libration is suitable. The Leibnitz range averages 5970 meters height (19,600 feet). In the central portion of the disk, Mount Huygens rises to 5500 meters (18,000 feet). Thus the higher lunar mountains are comparable to the terrestrial Andes, but considerably lower than the main summits of the Himalayas.

Large telescopes reveal many hundreds of long, narrow, snakelike valleys. Today the name *rille* has largely supplanted the earlier syno-

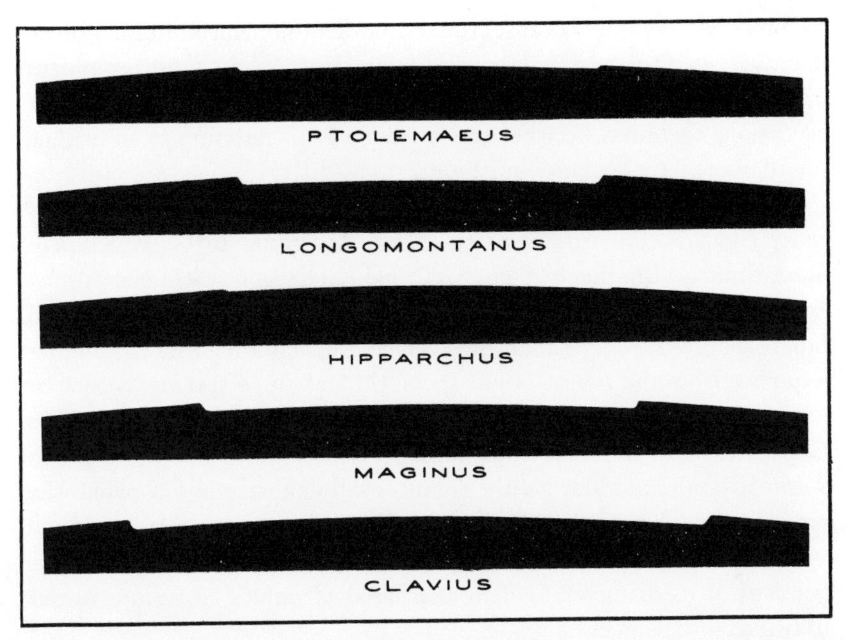


*Fig. 94.* These profiles, drawn to scale, show the extreme shallowness of the largest lunar walled plains. (After Dinsmore Alter in Vol. 68 of the *Publications* of the Astronomical Society of the Pacific)

nyms cleft, crack, and rill. These features are easiest seen in the maria, and often run more or less parallel to their "shores" for long distances. Sometimes, as near the craters Triesnecker and Prinz, large numbers of rilles join and intersect in elaborate patterns. Despite widespread current interest in rilles, the last general catalogue of these objects was published as long ago as 1866!

Many important types of lunar features have been relatively neglected

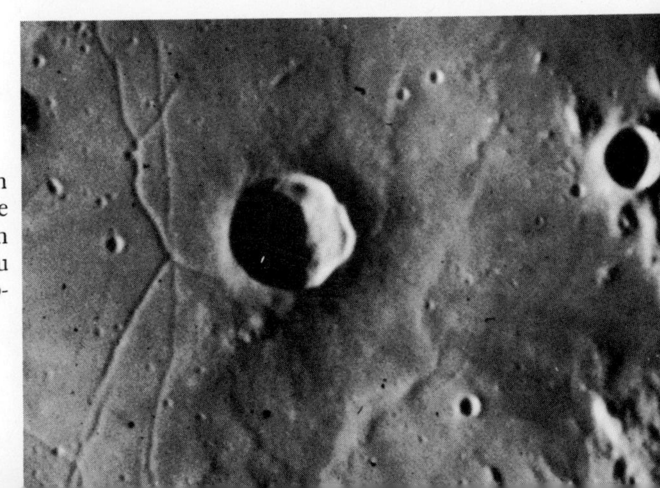

*Fig. 95.* The intricate pattern of shallow rilles adjoining the crater Triesnecker is shown in this photograph. (Pic du Midi Observatory photograph).

by observers, simply because the traditional nomenclature has been mainly limited to craters, maria, and mountains. All the most prominent of these have individual names on maps. On the other hand, with few exceptions there has been no convenient way of referring to individual bright spots, rays, domes, and faults.

Small diffuse white spots occur in vast numbers, being particularly conspicuous in the dark, smooth maria. According to G. P. Kuiper's observations with the 82-inch McDonald telescope, each one always contains a central craterlet. The famous object Linné is a normal bright spot, much larger than the average. Possibly there is a continuous sequence from the tiniest bright spots, through large specimens such as Linné, to the extensive white splashes seen surrounding the craters Copernicus and Kepler at full moon.

Lunar domes are low, gently sloping swellings, shaped somewhat like paint blisters. A typical specimen is the large dome east of Arago, which was known as early as 1866. Its height of 500 meters is only about two per cent of its diameter. Usually the flanks of domes have slope angles of two to four degrees.

Closely related are other, little-studied forms, such as very low extensive blisters, recognizable only on the terminator. The formation Rümker seems to consist of overlapping domes, and it is possible that the entire Aristarchus uplift is an extreme case of a dome. The rational classification of these forms is an inviting study.

Selenography is a rapidly expanding and changing science. There has been a great recent improvement in lunar cartography. Much quantitative information about heights and slopes is accumulating. Rectified photographs of exquisite quality now give us detailed, unforeshortened views. More emphasis is being placed on patterns of objects, and less on individual formations. For example, there is much current interest in the lunar grid system—the apparently moonwide pattern of intersecting families of parallel ridges and grooves. At last, it seems, a sound observational basis for selenology is taking form.

# A Lunar Contour Map

RALPH B. BALDWIN

(*Sky and Telescope*, February 1961)

It is clearly apparent, even to the naked eye, that the moon is not a smooth and perfect sphere. The terminator, or boundary between the sunlit and dark parts of the disk, shows large irregularities, and these must be caused by real differences in height of various portions of the lunar surface.

Several astronomers have attempted to determine these variations in height by measuring the deformation of the terminator, but without much success. The observations are extremely difficult to make accurately, for they usually refer to areas where the sun's rays strike the moon tangentially, so the sunlit portion fades out gradually. Telescopic measures are affected by individual bias, and those on pictures by photographic effects as well. No satisfactory contour maps of the moon have been made from terminator studies.

A second method may be used, taking advantage of the moon's librations.[1] At different times, we see the lunar globe as if it had turned through some 14 degrees. The resulting variation in the apparent direction of lunar features allows height determinations to be made on the stereoscopic principle.

In theory, if the moon were spherical, we could measure the positions of lunar formations on one photograph, and from these positions we could predict exactly where such formations would appear on photographs taken at different librations. The displacement of an object from its predicted co-ordinates on a second picture depends on the height of the object above or below a mean sphere.

By this procedure, the German astronomer J. Franz in 1899 prepared a very rough contour map from 55 points. In 1958 at Vienna University

[1] Although the moon keeps one face toward the earth as it circles around us, there is a "wobble", or libration, due primarily to its elliptical orbit. From the earth, we can see first further around one side of the moon, then further around the other side, as if the moon were rocked through an angle of 14°.—TLP

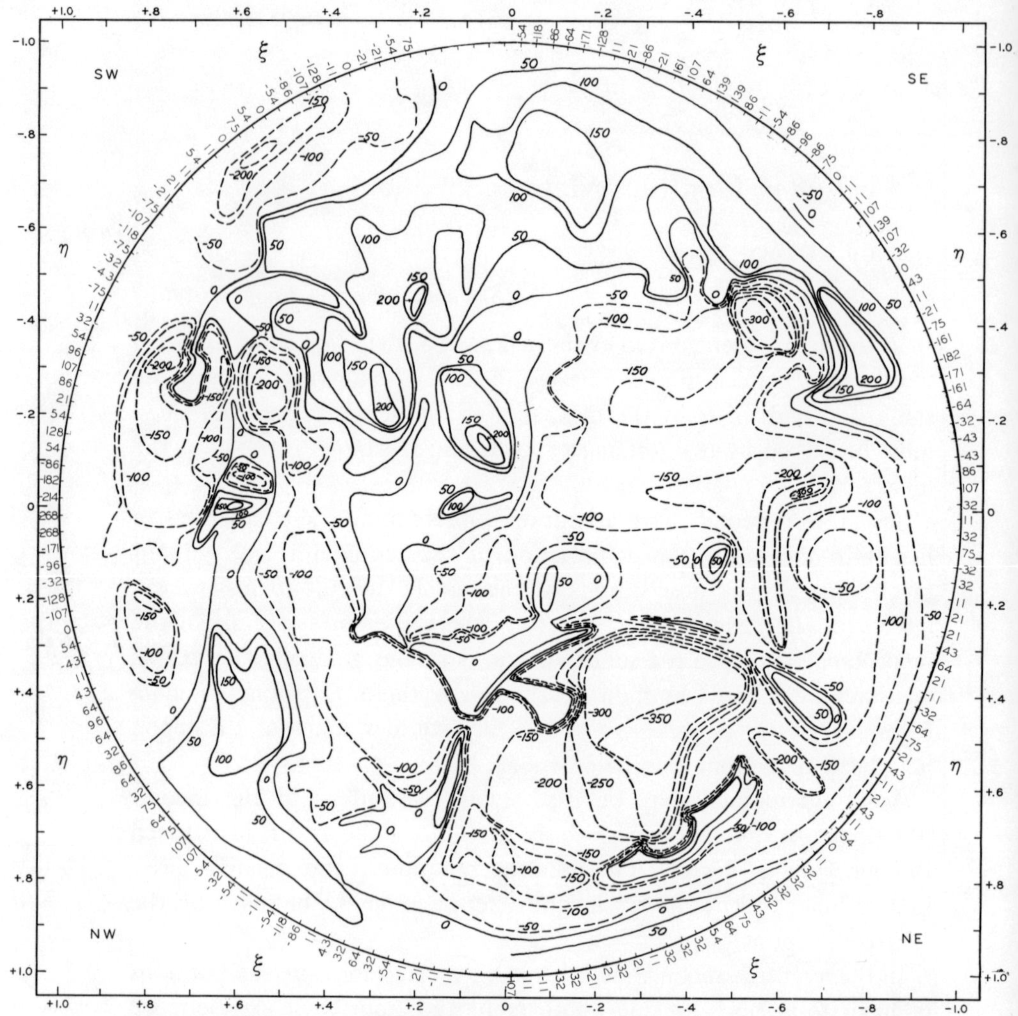


*Fig. 96*. Contour map of the visible face of the moon. Solid lines indicate the regions above the general level and dashed lines, depressed areas. Contours are labeled in units of 0.00001 lunar radius (57.1 feet). (Courtesy Ralph B. Baldwin)

*Fig. 97*. *(Opposite)* A simplified version of Fig. 96, with only the +100 and −100 contours drawn (the latter dotted). The larger seas are shaded. Numbers mark the following maria: *1*, Australe; *2*, Foecunditatis; *3*, Crisium; *4*, Nectaris; *5*, Tranquillitatis; *6*, Serenitatis; *7*, Vaporum; *8*, Imbrium; *9*, Nubium; *10*, Humorum; *11*, Oceanus Procellarium. (Courtesy Ralph B. Baldwin)

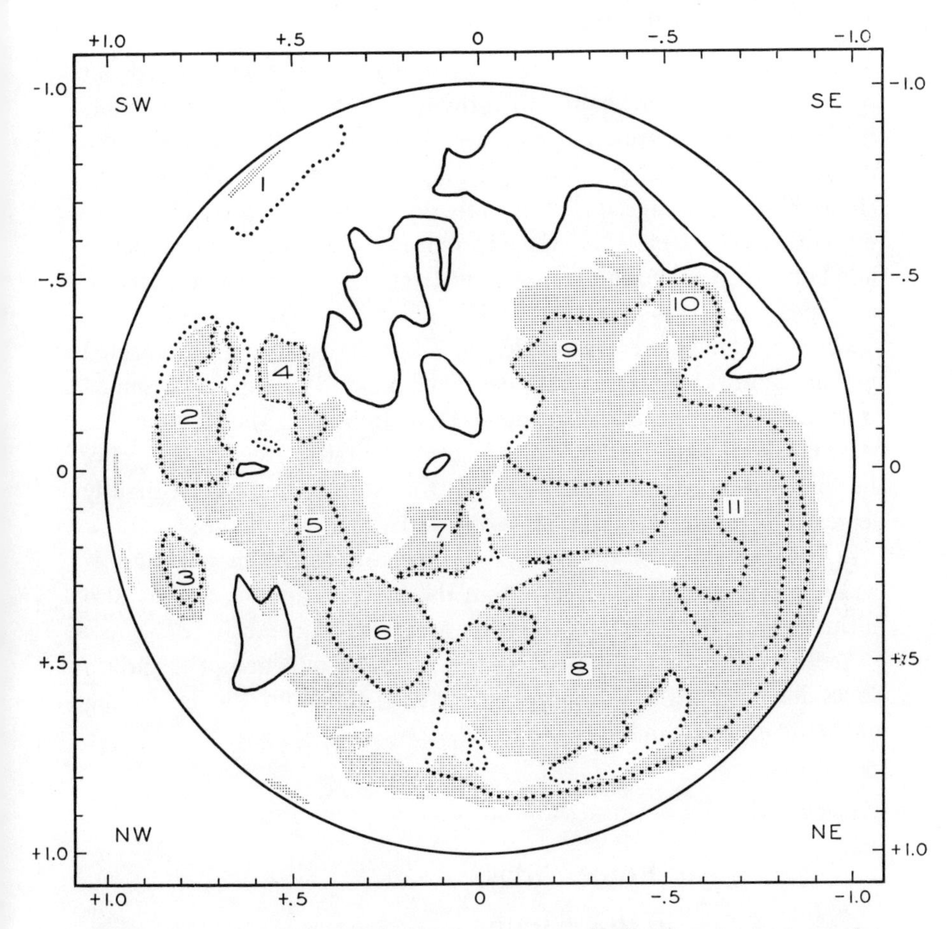


Observatory, G. Schrutka-Rechtenstamm recalculated measurements by Franz of 150 lunar features, and in collaboration with J. Hopmann published a somewhat better chart. No other contour maps based on the stereoscopic principle are available.

In September 1960, I completed the accompanying contour map of the moon (Fig. 96), from an extensive series of measures of 696 points on five photographs taken with Lick Observatory's 36-inch refractor. The coordinates were determined with a precision measuring engine at Dearborn Observatory of Northwestern University. An accuracy approaching that of stellar parallax work is needed, but the tiny craters involved are by no means as sharp as stellar images. They range from about one to 10 miles in diameter.

The probable error for a single determination of height turned out to be ±2270 feet, or about two fifths of a mile. This is considerably smaller than the six-mile range of heights found for the surface at the positions of these craters. Hence the map should be reasonably reliable. The contour lines are labeled in units of $10^{-5}$ lunar radius, which corresponds to 57.1 feet. Thus, the difference in elevation is about half a mile between neighboring contour lines, for they are drawn for 50-unit intervals.

The map shows several facts clearly. All of the great maria (indicated by shading in the key chart) are depressed areas. The regions presumed to be formed by asteroidal impacts—Mare Imbrium, Mare Humorum, Mare Crisium, Mare Nectaris, and Mare Serenitatis—are very low. Also, the shelf around Mare Nectaris, inside the Altai Mountains, is slightly depressed. Oceanus Procellarum is low and variable in depth.

In the highlands of the southwest quadrant of the moon, there is evidence of a rise in the surface from the limb toward the center. Also in this region, there is an extensive low area near Mare Australe.

Another noteworthy property is that in most directions the surface slopes down toward the dark areas for at least 100 miles, the descending gradient continuing out onto the maria. . . .

## Air Force Atlas of the Moon

JOSEPH ASHBROOK

(*Sky and Telescope*, April 1962)

Some years from now, an astronaut in the first manned American spacecraft traveling toward the moon may be consulting the map of which a small section is seen in Figure 98. This is a reproduction, slightly reduced, from sheet LAC 58 of the Air Force *Lunar Chart*, now being prepared by the USAF Aeronautical Chart and Information Center for the National Aeronautics and Space Administration. When this great atlas is complete, it will show the visible hemisphere of our natural satellite on 68 large sheets, to a scale of 1:1,000,000.

In these maps the resources and skills of professional cartographers have finally been applied to the moon. Terrestrial mapmaking has reached high standards of excellence, spurred by the practical needs of navigators, geographers, government agencies, and armies. Lunar charting, on the other hand, has hitherto usually been by private individuals, working alone and at their own expense.

One look at this picture of Copernicus and its environs will show the clarity with which vertical relief is indicated. The original chart is lithographed in three colors, giving much greater flexibility than line drawings in displaying elevations and depressions. Clearer rendition of such features as rays and bright spots is also possible.

For each individual formation, the shadowing corresponds to illumination by an afternoon sun, whose altitude is about equal to the slope angle of the surface. Inside the larger craters are approximate contour lines, carrying little tick marks that point downhill.

The surface features in this map have been entered from photographs taken with large telescopes at Lick, McDonald, Pic du Midi, Mount Wilson, and Yerkes observatories—much the same material from which G. P. Kuiper's *Photographic Lunar Atlas* was compiled. The two projects supplement each other. Each of the new charts combines information from many photographs taken at different phases of the moon; yet it cannot exhaust all the content of any one photograph. In fact, Dr. Kuiper and his group in Tucson, Arizona, have collaborated closely with the Air Force cartographers.

On the final *Lunar Chart* many of the larger craters will bear two numbers, 5200 and (3500) in the case of Copernicus. The latter figure, always given in parentheses, is the depth in meters from the crater rim to its floor. The former figure, 5200 meters, is the elevation of the rim above an arbitrary datum level. This datum is the surface of a sphere of 1735.4 kilometers radius, lying 2.6 kilometers below the mean level of the lunar surface.

The dashed contour lines, at intervals of 300 meters, are referred to the same datum level, whose choice allows all heights, even in the deepest mare basins, to be positive numbers. This is the first lunar atlas in which the contour lines are based on actual measurements. They were constructed from motion-picture studies of the travel of shadows across the moon's surface, by Z. Kopal and his co-workers.

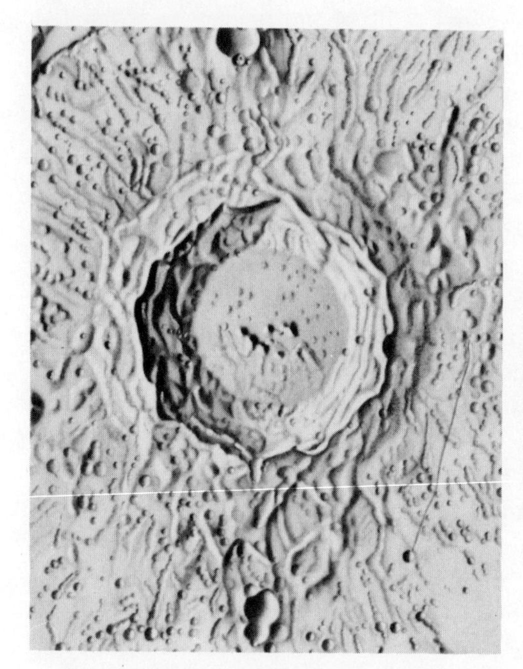

*Fig. 98.* Area surrounding the crater Copernicus, an immense depression about 56 miles from rim to rim and slightly more than two miles deep. (From Lunar Chart, LAC 58, the Aeronautical Chart and Information Center, USAF, St. Louis, Mo.)

The anticipated requirements of the astronaut are not the same as those of a terrestrial selenographer at the eyepiece of his telescope. This will explain why the Air Force *Lunar Chart* has north upward, instead of south as in all previous moon atlases. In addition, the map grid is selenographic latitude and longitude, instead of the rectangular coordinates that earthbound observers find more convenient in specifying crater locations. . . .

*After all this discussion of what can be seen of the moon from the earth, we now turn to observations of it from space probes. The fact that the moon swings around the earth with the same side always facing us has limited earthbound astronomers, and there was great interest in what the far side might show. A dispassionate attitude might be: "Why should the other side be any different from the side we see?"*

*At least one astronomer suggested a basic difference: that the side we see originally faced forward in the moon's motion around the earth, and therefore received most of the impacts that produced craters long ago. If the crust could hold up under the load, the extra material col-*

*lected (like bugs on the windshield of a moving car) would make the moon swing around so that the former leading side now faces the earth. If the meteoric material were by then "used up," the far side of the moon would not be so pockmarked as the side we see.*

*In 1959 the first observations were obtained, from Lunik III. Although they represent a remarkable achievement of Soviet technology, they do not completely settle the question. A great deal of work has gone into interpreting the data, as shown below. Many more such "views" must be analyzed before the back side of the moon is well charted.*

TLP

## First Photographs of the Moon's Far Side

(*Sky and Telescope*, December 1959)

Like Columbus on October 12, 1492, Lunik III on October 7, 1959, obtained a tantalizing first glimpse of a new world. Only three fifths of the moon's surface had been observed before, some of it very obliquely and under rare conditions of libration. Now, about three fourths of the previously unseen portion has been recorded in photographs from the Russian satellite.

Figure 99 is comparable in quality with daguerreotypes of the moon taken in the 1840s. The film was exposed with a small camera when it was about 40,000 miles from the moon, development taking place automatically within the satellite. Then the negative was televised to earth, with a scan resolution of about 1000 lines per inch. After reassembly, the picture was transmitted by radio from Moscow to the United States, reprocessed, and photoprints made.

Each step in this complicated chain has lost some detail in the photograph, and doubtless certain features have been effaced. Also, because of the many hands through which the picture has passed, there has been an unknown amount of retouching. For these reasons, much may be discovered on the photographs under study in Russia that is not apparent on the samples now available in this country.

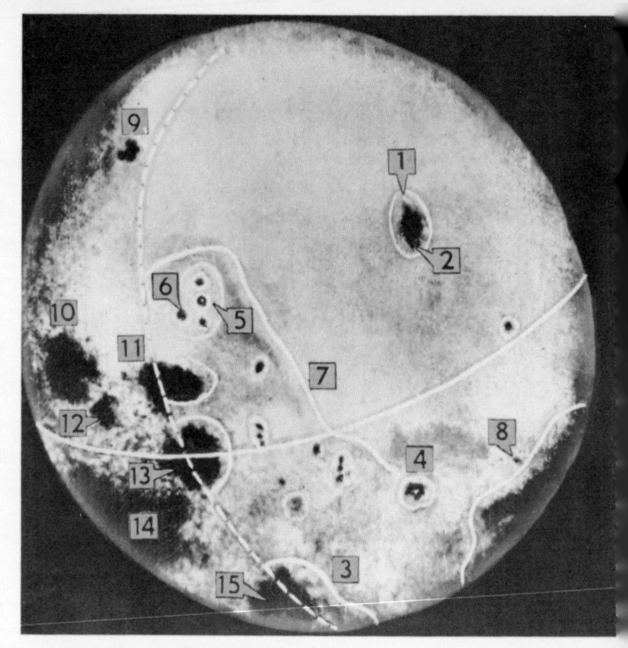


*Fig. 99.* The photograph at the right, taken on October 7, 1959, by the Soviet space probe Lunik III, is man's first view of the far side of the moon. The dashed line marks the edge of the normally visible hemisphere, and the solid line is the moon's equator. To the left is part of an earth-based photograph of the near side, showing some features that overlap the view from space. (Wide World Photos)

The moon's farther side appears to be mainly continental (mountainous) in character, with few of the large dark plains known as seas. The most extensive of these, the Sea of Dreams, appears to be a continuation of the great chain of maria (Mare Tranquillitatis, Serenitatis, Imbrium, and Oceanus Procellarum) that, half a century ago, it was conjectured, might girdle the moon.

The Soviet photographs mark the first serious beginning of what may be called *trans-selenography*, the science of the moon's hitherto hidden side. Some future steps in this field can be forecast. Evidently, much more detailed information will be available when Soviet astronomers have completed their analysis of the existing pictures. There is still a considerable area beyond the eastern limb of the moon awaiting a first view by future space probes.

One important task is the determination of precise selenographic longitudes and latitudes of features on the far hemisphere. This will involve measurement of overlapping photographs, in order to extend entirely around the lunar globe the coordinate network of the nearer face.

# Lunik III

MARSHALL MELIN

(*Sky and Telescope*, December 1959)

Launched on October 4 [1959], the Soviet space probe Lunik III continues in its immense orbit around the earth, after accomplishing the spectacular mission of photographing the moon's far side.

The rapid rotation of the probe was halted by jets of gas at about 3:30 UT on October 7. During the next 40 minutes, the stabilized satellite took photographs of the lunar surface from 37,300 to 43,500 miles above it. Two camera lenses, of 200 and of 500 millimeters focal length, were used. Then the 35-mm. film was developed and fixed at a temperature of 25° centigrade, maintained inside the satellite by radiation shutters.

Later the films were televised over the same frequency channel used for tracking the satellite and telemetering its experiments. When the transmissions began, at 274,000 miles from Earth, they were relatively slow, but became more rapid as the distance lessened—an arrangement to maintain a satisfactory signal-to-noise ratio.

All of the film was exposed on October 7, because Lunik III then passed closer to the moon than on its next few revolutions.

The path of the Soviet probe on its approach to the moon is represented on Fig. 100, prepared by the Smithsonian Astrophysical Observatory. On October 6, Lunik III passed less than 5000 miles from the moon's south pole. This close approach resulted in a radical modification of the object's orbit. After the satellite had receded far enough from the moon for the earth's attraction to dominate once more, it

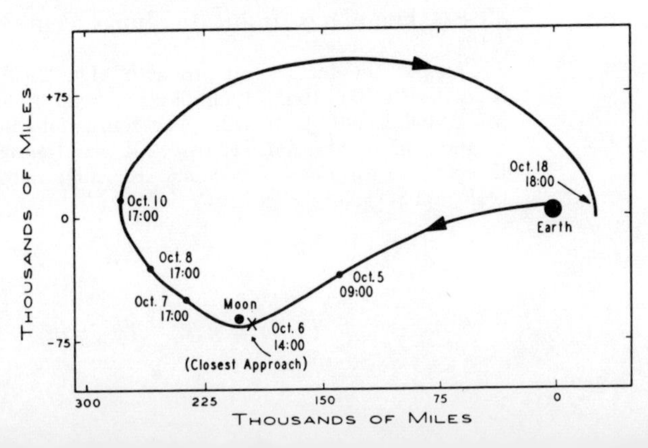


*Fig. 100.* Orbit of Lunik III deduced by C. A. Whitney, Smithsonian Astrophysical Observatory.

was moving in a highly elongated ellipse that lay in a plane inclined about 86 degrees to the moon's orbital plane.

According to Smithsonian calculations based upon Soviet news releases, the eccentricity of this orbit is 0.824, greater than that for any other satellite known, natural or artificial. (Neptune's second moon, Nereid, is runner-up with 0.749.) The distance of Lunik III in its present orbit varies between 29,000 miles from the center of the earth, at perigee, and about 300,000 miles at apogee. The period is now about 15.76 days, perigee having been passed on October 18 at 16:49 UT.

According to the Soviet press, the lifetime of Lunik III may be as short as six months. The orbital problem is, however, very difficult, and any forecast of the motion more than a revolution or two in advance requires step-by-step computation of the gravitational perturbations by the moon and the sun.

## Charting the Hidden Side of the Moon[1]

**Y. N. LIPSKY**

Translated from the Russian by R. M. Holdin and Burton Hobson

(*Sky and Telescope*, March 1961)

As is well known, on October 4, 1959, the Soviet Union launched its third cosmic rocket, which orbited Lunik III, an automatic planetary station (APS), which followed an orbit around the moon and returned toward the earth. Photographing the surface of the other side of the moon was begun by a special command, at 3:30 Universal time on October 7, at a distance of 65,200 kilometers from the moon's center.

The photographing ceased 40 minutes later, when the APS was 68,400 kilometers from the lunar center. The exposure times were

[1] This is the text of an article by Dr. Lipsky in the U.S.S.R. *Astronomical Journal*, 37, 1043-1052, 1960, "A Method for Studying the Reverse Side of the Moon and Results Obtained." The translation into English has been freely edited by the staff of *Sky and Telescope*. It was translated for the Geophysics Research Directorate, Air Force Cambridge Research Laboratories by the American Meteorological Society.

changed automatically. The camera had two objectives, with focal lengths of 200 and 500 millimeters, providing lunar images about 10 and 25 millimeters in diameter.

When a photograph had been made, the miniature camera developed, fixed, and dried the specially prepared 35-mm. film that was used to allow processing at a very high temperature. For televising to earth, the negative image was scanned and converted into electric signals showing changes in blackness of the negative.

To reduce the effect of noise, the signals of the image were modulated before being transmitted. When received at terrestrial stations, these signals were stored on magnetic tape and then, after demodulation, were recorded on different types of apparatus. Here we mention only the photorecorders that reproduced the images of the original APS negatives on 35-mm. film, and the magnetic recorders that produced the image from magnetic tape recordings. On the photorecorders, the images were about 10 and 25 millimeters in diameter, but were 10 times larger on the magnetic recorders. The details of the transmission process have been reported in an atlas published by the U.S.S.R. Academy of Sciences.

In Moscow, the Sternberg Astronomical Institute, together with the Central Scientific Institute of Geodesy, Aerial Photography, and Cartography, analyzed all data obtained. These organizations developed methods for interpreting the details of the lunar photographs, compiled a catalogue describing all recognizable formations, measured their coordinates, calculated the cartographic projections, and drew up a final map. The photographs were studied simultaneously and independently at the Pulkovo Observatory near Leningrad and at the Kharkov State University Observatory.

Interpreting the pictures involved two fundamental difficulties—the moon was almost full, as seen from the APS, and without exception all of the photographs had varying amounts of imperfections. Anyone who has examined full-moon pictures taken from ground observatories knows that it is extremely difficult to identify many familiar features. This is due to the lack of shadows and consequent loss of contrast. The density, size, and location of the defects relative to the lunar surface's image varied on different exposures. Thus, by comparing the details on several negatives we were able to test their reality.

We used various methods to bring out the details on the photographs. The principal ones are described here.

### Superposition of Negatives

When several negatives of the same object, taken under identical conditions, are superposed and viewed by transmitted light, the details on them become more clearly visible. But because the imperfections are randomly located on the different negatives they do not add up. This method made it possible to obtain exceptionally clear photographic images of the moon. In our case, the problem was complicated by the fact that the radio interference took the form of rather broad bands, consisting of a large number of points of varied density. Hence, we modified the method as follows:

Three film projectors were set up, each containing a different negative, and were used to project superimposed images. By turning the projectors properly, the edges of the lunar images could be made to coincide, and we could get the best possible coincidence of those features that were clearly visible on all three negatives. These included Mare Humboldtianum, Mare Marginis, Mare Australe, the Moscow Sea, the crater Tsiolkovsky, and others. Geometric distortions in some negatives were compensated by tilting the projected images of the moon.

Using this method, we were able to trace individual formations on a semitransparent screen. We outlined reliably part of the boundary of Mare Smythii, discovered an apparently elevated light spot within the Moscow Sea, detected several formations to the northeast of the Soviet Range, and so forth.

However, the interference bands on the several negatives, located randomly with respect to the moon's image, greatly limited the area free of clutter. Furthermore, the bands are not in the same direction on each negative, for while taking the pictures the APS slowly rotated around its axis. In regions where the interference bands intersected, interpretation was completely impossible. In some cases, when it became difficult to use the tracing technique, a visual estimate was made of the actual difference in contrast between the individual details. In any case, the aforementioned disturbances greatly limited use of the superposition method.

## Photographic Masking

. . . The photographic masking method reduces extreme contrast between different regions of the negative without weakening the slight contrasts of features within these regions. Essentially, the method involves three steps.

From a weak negative, we make a washed-out, indistinct positive on a transparent base, that is, a mask. The aim is to have the low-contrast fine details become indistinguishable on the mask due to equalization of density, so we use low-contrast film with its emulsion placed several millimeters from the negative. After exposure, the mask is developed until its range of densities is satisfactory. . . .

By adjusting the focus of the image on the mask, the density differences of the masked negative can be reduced to extremely small values. However, in this case, the negative and the mask must be made to coincide very accurately. We found the great number of defects often made it difficult to superimpose the two exactly and the combination became unclear.

Photographs 1 and 2 given in the *Atlas of the Opposite Side of the Moon* were obtained by masking the photometric cross sections (to be discussed below) of the original negatives 29 and 31. Quite clear pictures of the moon's far side were obtained in this way, but their maximum contrast is still very great. . . .

## Examining the Reproductions

On these photographs (Fig. 101) can be seen details located on the western part of the nearer lunar hemisphere, for example, the craters Endymion and Neper, Mare Crisium, and Mare Undarum. These familiar features in the Lunik photographs made it possible to orient the co-ordinate grid correctly and to determine the latitudes and longitudes of the newly detected formations. Their identification is a check on our accuracy in interpreting the photographs and in plotting the details on the map.

Many limb objects, observed from the earth only with extreme foreshortening, were for the first time observed practically without distortion. Among these are Mare Humboldtianum, Mare Smythii, Mare Marginis, and Mare Australe.

[A larger-scale photograph was also described by the author; it shows bright rays from the Giordano Bzuno crater, similar to rays from the craters Tycho and Kepler.] . . .

We have described here only a few of the important objects on the moon's hidden side. Study of all our data leads to the following general conclusions.

The two hemispheres of the moon are unlike in that there are no extensive depressions on the far side like Oceanus Procellarum and Mare Imbrium on the near side. Most of the latter two seems more than 200 meters lower than the general level. (See contour map, Fig. 97).

The assumption that there is an extensive lowland on the moon's opposite side near the western limb, continuing the belt of the seas, was not verified.

Formations on the farther hemisphere are not different in nature from those on the visible side. The presence of crater images in the photographs is beyond any doubt. The photometric cross sections of all the original negatives make it obvious that regions rich in bright craters occupy a large part of the hitherto unobserved side. We have also mentioned the ray systems and mountain ranges.

Left uncharted by the Lunik cameras is a sizable part of the moon's surface that is located beyond the eastern limb as seen from the earth.

*Fig. 101.* Two of the Lunik III lunar photographs televised to earth.

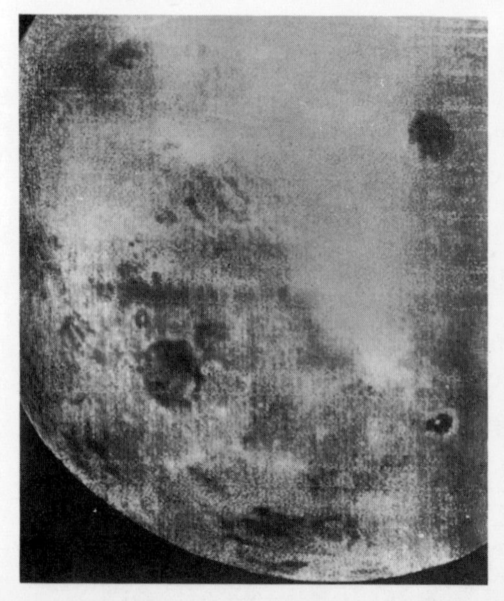

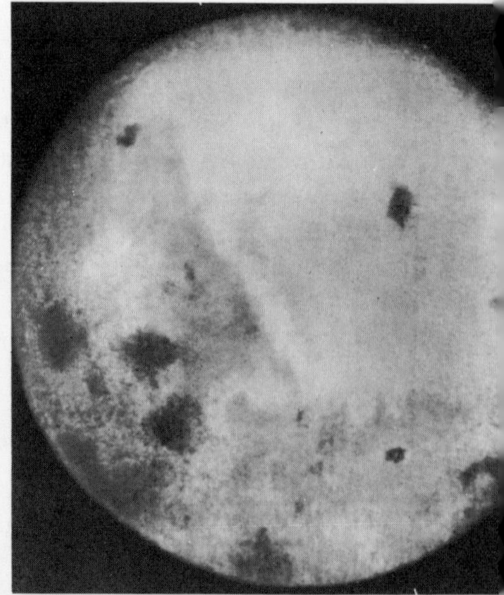

When new photographs of the moon are taken from space, at other phase angles and from other directions, our newly won information should be supplemented and made more accurate.
[As this volume goes to press the U.S. space probe Ranger 7 was successful in obtaining more extensive, close-up photographs of the moon's surface on July 29, 1964.]

*This Chapter has shown how much more we need to learn before men can understand what they see, even on our nearest astronomical neighbor. True, the moon's motion is accurately predictable; over half of its surface has been mapped, showing features as small as half a mile in extent; but we are not sure what the surface material is, or how all its irregularities are formed. Many other questions remain to be answered: How does the moon's interior compare with the earth's? Are any internal changes going on? Does it have a liquid core? A magnetic field? What materials or conditions account for its density being much less than the earth's?*

*Similar questions can be asked about Mars, Venus, and other planets, some to be discussed in Volume 2 of this series. This is scarcely the end of the story of the wanderers—although what scientists now accept is a long way from Ptolemy's version. We have seen the broad applications of Newton's mechanics and its modification in Einstein's general relativity. During the thirty years within which the articles in this book were written, effective new techniques have been introduced (among them, radioastronomy and rocket-powered vehicles), a wide new range of data has become available, and new wanderers have appeared in the sky. These new developments have stirred popular interest, but they are also the center of growing controversy, partly due to the costs involved.*

*Whatever the political outcome, men will continue to think about conditions on the moon (and on Mars, Venus, and farther places). A kind of exploration of the universe will take place, whether manned vehicles are used or not. The purpose, like that of most research in science, is just to learn more—to satisfy an insatiable curiosity. When asked why he wants to explore the moon, the manned-space-probe enthusiast can answer, simply: "Because it is there."*

TLP

## APPENDIX I
# The Origin of *Sky and Telescope*

In March 1931 publication of a small quarterly magazine, *The Telescope*, began at Perkins Observatory of Ohio Wesleyan University in Delaware, Ohio, with the director of the observatory, Dr. Harlan T. Stetson, as editor. By July 1933 the magazine had become a larger, bimonthly periodical. After Dr. Stetson moved to the Massachusetts Institute of Technology, the Bond Astronomical Club, a society of Cambridge amateur astronomers, and Harvard College Observatory assumed sponsorship of the magazine. Dr. Loring B. Andrews became editor, and in 1937 Dr. Donald H. Menzel succeeded him. *The Telescope* carried stories of important astronomical discoveries, reviews of current astronomical work, and articles on the history of the science.

In the meantime, the first issue of the small *Monthly Bulletin of the Hayden Planetarium* (New York City) had appeared in November 1935, edited by Hans Christian Adamson. In addition to a review of the current show at the Planetarium, it contained other astronomical notes and articles. Encouraged by the interest of its readers, in October 1936 its size and scope were enlarged, and its name changed to *The Sky*. In addition to its Planetarium ties, it became the official organ of the Amateur Astronomers Association in New York City, whose magazine, *Amateur Astronomer*, had been published from April 1929 to the spring of 1936.

*The Sky* grew in reputation and circulation. Various regular monthly departments, in addition to those describing the current Hayden Planetarium show and the activities of junior and amateur astronomers, were developed. Articles were contributed by members of the Planetarium staff and by many other professional astronomers. In February 1938 Dr. Clyde Fisher, curator-in-chief of the Planetarium, became editor.

On November 1, 1939, *The Sky* passed from the sponsorship of the Planetarium. The Sky Publishing Corporation was formed, owned by Charles A. Federer, Jr., who for four years had been a Planetarium lecturer, and his wife, Helen Spence Federer. They edited and published *The Sky* through its fifth volume, ending with the October 1941 issue.

Then, encouraged by Dr. Harlow Shapley, Director of the Harvard College Observatory, Sky Publishing Corporation moved to Cambridge, Massachusetts, and combined *The Telescope* and *The Sky* into *Sky and Telescope*, born with the November 1941 issue. The Federers continued as editors. The ties with Harvard have been strong. Until the middle 1950s the magazine's offices were in the Observatory—now, due to lack of space there, they are located less than a mile away.

During its twenty-two years, *Sky and Telescope* has been a distinguished and increasingly well-received publication, with two overlapping purposes: It has served as a forum where amateur astronomers can exchange views and experiences, and where they are furnished with observing data. It has brought to an ever-widening circle of scientists and educated laymen detailed and reliable information on new astronomical developments, and has, through its pages, introduced them to the important figures of modern astronomy.

## APPENDIX II

# Astronomy through the Ages

(A BRIEF CHRONOLOGY)

*ca. 3000* B.C.: Earliest recorded Babylonian observations of eclipses, planets, and stars.
Egyptian pyramids constructed, oriented north-south by the stars.
Babylonian story of creation: *Enuma Elish.*

*ca. 1000* B.C.: Beginnings of Chinese and Hindu astronomical observations.

*600–400* B.C.: Greek story of creation: Hesiod's *Theogony.*
Hebrew story of creation: *Genesis.*
Greek philosophers Thales, Pythagoras, and Meton note regularity of celestial motions.

*400–300* B.C.: Greek philosophers Plato, Eudoxus, and Calippus develop the concept of celestial motions on spheres.
Aristotle develops the idea of four elements and the concept that heavy things fall, light ones rise.

*300–100* B.C.: Aristarchus proposes that the earth moves.
Eratosthenes measures the size of the earth.
Hipparchus makes accurate observations of star positions.

*ca.* A.D. *150*: Ptolemy's *Almagest* summarizes the geocentric theory; the planets' motions are explained by epicycles and other motions in circles.

*ca. 1400*: Ulugh Beg in Samarkand reobserves star positions.

*1530*: Copernicus, in Poland, postulates that the earth and planets move around the sun because this involves fewer circular motions. This revolutionary idea later roused strong opposition.

*ca. 1600*: Tycho Brahe measures the motions of the planets accurately; Kepler uses these measurements to show that the orbits of planets are ellipses, rather than combinations of circles. Galileo uses the first telescope to observe the moons of Jupiter and the crescent shape of Venus, supplying strong support for the Copernican idea. Galileo also establishes that falling weights would all be accelerated in the same way if there were no air to hold the lighter ones back.

*1680*: Newton combines Kepler's and Galileo's findings, together with observations of moon and comets, into the fundamental laws of mechanics and gravitation. He also studies light, its colors and spectrum. By this time, accurate pendulum clocks are in use.

*1690*: Halley notes the periodic reports of a large comet every 75 years, and concludes they refer to one object moving in a long, thin ellipse around the sun.

*1755*: Kant postulates that the sun and planets were formed by the coagulation of a cloud of gas like the spiral nebulae.

*1780–1800*: William Herschel builds large telescopes, discovers the planet Uranus, and explains the Milky Way as a flat disk of stars around the sun.

*1700–1800*: Mathematical astronomy flourishes, involving many Europeans: Cassini, Bradley, d'Alembert, Laplace, Lagrange, and others who apply Newton's mechanics to celestial motions with remarkable precision.

*1800–1900*: Navigation has become a precise and important practical application of astronomy. The accurate observations of star positions show that annual parallax is due to the earth's orbital motion around the sun, confirming the Copernican idea, and providing a method of measuring distances to the stars. Other small motions show that the stars are moving.

*1840*: Draper obtains the first astronomical photograph (of the moon), at Harvard. By 1910 photography is well established for accurate observations with telescopes ranging up to 40 inches in aperture, photographing stars 10,000 times fainter than those visible to the naked eye.

*1843*: Doppler explains the effect of motion on the spectrum of a light source.

*1850–1900*: The laboratory study of light together with physical theory shows that spectrum analysis can be used to determine temperature and chemical composition of a light source.

*1877*: Schiaparelli observes "canals" on Mars.

*1900*: Chamberlin and Moulton speculate that the planets were formed after another star passed close to the sun.

*1904–1920*: Einstein formulates the theory of relativity.

*1905–1918*: Slipher and Hubble find that other galaxies are moving away from ours. De Sitter, Eddington, Lemaître, and others explain this recession by application of relativity theory.

Large reflecting telescopes are built at the Mount Wilson Observatory in California.

*1910–1930*: Russell and Eddington establish the theory of stellar structure.

*1920–1930*: Shapley, Lindblad and Oort establish the size, shape, and rotation of the Milky Way galaxy.

*1930*: Discovery of Pluto.

*1930–1960*: Bethe, Gamow, and others in the U.S. apply the results of nuclear physics to explaining the source of stellar energy. This is followed by the work of many astrophysicists on evolution of the stars from large, interstellar gas clouds.

Von Weizsäcker, Kuiper, Urey, and others develop theories of the origin of the solar system from a large gas cloud.

*1947–1960*: Instruments are shot by rocket above the atmosphere in the U.S. for astronomical observations.

*1957*: Sputnik I, the first artificial satellite of the earth, is launched by Soviet scientists.

*1959*: First space probe to hit the moon is launched by Soviet scientists.

*1961*: First manned space flight around the earth by Soviet astronaut, Yuri Gagarin.

*1964*: First close-up photographs of the lunar surface obtained by U.S. space probe, Ranger 7.

## APPENDIX III

# Notes on the Contributors

ASHBROOK, JOSEPH (1918– ), astronomer specializing in variable stars; on Yale astronomy department faculty from 1946–1953, when he joined the editorial staff of *Sky and Telescope*. (*Meteoric Satellites of the Earth, Air Force Atlas of the Moon*)

ATWELL, CLARENCE A. (1891– ), design engineer for Westinghouse Electric Corporation in Pittsburgh, Pa., until his retirement in 1958 after 38 years; former president of the Amateur Astronomers Association of Pittsburgh. (*Twenty-Nine Satellites*)

BALDWIN, RALPH B. (1912– ), manufacturer and astronomer, was a lecturer at the Adler Planetarium in Chicago and associated with the Applied Physics Laboratory of The Johns Hopkins University, before becoming vice-president of Oliver Machinery Company, East Grand Rapids, Mich.; author of *The Face of the Moon*. (*A Lunar Contour Map*)

BARTON, WILLIAM H., JR. (1893–1944), civil engineer, teacher of astronomy, and a regular contributor to *The Sky* and *Sky and Telescope*; curator and lecturer at the Hayden Planetarium, New York, from 1935 until 1942, when he became its chairman. Author, with

S. G. Barton, of *A Guide to the Constellations.* (*Comets and Meteors*)

BROUWER, DIRK (1902– ), astronomer, born and educated in the Netherlands; director of the Yale University Observatory since 1941, and a specialist in celestial mechanics. (*The Motions of the Five Outer Planets,* with G. M. Clemence)

CHERRINGTON, ERNEST, JR. (1909– ), astronomer, since 1948 Professor of Astronomy and Dean of the College of Liberal Arts of Akron University, Ohio. (*Old and New Ideas of the Solar System*)

CHRISTIANSEN, HAROLD A. No biographical information available. (*Phases of the Moon*)

CLEMENCE, G. M. (1908– ), astronomer, specialist in positional astronomy and motions of the planets; now Lecturer at Yale University, having been with the U.S. Naval Observatory since 1930 and its Head Astronomer since 1945. (*The Motions of the Five Outer Planets,* with Dirk Brouwer)

COHEN, I. BERNARD (1914– ), educator and historian of science; since 1959 Professor of the History of Science at Harvard University, author of a number of books, among them *Benjamin Franklin's Experiments; Science, Servant of Man;* and *The Birth of a New Physics.* (*The Astronomical Work of Galileo Galilei, 1564–1642; Isaac Newton, 1643–1727*)

FIELDER, GILBERT (c. 1930– ), British astronomer, now at the University of London Observatory, author of *Structure of the Moon's Surface* and co-author of *Astronomy and Spaceflight.* (*A Theory of the Origin of Lunar Rills*)

FITZPATRICK, JESSE A. (c. 1880–1945), engineer and amateur astronomer; editor and chief contributor to "The Observer's Page" of *Sky and Telescope* from January 1941 until his death. (*Jupiter and the Lunar Atmosphere*)

FOSTER, J. FOSTER (1918– ), mathematician, on the faculty of the University of Arizona; studied meteors and white dwarf stars at Harvard College Observatory. (*Lunar Crater Theories*)

FRANK, PHILIPP (1884– ), physicist, lecturer in mathematics and physics at Harvard University since 1941. (*Relativity and Its Astronomical Implications*)

GALE, S. I. (1899– ), chemist with American Cyanamid Company until his retirement in 1962. He is now a special lecturer at the Hayden Planetarium. (*Laboratory Craters; Lunar Craters in the Laboratory*, with F. H. Megson)

HERSCHEL, SIR WILLIAM (1738–1822), astronomer and musician, born in Hanover, Germany, and moved to England in 1757. He made his first telescope in 1774, which was followed by the construction of several larger ones. In 1781 he discovered the planet Uranus; he also made the first estimate of the size and shape of the Milky Way galaxy and compiled the first catalogue of nebulae. (*An Account of Three Volcanoes on the Moon*)

HOFFLEIT, DORRIT (1907– ), astronomer, conducted the "News Notes" page of *Sky and Telescope* from 1941 through 1956, while associated with Harvard College Observatory; since June 1957 director of the Maria Mitchell Observatory, Nantucket, Massachusetts. (*Celestial Target Practice*)

HUFFER, C. M. (1894– ), astrophysicist, at Washburn Observatory, University of Wisconsin from 1948–1961, now at University of California, San Diego. (*The Astronomy of Tycho Brahe*)

KANE, JOHN T. No biographical information available. (*Asaph Hall and the Moons of Mars*)

KOZYREV, NIKOLAI A., staff member of Pulkovo Observatory, Russia. (*Observations of a Volcanic Process on the Moon; Letter to the Editor*)

KUIPER, GERARD P. (1905– ), Dutch-born astronomer; formerly director of Yerkes and MacDonald observatories and now head of the Lunar and Planetary Laboratory at the University of Arizona. He is editor of *The Atmospheres of the Earth and Planets, The Solar System* (4 vols.), and *Stars and Stellar Systems.* (*Letter to the Editor*)

LEY, WILLY (1906– ), German-born author and educator, now resident in the U.S. Former science editor of the newspaper *PM*; author of a number of books, among them *Rockets, Missiles, and Space Travel; The Conquest of Space; Harnessing Space* (editor); and *Our Work in Space.* (*Attack on the Third Dimension*)

LIPSKY, Y. N., staff member of the Sternberg Astronomical Institute, Moscow University, Russia. (*Charting the Hidden Side of the Moon*)

MAC CALLA, W. A. (1908– ), Supervisor of Industrial Sales, West Penn Power Co., Greensburgh, Pa.; one of the pioneers of the Amateur Astronomers Association of Pittsburgh, and its president 1946–

47; active in introducing astronomy to the public. (*The Moon's Change in Apparent Diameter*)

MAKEMSON, MAUD W. (1891– ), astronomer, now teaching at the University of California at Los Angeles; former director of the Vassar College Observatory. (*Tribute to Copernicus*)

MATTERSDORF, LEO (1903– ), certified public accountant, former president of the Amateur Astronomers Association, New York City; author of *Insight Into Astronomy* (paperbound edition titled *A Key to the Heavens*). (*The Discovery of Neptune*)

MEGSON, F. H. (1917– ), chemist at the American Cyanamid Co. (*Lunar Craters in the Laboratory*, with S. I. Gale)

MELIN, MARSHALL (1917– ), biochemist, amateur astronomer and expert on visual observations of artificial satellites; member of Bond Astronomical Club, Cambridge, Massachusetts. (Author of ten short articles in this volume concerning satellites and space travel)

MENZEL, DONALD H. (1901– ), astrophysicist, Director of the Harvard College Observatory; author of *Stars and Planets, Story of the Starry Universe, Our Sun, Flying Saucers*, and *The Universe in Action*. (*What Is the Solar Corona?*)

MOORE, PATRICK (1925– ), author of many books and articles on astronomy; director of the Mercury and Venus Section of the British Astronomical Association; conducts BBC-TV program on astronomy. (*Lunar Domes*)

NICHOLSON, SETH B. (1891–1963), astronomer and astrophysicist, a staff member of the Mount Wilson Observatory for forty-two years. He was the discoverer of four satellites of Jupiter. (*Two New Satellites of Jupiter*)

PATERSON, E. RUSSELL (1887– ), Professor of Natural Sciences at Sir George Williams University, Montreal, Canada, teaching courses in descriptive astronomy, geology, and the history of science. (*The Pardonable Errors of Christopher Columbus*)

PENDRAY, G. EDWARD (1901– ), American rocket pioneer, president of Pendray & Co., Bronxville, N. Y.; author of *The Coming Age of Rocket Power; Men, Mirrors, and Stars*. (*To the Moon via Rocket*)

PRUETT, J. HUGH (1886–1955), popularizer of astronomy, associated with the University of Oregon from 1920 until his death. His "Terminology Talks" appeared in each issue of *Sky and Telescope* from 1947 to 1952. (*Direct and Retrograde Motion*)

ROGERSON, JOHN B., JR. (1922– ), astrophysicist, a research associate and lecturer at Princeton University since 1956. (*Project Stratoscope —Solar Photographs from 80,000 Feet*)

ROSEN, EDWARD (1906– ), historian of astronomy, member of the history faculty at the City College of New York; author of *Three Copernican Treatises, The Naming of the Telescope,* and *Kepler's Dream.* (*The Copernican Theory*)

STRUVE, OTTO (1897–1963), astrophysicist, last of a family which had produced four generations of renowned astronomers in Russia; directory of the Yerkes Observatory 1932–1949, of the McDonald Observatory 1938–1949, of the Leuschner Observatory, 1949–1959, and of the National Radio Astronomy Observatory, Green Bank, West Virginia, 1959–1962. He was the author of many research papers and books, his latest book being *Astronomy of the 20th Century.* (*Cosmic Dust*)

SUTER, RUFUS (1904– ), retired now from the Library of Congress and the Army Map Service; member of History of Science Society; author of *A Gallery of Scientists,* co-translator of Pasquale d'Elia's *Galileo in China.* (*Johann Kepler and the Laws of Planetary Motion*)

TOMBAUGH, CLYDE W. (1906– ), astronomer, discoverer of the planet Pluto at Lowell Observatory, Flagstaff, Arizona; now on the staff of New Mexico State University. (*Reminiscences of the Discovery of Pluto*)

UREY, HAROLD C. (1893– ), a leading American chemist and an authority on the structure of the atom, winner of the 1934 Nobel Prize for the discovery and isolation of deuterium, a student of the chemical problems of the origin of the earth. He was associated with the early development of atomic energy at University of Chicago from 1940–1952, and is now at University of California, San Diego. (*The Origin of the Moon's Surface Features*)

WARWICK, CONSTANCE (1926– ), astronomer, specializing in the study of solar-terrestrial relations; since 1958 she has been at the National Bureau of Standards in Boulder, Colorado. (*Solar Particles in Interplanetary Space*)

WHIPPLE, FRED L. (1906– ), astronomer, chairman of the Department of Astronomy at Harvard from 1949–1956, and director of the Smithsonian Astrophysical Observatory since 1955; he is noted for his studies of comets, spectrophotometry of variable stars, colors of external galaxies, novae, meteor orbits, stellar and planetary evolution; author of *Earth, Moon, and Planets.* (*Astronomy from the Space Station; Meteor Problems and Photographs of the Perseids*)

WILSON, RAYMOND H., JR. (1911– ), astronomer, whose fields of specialization include binary stars, mathematical astronomy, and high-temperature physics; now associated with the National Aeronautics and Space Administration in Washington, D.C., after working with rocket development at the Naval Research Laboratories. (*Magnetic Field Effects on Artificial Satellites*)

WITHERELL, PERCY W. (1877– ), graduate of MIT and still an active amateur astronomer; past president of the Bond Club at Harvard College Observatory; for many years treasurer of the American Association of Variable Star Observers, and now its auditor. (*Astronomy in the Dark Ages; The Eclipse of the Moon*)

---

## The Greek Alphabet

| | Capital | Lower Case | | Capital | Lower Case |
|---|---|---|---|---|---|
| Alpha | Α | α | Nu | Ν | ν |
| Beta | Β | β | Xi | Ξ | ξ |
| Gamma | Γ | γ | Omicron | Ο | ο |
| Delta | Δ | δ | Pi | Π | π |
| Epsilon | Ε | ϵ | Rho | Ρ | ρ |
| Zeta | Ζ | ζ | Sigma | Σ | σ |
| Eta | Η | η | Tau | Τ | τ |
| Theta | Θ | θ | Upsilon | Υ | υ |
| Iota | Ι | ι | Phi | Φ | ϕ |
| Kappa | Κ | κ | Chi | Χ | χ |
| Lambda | Λ | λ | Psi | Ψ | ψ |
| Mu | Μ | μ | Omega | Ω | ω |

# Glossary

**acceleration** Rate of change of velocity, including the effect of changing direction.

**albedo** The fraction of visible light reflected by a planet, satellite, asteroid, or solid fragment. A perfectly white object has albedo 1.0, a perfectly black one, albedo zero.

**angle** Angular distance measured in degrees, minutes, and seconds of arc. All the way around the sky is 360°; $1° = 60'$ (minutes of arc), $1' = 60''$ (seconds of arc).

**angstrom** Unit of length used to measure wavelengths of light, abbreviated A. One centimeter (about 0.4 inch) is 100 million A.

**aphelion** The point farthest from the sun on an orbit around the sun.

**apogee** The point farthest from the earth on an orbit around the earth.

**apparent motion** The change in direction of an astronomical body, including the effect of the observer's motion.

**asteroid** A "minor planet" moving around the sun generally near the plane of the nine major planets.

**astronomical unit** The average distance from earth to sun, about 93 million miles.

**atmosphere** The layer of gas around the earth or another planet. Layers of the sun near the surface we see are also called an atmosphere.

**atomic clock** A very accurate electronic clock based on natural atomic vibrations.

**bolide** A very bright meteor, especially one that explodes.

**celestial sphere** The "sphere of the sky" that appears to arch over us on a clear, dark night with moon, stars, and planets attached. Maps of the sky are maps of this sphere. The position of a star on the celestial sphere indicates a direction in space.

**coma** The fuzzy region around the head of a comet, from which the tail extends.

**comet** A fuzzy, white object, usually with a tail, falling toward the sun, swinging around it at closest approach and moving back out to a great distance. Comets consist of three parts: head, coma, and tail.

**corona** A faint haze and streamers around the sun visible only during total solar eclipse.

**cosmic rays** High-energy particles (ions) striking the earth's atmosphere, coming from all directions.

**craters, lunar** Bowl-shaped depressions on the moon's surface, some of them 100 miles across.

**diastrophism** The process by which the earth's crust is deformed by forces from below.

**diffraction** The bending of light around an obstruction of any size, such as the edge of the moon or the edges of small particles.

**direct motion** Motion in orbits around the sun in the same direction the earth is moving (counterclockwise as seen from the north side of the solar system). Satellite motion around a planet and rotations (spinning) of planets or satellites are called direct if they turn in the same way as the earth. Direct motion of a planet in the sky is eastward among the stars.

**Doppler shift** A slight shift in wavelength in the spectrum of a light source moving toward or away from the observer. The shift is toward shorter wavelength (more violet color) for an approaching source, and toward longer wavelengths (redder color) for a receding source.

**ecliptic** The path of the sun among the stars; also the plane of the earth's orbit.

**electrons** The small, negatively charged particles in the outer region of any atom, in motion about its nucleus. Sometimes electrons are removed from atoms and move independently, as in a stream forming an electric current.

**ellipse** An oval-shaped closed curve, precisely defined by the equation in rectangular coordinates, $x^2/a^2 + y^2/b^2 = 1$.

**ephemeris** A list of predicted positions in the sky for planets, satellites, or other moving objects.

**epicycles** Curves traced by a point moving uniformly around a circle as the circle itself moves around another circle. Used by early astronomers to explain apparent motions of planets.

**equinox** Two dates of the year (about March 21 and September 21) when the sun is above the horizon just twelve hours. The *vernal* equinox is a point in the sky (or direction in space) marking the center of the sun on March 21, and is used as an origin of coordinates in the sky.

**fault** A crack in surface layers of rock along which the rock has slipped, one side past the other.

**Fraunhofer spectrum** *See* **spectrum**

**galaxy** A vast disk-shaped assemblage of stars, gas, and dust. The sun is located in the Milky Way galaxy.

**geocentric system** The concept that considers the earth to be at the center of the motions of the solar system.

**gnomon** A pillar or prong which casts a shadow in sunlight, from which the time of day can be measured.

**heliocentric system** The concept of our sun at the center of the motions of the solar system.

**inertia** The tendency of massive bodies to remain at rest or continue moving in a straight line.

**ion** An atom with one or more electrons removed or added; therefore it is electrically charged.

**ionosphere** The upper regions of the earth's atmosphere, consisting mostly of ions.

**jet** A swiftly moving stream of gases or particles; the thrust-producing factor of a rocket motor.

**libration** The wobbling of the moon which allows us to see more than half its surface from the earth.

**magma** Molten rock material, including gases, that pushes up from beneath the earth's surface to form igneous rocks, lava flows, and volcanoes.

**magnetometer** An instrument used to measure the strength of a magnetic field.

**magnitude** An indication of the brightness of a celestial object. The brightest stars are "of the first magnitude" and the faintest stars visible to the naked eye are of sixth magnitude (6 mag.). With telescopes, the scale has been extended to over 20 mag. Every 5 magnitudes correspond to 100 times fainter.

**maser** An electronic circuit able to oscillate at only one precise frequency, used for the production of standard-frequency radio waves.

**maria** Large dark areas, roughly circular in shape, on the moon's surface.

**meteor** A "shooting star," caused by a small chunk of material moving through the earth's atmosphere at such high speed that it becomes white hot.

**meteorite** A meteoroid that has survived passage through the earth's atmosphere. Micrometeorites are very small meteorites.

**meteoroids** The fragments that will produce meteors if they strike the earth's atmosphere.

**micrometeorite** *See* **meteorite**

**nebulae** Vast clouds of gas between the stars.

**nova** A faint star that suddenly became visible or more apparent as it brightened because of an explosion or sudden change in structure.

**nuclear processes** Interactions between the nuclei of atoms that generally release vast quantities of energy as one kind of atom is changed into another.

**oblateness** The bulging at the equator of the earth or any other rotating body, compared to a perfectly spherical shape.

**occultation** The "eclipse" of a star or planet by the moon.

**opposition** Position in the sky opposite that of the sun. Planets and asteroids outside the earth's orbit are closest to the earth at the time of opposition and are then in retrograde motion.

**parallax** Change in direction of a distant object due to displacement of the observer. Stellar distances are measured by parallax due to the earth's motion around the sun. Distances of nearby planets are measured by parallax (triangulation) from two places on the earth.

**perigee** The point closest to the earth on an orbit around the earth.

**perihelion** The point closest to the sun in an orbit around the sun.

**period** The time for one complete circuit of an orbit, or one complete rotation of a rotating body, or the complete cycle of any periodic change.

**perturbations** Deviations from an ideal elliptical orbit caused by the gravitational attraction of other planets or satellites.

**photodiode** and **photomultiplier** Photoelectric cells.

**photometer** An instrument designed to measure the brightness of light falling on it. It is described as visual, photographic, or photoelectric, depending on the detector used.

**precession** The slow change in direction of the earth's axis of rotation due to gravitational action of the moon on the oblate earth.

**prism** A wedge-shaped object; the prism of glass or quartz in a spectrograph serves to separate white light into its component colors. (*See* **spectrum**)

**proton** A hydrogen atom with its one electron removed.

**quantum** The energy packet associated with light of frequency, $f$ (or wavelength $\lambda$). The smallest amount of energy that can be interchanged by light of this color is $E = hf = hc/\lambda$; where $c$ is the velocity of light; and $h$ is Planck's constant.

**radiant** A point of the sky from which parallel-moving meteors seem to diverge. The tracks of shower meteors plotted on a star map can be extended back to cross at the radiant.

**radioactive dating** Computing the length of time since a material was solidified, based on the measured quantities of chemical elements involved in radioactive decay.

**radioactive decay** The spontaneous nuclear reactions that continue at a predictable rate, resulting in decomposition of a heavy element into a less heavy one, such as uranium decaying to radium and then to lead.

**reaction motor** *See* **jet.**

**refrangibility** The different tendencies of the various colors of light to be deflected on passing through a glass prism.

**relativity** A concept of physics that allows no use of absolute motion in space. (*See* p. 94.)

**retrograde motion** The seemingly backward (westward) motion of a planet as the earth overtakes it in orbit around the sun. (*See* p. 14).

**seismic wave** Sound waves in the earth's interior, caused by earthquakes or explosions.

**seismograph** An instrument designed to record earthquake waves (or any shaking of the foundation on which it rests). Three instruments are generally required to record the shaking up and down, east-west, and north-south.

**seismology** Study of earthquake waves passing through the internal layers of the earth.

**selenology** Study of the structure of the moon, and its history.

**solar wind** Thin clouds of gas, mostly ions and electrons, moving away from the sun, caused by eruptions on the sun, and influenced by magnetic fields.

**specific impulse** The characteristic of a rocket fuel that indicates the "lifting power" per pound of fuel.

**spectral bands** Closely packed lines in a spectrum caused by molecules absorbing or emitting light. Each band is characteristic of one kind of molecule. Some bands have names; *e.g.*, the Swan band of carbon.

**spectrogram** Photograph of a spectrum.

**spectrum** The various colors of light from a source spread out in the sequence from red to violet (long wavelength to short wavelength) as in a rainbow. Invisible wavelengths extend from the red to infrared to radio waves, and from blue-violet to ultraviolet and X rays. The spectrum of the sun is often called a Fraunhofer spectrum which, like the spectra of most stars, lacks certain colors in gaps called Fraunhofer lines, or absorption lines.

**stratosphere** The cold and steady layers of air high in the atmosphere (above the region of winds called the troposphere).

**summer solstice** The day in June (about the 21st) when the sun rises farthest toward the north.

**superior planet** A planet farther from the sun than the earth (Mars, Jupiter, Saturn, Uranus, Neptune, or Pluto).

**Swan band** *See* **spectral band.**

**thrust** The forward push on a rocket vehicle caused by the ejection of hot gases through a jet toward the rear.

**triangulation** Determining the distance to an inaccessible object by measuring its direction from the two ends of a base line of known length.

**Universal time** The time of day (and date) at Greenwich, England (Longitude 0°), used by astronomers to avoid the confusion of different times used at different longitudes around the earth.

**Van Allen belt** The region from about 1000 to about 15,000 miles above the earth's equator in which there are many high-speed electrons and ions moving back and forth in the earth's magnetic field.

**wavelength** The distance between the crests (or troughs) of regular waves. Visible light of various colors has wavelengths ranging from about 1/70,000 inch to about twice that length. *See* **spectrum.**

**X rays** Light of too short a wavelength to be visible, that can penetrate some distance into most materials. X rays from the sun are entirely absorbed in the ionosphere.

# Suggestions for Further Reading

### GENERAL

Abell, George O. *Exploring the Universe.* New York: Holt, Rinehart, and Winston, 1964. (Very broad coverage)

Baker, R. H. *Astronomy,* 8th ed. Princeton, N.J.: D. Van Nostrand and Co., 1964. (Textbook)

Inglis, S. J. *Planets, Stars, and Galaxies.* New York: John Wiley and Sons, 1961.

Struve, Otto, and Zebergs, Velta. *Astronomy of the Twentieth Century.* New York: The Macmillan Company, 1962.

### Chapter 1

Brown, N. O. (tr.). Hesiod's *Theogony.* New York: Liberal Arts Press, 1953. (Greek mythology of creation)

Crew, Henry, and de Salvio, Alfonso (trs.). Galileo's *Two New Sciences.* Evanston, Ill.: Northwestern University Press, 1946. (Galileo's physics)

*Dreyer, J. L. E. *History of Astronomy from Thales to Kepler.* New York: Dover Publications, Inc., 1953. (A thorough history)

Koestler, Arthur. *The Sleepwalkers.* New York: The Macmillan Company, 1958. (History from Copernicus to Newton)

———. *The Watershed.* Garden City, N.Y.: Anchor Books, 1960. (An Excerpt from *The Sleepwalkers*)

Munitz, M. K. *Theories of the Universe*. Glencoe, Ill.: The Free Press, 1957. (Historical)

Noyes, Alfred. *Watchers in the Sky*. London: Frederick A. Stokes, 1922.

## Chapter 2

*Barnett, Lincoln. *The Universe and Dr. Einstein*. New York: New American Library, 1952. (Relativity in simple terms)

Cajori, Florian (tr.). Newton's *Principia Mathematica*. Berkeley: University of California Press, 1934.

*Russell, Bertrand. *The ABC of Relativity*. New York: New American Library, 1962.

## Chapter 3 and 4

*Jet Propulsion Laboratory Staff. *Mariner, Mission to Venus*. New York: McGraw-Hill Book Co., Inc., 1963.

*Mishkin, A. B. *The Complete Guide to Orbiting Satellites*. New York: Space Products Corp., 1962.

*New York Times Staff. *Project Apollo*. New York: Random House, 1962.

*Ovenden, M. W. *Artificial Satellites*. Baltimore, Md.: Penguin Books, Inc., 1960.

Odishaw, Hugh. *The Challenges of Space*. Chicago: University of Chicago Press, 1962.

## Chapter 5

Baldwin, R. B. *The Face of the Moon*. Chicago: University of Chicago Press. 1949. (Evidence of impact craters)

Kuiper, Gerard P. *Photographic Lunar Atlas*. Chicago: University of Chicago Press, 1960.

Moore, Patrick. *Guide to the Moon*. London: W. W. Norton Ltd., 1953.

*Paperbound editions.

# Index